Handbook of Thermoplastic Elastomers

Handbook of Thermoplastic Elastomers

Edited by
Benjamin M. Walker
President, Walker Engineering Associates

VNR VAN NOSTRAND REINHOLD COMPANY
NEW YORK   CINCINNATI   ATLANTA   DALLAS   SAN FRANCISCO
LONDON   TORONTO   MELBOURNE

Van Nostrand Reinhold Company Regional Offices:
New York Cincinnati Atlanta Dallas San Francisco

Van Nostrand Reinhold Company International Offices:
London Toronto Melbourne

Library of Congress Catalog Card Number: 78-15350
ISBN: 0-442-29163-9

Manufactured in the United States of America

Published by Van Nostrand Reinhold Company
135 West 50th Street, New York, N.Y. 10020

Published simultaneously in Canada by Van Nostrand Reinhold Ltd.

15 14 13 12 11 10 9 8 7 6 5 4 3 2 1

Library of Congress Cataloging in Publication Data

Walker, Benjamin M
  Handbook of thermoplastic elastomers.

  Includes index.
  1. Elastomers. 2. Thermoplastics. I. Title.
TS1925.W34   678   78-15350
ISBN 0-442-29163-9

To My Wife
ALICE

Preface

A most exciting development in recent years has been the introduction of several new types of rubbers called *thermoplastic elastomers.* These materials have the properties of conventional rubbers but, unlike conventional materials, they do not require curing or vulcanizing. Instead, they are readily fabricated by such melt-processible techniques as injection molding or extrusion, which are characteristic of plastics materials.

The economic advantages of this type of elastomer and its rapidly increasing commercial importance, supplanting conventional rubbers for many applications, make it of great interest to design engineers and processors. Despite this great interest, it has been difficult for potential users to obtain broad information on the types of TPEs available or guidance as to which ones to choose and how to use them. A great deal of information is available in published articles and from material suppliers, but up until now there has been no adequate single source of in-depth information on all types of TPE.

It is the purpose of this *Handbook* to serve as such a reference source for TPEs and to give detailed guidance in their selection and use. The *Handbook* is directed to anyone who is interested in using rubber, including product designers, product users, compounders, and processors, who would like to know how to go about molding, extruding, or otherwise converting TPEs to useful products. It will also be of interest to those who would like to know how TPEs compare with conventional rubbers, where they could benefit by using them, and what their limitations might be.

The authors contributing to this volume are well qualified in their fields, and the thoroughness and high quality of their work are appreciated. I also thank them for their close cooperation during the two years it has taken to complete the job. These contributors join me in thanking the many individuals, material suppliers, publications, and others not otherwise credited in references in the text for their assistance.

I especially thank the editorial staff of Van Nostrand Reinhold, including Ashak M. Rawji, Alberta Gordon, and Patricia Mansfield, for their pleasant, capable, and dedicated guidance in putting this volume together.

BENJAMIN M. WALKER

Contents

3. Block Polymers, *J. R. Haws and R. F. Wright*

7. Compounding Thermoplastic Elastomers for Specific Applications, *Patrick A. DePaolo and David P. DaVia*

8. Borderline Materials, *Benjamin M. Walker, Ph.D.*

9. Markets, Applications, Desirable Future Improvements,
*Robert D. Lundberg, Ph.D., Clarence M. Alsys, and
Benjamin M. Walker, Ph.D.*

Handbook
of
Thermoplastic
Elastomers

1

Introduction

Harry S. Katz
Utility Research Co.
Montclair, New Jersey

Benjamin M. Walker, Ph.D.
Walker Engineering Associates
Madison, Connecticut

1.1 GENERAL

Rubber goods, such as rubber coatings on fabrics, were manufactured in 1823 by Charles Macintosh in Glasgow, Scotland. The growth of the modern rubber industry was initiated in 1838, when Charles Goodyear discovered that sulfur could be used to vulcanize rubber and that the cured material had a high degree of elasticity and no residual tackiness. Since that date, there have been many modifications and improvements in the formulation of natural rubber compounds. Also, many synthetic rubber polymers have been developed, and there is now a wide spectrum of natural and synthetic polymers that can be compounded to meet the requirements of different rubber end products.

1.2 PRODUCTION STATISTICS

The unique properties of rubber, such as its capability of stretching and then snapping back to its original configuration, have made it the preferred (and often the only) material choice for many applications. Therefore, it is not surprising to observe the continued excellent growth of rubber production, as shown in Table 1-1. More detailed statistics and discussion of this subject are given in Chapter 9.

1.3 ADVANTAGES OF TPEs vs. CONVENTIONAL RUBBERS

During recent years, thermoplastic elastomers (TPEs) that have properties similar to vulcanized rubber have been developed and marketed. Conventional vulcan-

Table 1-1. U.S. consumption in long tons of specialty and general purpose elastomers.[a]

	1966	1969	1973	1974	1978
Conventional cured rubbers	2,203,110	2,629,312	3,160,637	3,079,050	3,860,831
Thermoplastic elastomers	7,370	17,720	57,240	65,000	98,400
Total	2,210,480	2,647,032	3,217,877	3,144,050	3,959,231
TPEs, % of total	0.33%	0.67%	1.78%	2.07%	2.49%

[a]Based upon data from *Rubber World*, February 1975, p. 43. For complete tabular presentation of these data, see Chapter 9, Table 9-2 (p. 309).

ized rubbers, whether natural or synthetic, have the common characteristic that the vulcanizing or curing process leads to a cross-linked thermoset structure, which cannot be softened or melted by reheating to the original molding temperature. Therefore, rejected parts, runners, and sprues cannot be reprocessed. In contrast, the TPE materials can be repeatedly softened by heating to the molding temperature, and scrap material and parts can be effectively reprocessed. In addition, thermoplastic molding processes, such as injection and blow molding, can provide faster molding cycles than would be attainable with the usual compression or transfer molding of vulcanized rubbers. Also, in extrusion processes, the TPE materials can provide higher extrusion rates than are attainable with conventional rubbers, and may require considerable less capital investment in postcuring equipment. The TPE resins can be used in processes where conventional rubber would not be applicable, such as vacuum forming, blow molding, and for hot melt adhesives.

1.4 FUTURE MARKETS

Because of the many advantages of TPEs over vulcanized rubber, it is not surprising that the TPE materials have experienced a rapid rate of growth. Although TPEs at present account for only a relatively small percentage of the total United States consumption of elastomers, the rate of growth is much more rapid than for cured rubbers. (See Table 1-1.) As design and process engineers become more familiar with the advantages of thermoplastic elastomers, and as more and more applications are found that can benefit from TPE use in preference to cured rubber, the relative importance and rate of growth of TPEs will probably accelerate. For a more detailed discussion of this economic and marketing aspect of the subject, see Chapter 9, pp. 306–338.

1.5 CHAPTER COVERAGE

This *Handbook* is divided into nine chapters, of which Chapters 2 through 5 are devoted to detailed descriptions of, and discussions and data on, the four present commercial types of thermoplastic elastomers.   Chapter 2 covers a number of polyolefin types of TPEs offered by several companies, including Uniroyal Inc.'s TPR, E. I. du Pont de Nemours & Company's Somel, B. F. Goodrich Co.'s Telcar, Allied Chemical Corporation's ET Polymer, and Hercules Incorporated's Profax. Details of available property, processing, and application data are included. Chapter 3 covers block copolymer types of TPEs, based upon styrene copolymerized with butadiene and isoprene.   It includes Phillips Petroleum Co.'s Solprene and Shell Chemical Company's Kraton and Elexar TPEs.   Chapter 4 gives a very thorough treatment of the properties and uses of polyester TPEs, which are produced by Du Pont under the trade name Hytrel.   Chapter 5 is devoted to polyurethane TPEs of both the ester and ether types supplied by many producers.   The major suppliers are Uniroyal (Roylar), Goodrich (Estane), Mobay Chemical Corp. (Texin), Upjohn Co. (Pellethane), American Cyanamid Company (Cyanoprene), and Hooker Chemicals & Plastics Corp. (Rucothane). TPEs that are readily soluble in solvents and that could be used for applications such as cast films and coatings, are available from Shell Chemical, Goodrich, Hooker, K. J. Quinn, and Uniroyal.

The field of TPEs is progressing rapidly, and new materials are continually appearing.   Chapter 6 describes some of the newer offerings now becoming commercial, and which may be increasingly important in the future.

Although the TPEs presently available offer a wide range of properties for increasing numbers of applications, it is sometimes advantageous to further modify these types to obtain the optimum properties desired for a specific application. Chapter 7 discusses the approach to compounding TPEs for specific applications.

Two borderline TPE materials are described in Chapter 8. Some arbitrary decisions were made regarding some materials that could have been included in this book.   The borderline materials mentioned here are not normally classified as TPEs, but some of their grades and types do qualify. Therefore, they are included for the sake of completeness, and references for further information are included for each.

Finally, Chapter 9 gives a general discussion of present uses and markets for TPEs, and some criteria for successful application engineering.   It also briefly considers future possibilities for TPEs and desirable improvements that could enhance their future.

1.6 OVERLAPPING IN CHAPTERS

In a number of the chapters, there has been some duplication of information that occurs in another chapter. This overlapping or repetition was considered necessary in order to permit each author to present his subject as an independent unit.

1.7 NEW MATERIALS

The recognition of the great potential of TPE materials is evident from the increasing number of technical papers on related topics that are being presented at meetings and conferences, and from the rapidly growing number of TPE resins that are being introduced to the market. During the months preceding this write-up, there has been publicity regarding a line of Ren-Flex compounds manufactured by Ren Plastics, a division of Ciba-Geigy Corporation, and a line of Dutral polyolefinic TPE materials by Montedison USA Inc. Another recent announcement stated that Shell Chemical intends to boost production of Kraton thermoplastic rubbers from 100 million to 200 million lb/yr at Marietta, Ohio. In addition, the University of Akron Institute of Polymer Science has received the largest grant in its history, $256,700, from the National Science Foundation to continue research on thermoplastic elastomers. These activities indicate the expanding horizons of TPE products.

We hope that the reader will find this *Handbook* a useful reference and introduction to the TPE field.

1.8 COMMENTS WELCOME

The editor anticipates that there will be a revision and updating of this *Handbook* about 4 years after this first edition, so comments and additional data on current materials will be appreciated.

2

Polyolefin Thermoplastic Elastomers

Harris L. Morris, Ph.D.*
Xerox Corporation
Webster, New York

2.1 INTRODUCTION

The polyolefin thermoplastic elastomers represent a distinctly new type of thermoplastic elastomer; they differ from the earlier ones, which are based on block polymer systems. Most of the commercially available olefinic thermoplastic elastomers are based on ethylene-propylene chemistry and/or are an extension of EPDM rubber technology. The characteristics of this type of thermoplastic elastomer are dependent on both the thermoplastic and elastomeric polymers used as well as the manner in which they are combined. The first polyolefin thermoplastic elastomers were formally introduced to the marketplace by Uniroyal in the fall of 1972. By the end of 1974, a number of olefinic-type thermoplastic elastomers had been commercialized by E. I. du Pont de Nemours & Company, B. F. Goodrich Co., Hercules Incorporated, and Exxon. These more recent polyolefin thermoplastic elastomers are essentially mechanical blends of an ethylene-propylene or ethylene-propylene-diene rubber and a thermoplastic such as polypropylene. Developmental thermoplastic elastomers based on butyl rubber-grafted polyethylene were reported by Allied Chemical Corporation as early as 1970, but they have only recently been commercialized.

This unique class of polymers can be processed into finished parts having the properties of a vulcanized rubber using conventional thermoplastic equipment.

---

*Formerly associated with the Chemical Division of Uniroyal, Inc., Naugatuck, Connecticut.

Useful articles can be fabricated by rapid, economical methods such as injection molding, extrusion, blow molding, calendering, and vacuum forming. The thermoplastic elastomers are completely reprocessable without any appreciable loss in properties or processing characteristics. Because they can be repeatedly reprocessed, scrap and defective articles can be recycled. The reworked material is usually recycled with up to an equal amount of virgin material; this greatly increases the efficiency of material utilization.

Because of their thermoplastic nature, the thermoplastic elastomers have an advantage in processing economics relative to vulcanized rubbers. A thermoplastic elastomer is more than competitive with a cured rubber fabricated part on the basis of finished product cost. The faster molding cycles and higher extrusion rates permitted with the thermoplastic elastomers result in a significant reduction in manufacturing cost. The increased production rates and reduction of scrap more than offsets their higher raw material cost.

All of the olefinic thermoplastic elastomers are supplied as ready-to-use materials and require neither compounding prior to processing, nor vulcanization after processing. Molding and extrusion grade materials are usually available in pellet or diced form. Most of the products are offered in both natural and black colors, although some highly stabilized grades are white. The unpigmented grades can be easily colored by blending in compatible color concentrates or dry color pigments. Uniform color dispersion can be achieved by dry tumble mixing at the processing site. Thermoplastic elastomers are generally not hygroscopic, but highly loaded carbon black materials may require drying before they are processed.

Most of the general purpose grades are compatible with one another and can be blended in all proportions to obtain the desired characteristics. The olefinic thermoplastic elastomers can also be modified by blending them with a number of other polymers such as polyolefins. Modification is also possible using different fillers, but this route has been somewhat limited to date. Specially formulated grades are also offered that are easier to process, highly stabilized, oil resistant, flame retardant, semiconductive, electrically stable, and electrostatically paintable. Most of these specialty grades have been commercialized, although some are still developmental products.

The polyolefin thermoplastic elastomers are produced by a number of different manufacturers in the chemical and rubber industry, which also produce one of the raw materials needed. Uniroyal Inc., Goodrich, and Du Pont manufacture a wide variety of EPDM rubbers. Hercules and Allied Chemical are not basic in rubber technology, but both produce polyethylene and polypropylene resins. Exxon produces both EPDM and polypropylene (their ionic thermoplastic elastomers and recently commercialized materials are covered in Chapter 6). This chapter will concentrate on the polyolefin thermoplastic elastomers made by

Uniroyal, Du Pont, Goodrich, Hercules, and Allied Chemical. Other recently commercialized or developmental thermoplastic elastomers are not included here due to the lack of information available on these newer products.

2.1.1 Uniroyal TPR®*

Uniroyal, which has the largest selection of commercially available olefinic thermoplastic elastomers, offers six series of thermoplastic rubbers under the trademark *TPR*. The TPR 1000 and 2000 series were the first polyolefinic thermoplastic elastomers to be commercialized. There are five basic types within the TPR 1000/2000 series that cover a wide range of hardness. TPR 1600 is the most elastomeric grade material in this series and is therefore soft and quite flexible. It has the lowest set of all the different types of TPR thermoplastic rubber. In contrast, TPR 1900 is the least elastomeric type and is much harder and stronger. TPR 1700, 1800, and 2800 types have intermediate hardnesses and properties, combining properties inherent to both elastomers and plastics. Typical injection molded properties of these products are summarized in Table 2-1.

All of these TPR thermoplastic rubbers are available in natural and white pellets. Two levels of stabilization are also offered; a standard stabilizer series (i.e., TPR XX00) and a higher stabilization level for outdoor and heat aging applications (i.e., TPR XX22). The color is governed by the level of stabilization. For example, TPR 1700 is natural in color with standard stabilization, whereas TPR 2822 is white and is highly stabilized for environmental resistance.

The TPR 3000 series is a specialty grade of thermoplastic elastomer that is both oil resistant and fire rated. Two grades have been manufactured; TPR 3700 is natural, and TPR 3812 is black and highly stabilized. These two extrusion grade polymers have been designed to compete with thermoset synthetic rubbers such as neoprene, chloroprene, and Hypalon in wire sheathing and jacketing for control cable. They meet all of the requirements of cured elastomers including abrasion resistance, low temperature flexibility, high temperature resistance, and weather resistance. They also have excellent retention of physical properties after environmental heat agings and oil-immersion aging tests. These fire-rated polymers meet the flammability requirements of Underwriters' Laboratories 94VE-0 rating and also pass the CSA C22.2 standard specifications. The oxygen index of the TPR 3000 series is 28. Typical extruded properties of TPR 3700 and 3812 are summarized in Table 2-2.

The TPR 4000 series has better room-temperature tensile properties relative to the TPR 1000/2000 series, particularly when extruded. Three grades (TPR 4700, 4800, and 4900), which cover a wide range of hardness, are commercially available. They are all available in natural or white color and in standard or

*Registered trademark for Uniroyal's olefinic thermoplastic elastomers.

Table 2-1. Typical properties of TPR 1000/2000 series.[a]

	ASTM METHOD	TPR 1600	TPR 1700	TPR 1800	TPR 1900	TPR 2800
Specific gravity	D-297	0.88	0.88	0.88	0.88	0.88
Hardness (Shore A)	D-2240	67	77	88	92	87
Tensile strength, psi	D-412	650	950	1400	1850	1300
MPa		4.5	6.6	9.7	12.8	9.0
Ultimate elongation, %	D-412	230	200	210	230	150
100% modulus, psi	D-412	500	800	1250	1850	1250
MPa		3.5	5.5	8.6	12.8	8.6
Tensile set at break, %	D-412	10	20	25	50	30
Compression set, %	D-395-E					
After 22 hr @ 73°F (23°C)		25	30	35	40	30
After 22 hr @ 158°F (70°C)		45	50	64	70	70
Torsional modulus, psi	D-1053	300	500	1060	3000	1200
Kgf/cm^2		21.1	35.2	74.6	210.4	84.4
Flex modulus, psi	D-790	1500	2700	10,000	35,000	8000
MPa		10.3	18.6	69.0	241.3	55.2
Bashore resilience, % rebound		50	50	43	45	50
Split tear, pli	D-470	30	45	55	100	85
kN/m		5.3	7.9	9.6	17.5	14.9
Split tear, pli	D-624	140	220	270	500	350
kN/m		24.5	33.5	47.3	87.5	61.3
Abrasion resistance, g/kc	D-1044	0.6	0.3	0.3	0.4	0.3

[a]Data based on injection molding TPR into 2 × 6 × 0.075 in. (50.8 × 152.4 × 1.905 mm) slab using a 0.075-in. (1.905 mm) deep, 0.125-in. (3.175 mm) wide gate at one end of the plaque. Slabs are then die cut to ASTM specifications.

Table 2-2. Typical properties of TPR 3000 series.

Physical Properties[a]	
Shore A hardness	80
Tensile strength	1700 psi (11.8 MPa)
100% modulus	740 psi (5.1 MPa)
200% modulus	1060 psi (7.3 MPa)
Ultimate elongation	360%
Elongation set and break	25%
Set @ 200% elongation (D-470)	15%
Brittle point, °F	−30
Aging Properties[a]	
Air oven 168 hr @ 113°C (235°F)	
Tensile strength retention	142%
Elongation retention	116%
Air oven 168 hr @ 121°C (250°F)	
Tensile strength retention	145%
Elongation retention	105%
ASTM oil No. 2 18 hr @ 121°C (250°F)	
Tensile strength retention	138%
Elongation retention	108%
ASTM oil No. 3 18 hr @ 121°C (250°F)	
Tensile strength retention	115%
Elongation retention	102%
Oxygen bomb 96 hr @ 70°C (158°F)	
Tensile strength retention	100%
Elongation retention	93%
Air bomb 20 hr @ 127°C (260°F)	
Tensile strength retention	136%
Elongation retention	134%

[a]Initial physical properties and agings measured on 0.060-in. extruded strip.

highly stabilized grades. These modified polymers are designed for use as insulation and jacketing in flexible low voltage cables. TPR 4000 series polymers meet the requirements of UL-62 Class 34 and may be used in all applicable cable types. Typical properties of TPR 4700, 4800, and 4900 are summarized in Table 2-3.

The TPR 5000 series was recently introduced as a new, expanded line of thermoplastic rubbers for extruded wire and cable applications. This latest series is available only in natural color; however, it can be easily colored to any desired color coding. TPR 5160, 5180, and 5190 were developed for applications requiring maximum high temperature deformation resistance combined with low temperature flexibility. The TPR 5100 types are analogous to the TPR 1000 series except that they are specially formulated for electrical applications. TPR 5260 and 5280 are less expensive versions, which also have good high temperature deformation resistance. TPR 5370 is designed for use where oil resistance is required. TPR 5470 and 5480 are used for flexible insulation and jacketing for

Table 2-3. Typical properties of TPR 4000 series.

	ASTM TEST METHOD	TPR 4700	TPR 4800	TPR 4900
Specific gravity	D-297	.88	.88	.88
Hardness, Shore A	D-2240	78	84	90
Tensile strength, psi	D-412	950	1200	1800
MPa		6.6	8.3	12.4
Ultimate elongation, %	D-412	400	360	300
100% modulus, psi	D-412	900	850	1750
MPa		6.2	5.9	12.1
Tensile set at break, %	D-412	40	170	80
Compression set, %	D-395B			
After 22 hr @ 73°F (23°C)		41	34	56
After 22 hr @ 158°F (70°C)		90	92	84
Torsional modulus, psi	D-1053	650	850	3800
KgF/cm^2		45.7	59.8	267.2
Flexural modulus, psi	D-790	4600	6000	32,000
MPa		31.7	41.4	. 220.7
Bashore resilience, % rebound		47	51	48
Split tear, pli	D-470	70	90	140
kN/m		12.3	15.8	24.6
Abrasion resistance, g/kc	D-1044	0.4	0.4	0.3

low voltage cable. Typical extruded properties for these eight electrical grade TPR thermoplastic rubbers are summarized in Table 2-4.

TPR 6400 is a low-cost impact modifier for homopolymer polyethylene or polypropylene. A highly stabilized version, TPR 6422, is also commercially available. TPR 6400 and 6422 can be directly blended with polyethylene and/or polypropylene at the injection molding machine or extruder. Modification of polyethylene with the TPR 6400 series significantly improves its impact and chemical stress crack resistance. Modification of polypropylene homopolymer results in a higher level of impact resistance than can be gained by using polypropylene copolymer, particularly at lower temperatures.

2.1.2 Du Pont Somel®*

Somel thermoplastic elastomers are described by Du Pont as polyolefinic materials based on ethylene-propylene chemistry. These latest materials, an extension of Du Pont's original TPN thermoplastic Nordel®† type, complement Du Pont's high-performance Hytrel®† polyester thermoplastic elastomers. The

*Registered trademark for Du Pont's olefinic thermoplastic elastomers.
†Du Pont's registered trademark.

Table 2-4. Typical properties of TPR 5000 series.

	ASTM METHOD	TPR 5160	TPR 5180	TPR 5190	TPR 5260	TPR 5280	TPR 5370	TPR 5470	TPR 5480
Specific gravity	D-297	.88	.88	.88	.88	.88	1.18	.88	.88
Hardness, Shore A	D-2240	60	80	91	67	71	77	64	75
Tensile strength, psi	D-412	450	900	1250	1190	1210	1900	1250	2000
MPa		3.1	6.2	8.6	8.2	8.3	13.1	8.6	13.8
Ultimate elongation, %	D-412	600	600	400	790	700	400	790	700
100% modulus, psi	D-412	210	490	840	350	400	1000	350	470
MPa		1.4	3.4	5.8	2.4	2.8	6.9	2.4	3.2
200% modulus, psi	D-412	300	650	950	470	530	1300	530	580
MPa		2.1	4.5	6.6	3.2	3.7	9.0	3.7	4.0
Tensile set at break, %	D-412	60	120	220	225	215	25	300	285
Split tear, pli	D-470	20	45	52	48	50	50	47	60
kN/m		3.5	7.9	9.1	8.4	8.8	8.8	8.2	10.5

Somel line offers a more economical material for applications where lower physical strength properties and lesser degree of heat resistance are acceptable. Somel thermoplastic elastomers are supplied in the form of free-flowing pellets ready for processing.

The Somel products are believed to be mechanical blends of EPDM rubber and polypropylene. Three types of Somel thermoplastic elastomer are commercially available. All of them have a Shore A hardness above 90. Two of these products are highly filled with carbon black to achieve electrostatic painting. Typical injection-molded properties of these thermoplastic elastomers are summarized in Table 2-5.

Somel 301G, a general purpose material with good outdoor weathering properties, is black and is the most flexible Somel type. This easy processing material is moisture sensitive and may require drying if it is exposed to high humidity prior to processing.

Somel 401T is harder and has greater toughness and stiffness than the 301G type. It is also black and moisture sensitive. The 401T type has good resistance to ultraviolet light and outdoor weathering. Somel 401T is easier to extrude than the 301G type, but is harder to injection mold. It has relatively high tensile strength and impact, and is recommended in applications where maximum impact is required, particularly at low temperatures.

Somel 402T is white and has properties similar to the 401T type. Its specific gravity is only 0.89 compared with 1.02 for the two black grades. The higher priced 402T type is the easiest grade to mold and extrude. It is the stiffest Somel, and its impact resistance is also exceptional, approaching that of type 401T. Somel 402T can be colored if desired with color concentrates or dry pigments.

2.1.3 B. F. Goodrich Telcar®*

Telcar thermoplastic elastomers were introduced by Goodrich in November 1974, to complement its Estane polyurethane product line. The Telcars appear to be mechanical blends of EPDM rubber and polypropylene or polyethylene. Seven products are currently commercial with a wide range in hardness from 54 to 95 Shore A durometer. This is the widest flexibility range of all olefinic thermoplastic elastomers that are commercially available from any manufacturer. Telcar thermoplastic elastomers are sold in granule form and are available in natural and black colors. All of the Telcar products can be properly pigmented for good weathering properties in outdoor applications.

Typical injection-molded properties of Telcar thermoplastic elastomers are summarized in Table 2-6. The Telcar TR 100 series is the hardest and stiffest of

*Registered trademark for Goodrich's olefinic thermoplastic elastomers.

	ASTM METHOD	SOMEL 301G	SOMEL 401T	SOMEL 402T
Specific gravity	D-792	1.02	1.02	0.89
Hardness, Shore D	D-2240	40	50	50
Tensile properties at 2 in./min	D-412			
Tensile strength, psi (MPa)				
−20°F (−29°C)		3800(26.2)	6320(43.6)	4870(33.6)
73°F (23°C)		1660(11.4)	3160(21.8)	4460(30.8)
158°F (70°C)		950(6.6)	1085(7.5)	870(6.0)
Tensile at 100% elongation, psi (MPa)				
73°F (23°C)		1550(10.7)	2035(14.0)	1990(13.7)
Elongation at break, %				
−20°F (−29°C)		45	135	10
73°F (23°C)		230	390	595
Tensile properties at 20 in./min	D-412			
Tensile strength, psi (MPa)				
−20°F (−29°C)		4280(29.5)	4460(30.8)	4790(33.0)
73°F (23°C)		2200(15.2)	2800(19.3)	2400(16.6)
158°F (70°C)		1350(9.3)	1270(8.8)	1440(9.9)
Tensile at 100% elongation, psi (MPa)				
73°F (23°C)		2050(14.1)	2600(17.9)	2250(15.5)
Elongation at break, %				
−20°F (−29°C)		50	60	35
73°F (23°C)		120	140	160
Flexural modulus, psi (MPa)	D-790B			
−20°F (−29°C)		118,000(814)	127,000(876)	175,000(1207)
73°F (23°C)		33,000(228)	43,000(297)	56,000(386)
158°F (70°C)		13,000(89.7)	13,000(897)	16,000(110)
Stiffness in flexure, psi (MPa)	D-747			
73°F (23°C)		18,000(124)	27,000(186)	38,000(262)
Die C tear (2 in./min), pli (kN/m)	D-624			
73°F (23°C)		500(87.7)	750(131.6)	650(114.0)
Izod impact (notched)	D-256			
−40°F (−40°C)		NB[a]	NB	NB
Taber abrasion, CS 18 wheel				
500 gm load, mg/kc		180	100	40

[a]NB = no break.

Table 2-6. Typical properties of Telcars.

	ASTM METHOD	TELCAR TR 100	TELCAR TR 101	TELCAR TR 301	TELCAR TR 302	TELCAR TR 400	TELCAR TR 402	TELCAR TR 405
Specific gravity	D-792	0.89	0.89	0.84	0.84	0.91	0.93	0.88
Hardness, Shore A	D-2240	93	95	83	71	90	78	54
Shore D		45	55	—	—	—	—	—
Original properties Stress strain	D-412							
Yield tensile strength, psi.								
72°F (22°C)		1780	2560	400–550	300–400	585	320	200
100°F (38°C)		—	—	450	250	440	250	100
150°F (66°C)		—	—	175	60	260	130	—
Ultimate tensile strength, psi.								
72°F (22°C)		1800	2150	900–1150	800–1000	2575	1250–1500	650
100°F (38°C)		—	—	500	300	820	365	175
150°F (66°C)		—	—	175	75	305	157	—
250°F (121°C)		>390	>750	—	—	—	—	—
Ultimate elongation, %.								
72°F (22°C)		290	70	750–850	750–850	870	900	1000 NB
100°F (38°C)		—	—	900	900	900	900	NB
150°F (66°C)		—	—	900	—	NB	NB	—
250°F (121°C)		>620	>620	—	—	—	—	—
Modulus at 100% elongation, psi.								
72°F (22°C)		1780	—	450	310	600	360	200

Property	ASTM Method							
Modulus at 300% elongation, psi.								
72°F (22°C)		200	375	700	400	550	—	—
Flexural modulus, psi.								
-20°F (-29°C)		3750	10,150	40,000	12,500	22,000	162,000	76,000
0°F (18°C)		2300	7200	15,000	8000	16,000	53,600	23,000
72°F (22°C)		900	2450	4000	5000	4500	—	—
100°F (38°C)		216	1080	2500	1225	2750	22,600	5800
160°F (71°C)		—	—	—	—	—	—	—
Stiffness, psi.	D-747							
-20°F (-29°C)		—	—	—	—	—	155,000	93,500
72°F (22°C)		—	—	—	—	—	64,000	33,700
160°F (71°C)		—	—	—	—	—	22,600	12,700
Tear strength, Die C, ppi.	D-624							
72°F (22°C)		110	185	310	175	290	635	450
250°F (121°C)		—	43	53	40	47	240	105
Vicat softening point, °C	D-1525	—	—	—	—	—	91	59
Compression set Method B, %	D-395							
22 hours at 72°F (22°C)		30	28	24	32	37	48	45
22 hours at 158°F (70°C)		67	58	70	90	92	52	84
Brittleness temperature, °C	D-746	-65	-60	-60	-65	-65	-58	<-80
Clash-Berg stiffness, psi	D-1043	1450	4500	14,000	8000	18,000	67,000	27,000
Modulus of rigidity at								
-40°C (-40°F)		—	—	—	—	—	—	—
-35°C (-31°F)		—	—	—	1400	3400		
-10°C (14°F)					—	—		
T_f°C							-15	-41

the entire product line. Telcar TR 100 is more elastomeric than the TR 101 grade. Telcar TR 101 has significantly higher tensile strength and flexural modulus, but its ultimate elongation is much lower. These materials can be processed in hot roll coating operations, as well as injection molded and extruded. They offer excellent processability in slot-die extrusion for coated fabrics or free film.

Telcar TR 301 and TR 302 are the latest additions to the Goodrich product line. The Telcar TR 300 series is softer than the TR 100 series. The tensile strength is also lower, but the ultimate elongation is much higher. The relatively low specific gravity of 0.84 for these two new grades suggests the presence of amorphous polypropylene in the blend. No information is available on the specific applications of the TR 300 type grades.

The Telcar TR 400 series contains three types: TR 400, TR 402, and TR 405. Telcar TR 400 is considered a general purpose grade with good tensile properties. TR 402, which is softer and not as tough as TR 400, is also reported by Goodrich to contain about 1 percent moisture; thus, it must be dried before processing. The TR 405 type is the softest Telcar product and has the lowest tensile strength and modulus. The rather low properties at elevated temperatures suggest that this blend might be based on polyethylene rather than polypropylene.

2.1.4 Allied Chemical's ET Polymer®*

Allied Chemical has commercialized a unique type of thermoplastic elastomer designated as *ET polymer*. ET polymers are produced by a grafting reaction that chemically combines butyl rubber with polyethylene. The butyl rubber is grafted onto the polyethylene chains using a phenolic resin such as brominated hydroxymethylphenol. This butyl/ethylene graft polymer combines the thermoplastic properties of polyethylene with the elastomeric characteristics of butyl rubber. The butyl rubber forms the so-called soft segment, and the crystallinity of polyethylene provides the strength at service temperatures.

Four different ET polymers are commercially available from Allied Chemical. They are made by varying the amount of butyl rubber and using both low-density and high-density polyethylene. These formulations produce a variety of thermoplastic elastomers that have a wide range of flexibility. The properties of the four ET polymers are summarized in Table 2-7.

ET polymer L1100 is a 50/50-polyethylene/butyl rubber graft based on low-density polyethylene. Its flexural modulus is comparable to that of flexible polyvinyl chloride (PVC), but it has better chemical resistance. L1100 has a wide service-temperature range from -100 to 190°F (-73 to 88°C) and has excellent long-term aging resistance.

*Registered trademark for Allied Chemical's grafted thermoplastic elastomer.

Table 2-7. Typical properties of ET polymers.

	ASTM METHOD	ET L1100	ET H1100	ET L3100	ET H3100
Specific gravity	D-1505	.923	.939	.920	.944
Hardness, Shore D	D-1706	56	38	40	55
Tensile strength, psi	D-412	1650	2600	1750	3400
(MPa)		11.4	17.9	12.1	23.4
Tensile yield, psi	D-412	550	1100	950	2100
(MPa)		3.8	7.6	6.6	14.5
Ultimate elongation, %	D-412	375	375	400	450
Flexural modulus, psi	D-796	4000	6000	10,000	60,000
(MPa)		27.6	41.4	69.0	414
Compression set, %	D-395B				
After 22 hr @ 158°F (70°C)		37	33	62	49
After 22 hr @ 212°F (100°C)		50	37	69	57
Tabor, abrasion	D-1044	.012	.003	.012	.003

ET polymer L3100 is a 75/25 ratio graft polymer of low-density polyethylene/ butyl rubber. The relatively higher amount of polyethylene increases the flexural modulus but makes it softer than L1100. The low-density polyethylene used in ET polymers L1100 and L3100 has a density of 0.919 and a melt flow index of 1.0 at 230°C (446°F).

ET polymer H1100 is the high-density polyethylene analogue of ET polymer L1100. It is also a 50/50 blend of polyethylene and butyl rubber. H1100 has a higher tensile strength and flexural modulus relative to L1100. It also has a better retention of properties at elevated temperatures.

ET polymer H3100 is a 75/25-HDPE/butyl rubber blend. It is the high-density analogue of L3100. This graft polymer has the highest tensile strength, ultimate elongation, and flexural modulus of all the ET polymers. The high-density polyethylene used in ET polymer H1100 and H3100 is made by the Phillips process. It has a density of 0.950 and a melt flow index equal to 0.4.

2.1.5 Hercules Profax®*

Developmental grades of Profax SB 814 were introduced by Hercules in early 1974. By mid-1974, improved grades were introduced that had much better properties and processibility. Typical properties of the commercial grade of Profax SB 814 are summarized in Table 2-8.

Profax SB 814 is a high hardness thermoplastic elastomer that is believed to be a mechanical blend of EPDM rubber and polypropylene. It is available in natural

*Registered trademark for Hercules' olefinic thermoplastic elastomer.

Table 2-8. Typical properties of Profax SB 814.

	TEMPERATURE (°F)	ASTM METHOD	
Density, g/cm^3	75	D-792 A-2	0.89
Hardness, Shore D/A	75	D-2240	48/96
Tensile strength, psi (MPa)	75	D-412	1600(11.0)
(20 in./min.)	140		>960(>6.6)
	250		>290(>2.0)
100% tensile modulus, psi (MPa)	75	D-412	1385(9.6)
(20 in./min.)	140		590(4.1)
	250		170(1.2)
Elongation at break, %	75	D-412	500
(20 in./min.)	140		>640
	250		>660
Tensile modulus, psi (MPa) 1%	75	D-638	82,000(566)
100%	75	D-412	1385(9.6)
200%	75		1410(9.7)
300%	75		1500(10.3)
High-speed tensile strength, psi (MPa)			
1000 in./min.	75	–	3900(26.9)
Flexural modulus (1% sec)	–40	D-790	151,000(1041)
psi (MPa)	75		50,000(345)
	120		26,000(179)
Flexural strength, psi (MPa)	–40	D-790	4900(33.8)
	75		1600(11.0)
	120		960(6.6)
Notched Izod impact	–20	D-256A	No break
Falling dart impact, ft-lb	–80	–	108
0.1-in. textured plaque			
0.5-in. tip 18-lb weight			
75% extension set, %	75	D-412	34
Compression set, %			
After 22 hr	158	D-395B	78
Tear strength die "C", pli (kN/m)	75	D-624	566(99.3)
	250		143(25.1)

pellet form and is heat-stabilized. This material is distinguished from other thermoplastic elastomers by its ultrahigh impact resistance and excellent flexibility at low temperatures combined with stiffness at elevated temperatures.

2.2 PROPERTIES

The polyolefin thermoplastic elastomers differ from conventional thermoplastics because of their elastic memory or recovery from deformation. Elastomers are defined by ASTM in terms of these recovery characteristics. According to the ASTM definition, an elastomer is any material that can be stretched repeatedly to twice its original length at room temperature and that will return rapidly to approximately its original length after the applied stress is removed. All of the thermoplastic elastomers fulfill these criteria by virtue of their ultimate elongations in excess of 200% and their excellent elastic recovery characteristics. In contrast, even the most flexible conventional thermoplastics have much lower elongations and poor elastic recovery resulting in a nonrecoverable yield point at low stress levels.

The elastic recovery of the thermoplastic elastomers is demonstrated by their relatively low set in tension and compression. Low permanent set is usually obtained only in vulcanized elastomers, which require a lengthy vulcanization cycle. Because of their thermoset properties, vulcanized flash or scrap cannot be reprocessed. Thermoplastic materials can be processed rapidly and scrap can be reprocessed, but their permanent set is usually very poor. The olefinic thermoplastic elastomers combine the advantages of rapid processing and reprocessibility characteristic of thermoplastic materials with the property advantages of a vulcanized elastomer such as low permanent set.

The thermoplastic and elastomeric behaviors of the thermoplastic elastomers are obtained differently by the various manufacturers of these polymers. Most of the commercially available polyolefin thermoplastic elastomers are mechanical blends of a thermoplastic material such as polypropylene and an elastomer such as EPDM rubber. Their properties are dependent on the type of thermoplastic and elastomeric materials used as well as on the relative proportion of each component in the final blend. The properties of TPR-type thermoplastic rubbers are dependent on the types of polymers used but also on the manner in which they are combined. A wide range of properties can be obtained by controlling the level of primary cross-links that are present throughout the polymer system. The properties of ET polymers are dependent on both the butyl rubber content and on the type of polyethylene used. The low-density polyethylene graft polymers are more elastomeric than their high-density polyethylene analogues.

The properties of the olefinic thermoplastic elastomers are also dependent on the processing method used for their fabrication. This anisotropic effect is caused by the degree of orientation in the finished part. The final properties are generally improved when there is more orientation. The degree of orientation is a function of the magnitude of the shear applied to the polymer melt. Consequently, injection molded parts generally have better tensile properties than when extruded. The effect of anisotropy is also due to the orientation of the polymer melt relative to the applied shear stress. For example, tensile properties are greater when measured in the direction parallel to that of the applied shear relative to the perpendicular direction. This effect becomes more pronounced with increasing crystallinity in the thermoplastic elastomers. Most manufacturers report only the optimum properties obtained via injection molding.

2.2.1 Mechanical

The olefinic thermoplastic elastomers have good overall mechanical properties. Typical properties have been summarized in Tables 2-1 through 2-8 for all commercially available products. The properties of the thermoplastic elastomers cover a broad range and are dependent on their type and particular manufacturer. Their characteristic properties range from rubbery to rubbery-plastic and are generally dependent on hardness. The hardness can vary from about 55 to 95 Shore A durometer. The tensile properties show moderate strength and elongation with relatively very little set. The tensile strength commonly ranges

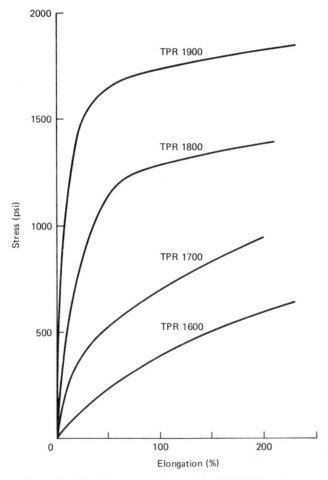

Figure 2-1. Typical stress-strain curves for TPR 1000 series.

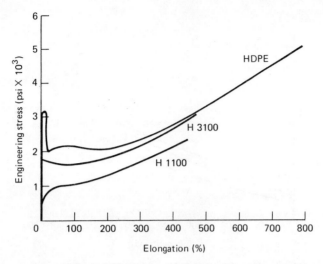

Figure 2-2. Stress-strain curves for ET polymers based on HDPE.

between 1000 and 2000 psi (6.9 and 13.8 MPa), although higher tensile strengths are obtained for the hardest materials. The softer materials are more rubbery and have lower set. The ultimate elongation is generally 200 to 300% for molded parts and even higher when extruded.

Stress-strain curves of the TPR thermoplastic rubbers show a monotonic increase in stress with increasing strain. Typical stress-strain curves for TPR 1600, 1700, 1800, and 1900 are shown in Figure 2-1. A pronounced *Mullins effect* is observed in the hysteresis response for these polymers; i.e., if a polymer is stretched to some initial elongation and then released, the subsequent stress-strain curve falls below the original curve up to that elongation. At strains above the initial elongation, the second stress-strain curve achieves the same level of stress that would have been observed if the initial stress-strain cycle had been run to higher elongations.

The stress-strain curves for ET polymers based on high-density and low-density polyethylene are shown in Figures 2-2 and 2-3, respectively. The pronounced yield point observed in the stress-strain curve for high-density polyethylene is significantly reduced in H3100, which has only a slight yield point. Even though there are significant differences in yielding behavior, the stress-strain curve of H3100 superimposes with that of high-density polyethylene at higher elongations. No yield point is observed in the higher rubber graft polymer, H1100, which remains softer than high-density polyethylene even at higher elongations. The stress-strain curves for ET polymers based on low-density polyethylene do not have a yield point. As before, the stress-strain curve for

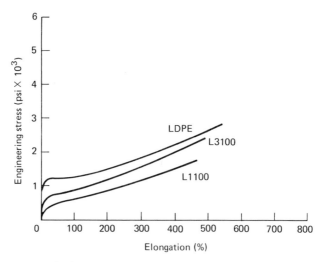

Figure 2-3. Stress-strain curves for ET polymers based on LDPE.

the 50/50-polyethylene/butyl rubber graft polymer is consistently below that of the corresponding 75/25 ratio graft polymer.

The rubbery character of the polyolefin thermoplastic elastomers is demonstrated by their rubbery feel and appearance, high resilience, good traction, and flexibility. They are generally elastic at normal service conditions and have high coefficients of friction. Other mechanical properties such as abrasion resistance, tear strength, and the Poisson ratio exemplify the elastomeric nature of the thermoplastic elastomers. For example, the Poisson ratio for TPR thermoplastic rubbers is in the range of 0.45 to 0.49, depending on hardness. The softer grades approach the limiting ratio of 0.5 for an ideal rubber.

2.2.2 Thermal

The olefinic thermoplastic elastomers have an exceptionally wide service-temperature range from approximately −50°F (−46°C) up to 250 to 300°F (121 to 149°C). Somewhat higher and lower temperatures can be tolerated in intermittent use. These thermoplastic elastomers have excellent flexibility and impact resistance at low temperatures combined with retention of properties at elevated temperatures. Good resistance to tear and stress cracking is also exhibited over this broad thermal service range.

Property retention at high temperatures is generally good. Available data for the retention of tensile strength at elevated temperatures are summarized in Table 2-9. Comparison of the data shows that the tensile strength of the TPR 1000

Table 2-9. High temperature property retention of polyolefin thermoplastic elastomers.

ELASTOMER	% TENSILE STRENGTH RETAINED AT						
	100°F 38°C	140°F 60°C	150°F 66°C	158°F 70°C	200°F 93°C	250°F 121°C	300°F 149°C
TPR 1600	93	–a	80	–	65	53	39
TPR 1700	94	–	82	–	68	56	42
TPR 1800	95	–	83	–	70	59	43
TPR 1900	94	–	84	–	73	63	52
TPR 2800	94	–	82	–	70	58	45
TPR 4700	67	–	32	–	–	11	–
TPR 4800	67	–	28	–	–	8	–
TPR 4900	86	–	55	–	–	18	–
Telcar TR 100	–	–	–	–	–	22	–
Telcar TR 101	–	–	–	–	–	35	–
Telcar TR 301	49	–	17	–	–	–	–
Telcar TR 302	33	–	8	–	–	–	–
Telcar TR 400	32	–	12	–	–	–	–
Telcar TR 402	27	–	11	–	–	–	–
Telcar TR 405	27	–	–	–	–	–	–
Somel 301G	–	–	–	61	–	–	–
Somel 401T	–	–	–	45	–	–	–
Somel 402T	–	–	–	60	–	–	–
Profax SB 814	–	60	–	–	–	18	–

aNo data available.

and 2000 series thermoplastic rubbers is retained to a greater degree at higher temperatures relative to the other thermoplastic elastomers. The tensile strength is plotted against temperature in Figure 2-4 for these TPR thermoplastic rubbers. The temperature dependence of the tensile modulus at 100% elongation and hardness is shown in Figures 2-5 and 2-6, respectively. The data show that the ultimate tensile strength and tensile modulus at 100% elongation are about 50% their room-temperature values at 300°F (149°C). The Shore A hardness of these polymers at 300°F (149°C) is about 80% of their corresponding room-temperature value.

The elastic recovery of the polyolefin thermoplastic elastomers is also retained to a large degree at elevated temperatures. This is demonstrated by the compression set of a number of thermoplastic elastomers summarized at various temperatures in Table 2-10. The compression set of the softer TPR thermoplastic rubbers is lower than the other thermoplastic elastomers listed including the Telcar polymers and Profax SB 814. Compression set is plotted against temperature in Figure 2-7 for the TPR 1000 and 2000 series. The time dependence of the compression set of TPR 1600 is plotted in Figure 2-8 at 73 and 158°F (23 and

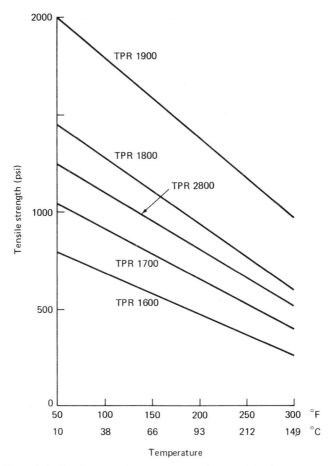

Figure 2-4. Tensile strength vs. temperature for TPR 1000/2000 series.

70°C). These time-temperature data are indicative of the long-term elastic re-coverability of the thermoplastic elastomers.

The heat deformation resistance of the olefinic thermoplastic elastomers is generally quite good. Heat-deformation data are shown in Figure 2-9 over a range of temperature for TPR 1812 and 1912. Comparison with a typical wire-coating grade of PVC shows the much better heat deformation resistance of these two hardness grades of TPR thermoplastic rubber. At 50% deformation, for example, TPR performs at temperatures 30°C (54°F) above that for plasti-cized PVC.

The low temperature properties of the polyolefin thermoplastic elastomers are

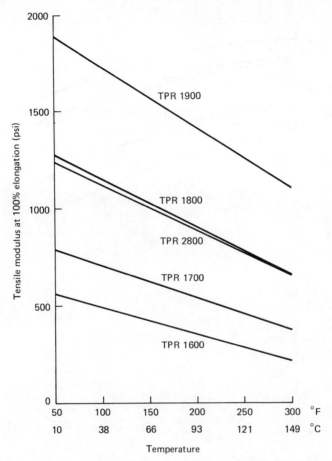

Figure 2-5. A 100% tensile modulus vs. temperature for TPR 1000/2000 series.

excellent. They do not become embrittled even at temperatures as low as −75°F (59°C). The thermoplastic elastomers also have exceptional impact resistance at low temperatures. No break is observed upon impacting most of these polymers at temperatures as low as −40°F (−40°C). The falling dart impact resistance of Profax SB 814 is reportedly over 100 ft lb at −80°F (−62°C).

Most of the thermoplastic elastomers remain flexible at temperatures down to −50°F (−46°C). This is demonstrated by the effect of temperature on the torsion modulus of TPR and Telcar blends summarized in Table 2-11. The limited data show that the Telcars are generally not as flexible as the TPR thermoplastic rubbers. If the conventional reference value of 10,000 psi is taken as the di-

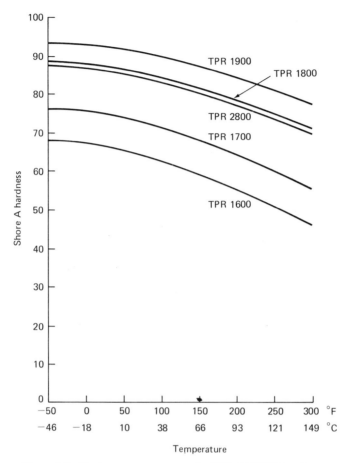

Figure 2-6. Hardness vs. temperature for TPR 1000/2000 series.

viding line between flexible and rigid properties, only Telcar TR 302, 402, and 405 are flexible at -40°F (-40°C). All of the TPR thermoplastic rubbers are flexible at -50°F (-46°C), with the exception of TPR 1900. This is shown more clearly by the plot of torsional modulus against temperature in Figure 2-10. Their flexibility is also demonstrated by the absence of cracking or crazing when bent over a 1-in.-diameter mandrel at -40°F (-40°C).

The relative flexibility of the olefinic thermoplastic elastomers can be seen from the flexural modulus data summarized in Table 2-12 over a wide range in temperature. The more rigid materials are characterized by a relatively high flexural modulus and include all three Somel blends, Profax SB 814, the Telcar TR 100 series, ET H3100, and TPR 1900. The more flexible thermoplastic materials include Telcar TR 405 and TPR 1600. The temperature dependence of

Table 2-10. Compression set percent at various temperatures for polyolefin thermoplastic elastomers.

ELASTOMER	TEMPERATURE			
	73°F 23°C	158°F 70°C	212°F 100°C	250°F 121°C
TPR 1600	23	43	49	54
TPR 1700	32	51	60	66
TPR 1800	41	68	77	85
TPR 1900	38	68	76	87
TPR 2800	32	72	82	91
TPR 4700	41	90	—[a]	—
TPR 4800	34	92	—	—
TPR 4900	56	84	—	—
Telcar TR 100	45	84	—	—
Telcar TR 101	48	52	—	—
Telcar TR 301	37	92	—	—
Telcar TR 302	32	90	—	—
Telcar TR 400	24	70	—	—
Telcar TR 402	28	58	—	—
Telcar TR 405	30	67	—	—
Pro-fax SB 814	—	78	—	—

[a]No data available.

the flexural modulus can be seen more clearly from the semilogarithmic plot in Figure 2-11. The slope of the flexural modulus curves is generally flatter for TPR thermoplastic rubbers, giving the advantage of better stiffness retention at higher temperatures and more flexibility at lower temperatures.

The coefficient of linear thermal expansion for the polyolefin thermoplastic elastomers is comparable to that of conventional thermoplastic materials. Somel 301G and 402T have linear thermal expansion coefficients equal to 5.5×10^{-5} in./in./°F. The value for Somel 401T is slightly higher at 7.2×10^{-5} in./in./°F. The coefficient of linear thermal expansion for TPR thermoplastic rubbers is generally between $5\text{-}7 \times 10^{-5}$ in./in./°F.

The thermal conductivity of the thermoplastic elastomers is comparable to that of natural rubber but much lower than thermoplastics such as polyethylene and polypropylene. TPR thermoplastic rubbers have a thermal conductivity of 1.0-1.2 Btu/ft^2/sec for a temperature gradient of 1°F/in. The value for Somel 402T is 1.7 Btu/ft^2/sec/°F/in. The thermal conductivity of DuPont's two black grades, Somel 301G and 401T, is somewhat higher at 2.2 Btu/ft^2/sec/°F/in.

2.2.3 Aging

Air-oven aging data are summarized in Table 2-13 for a number of thermoplastic elastomers. The retention of tensile strength and ultimate elongation is reported

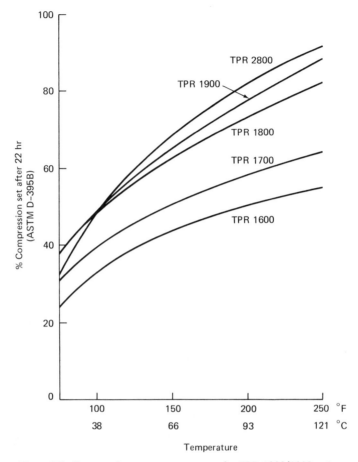

Figure 2-7. Compression set vs. temperature for TPR 1000/2000 series.

by Goodrich for the Telcar TR 100 series at 100°C (212°F) and the TR 300 and 400 series at only 38°C (100°F), indicating that property retention is poor at higher temperatures. ET polymers exhibit good retention of tensile properties after 4 days at 126°C (255°F). Aging data for TPR thermoplastic rubbers show their good property retention at even higher temperatures. TPR 1922 and 2822 meet the requirements for 105°C (221°F) service in accordance with UL 62 class 12 specifications. Both TPR products exceed the minimum requirements of 75% tensile strength retention and 65% ultimate elongation retention at 135°C (275°F). These data were obtained on 47-mil wall thickness insulation extruded onto No. 14 solid tinned copper wire.

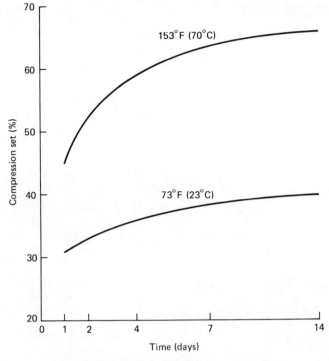

Figure 2-8. Compression set vs. time for TPR 1600.

Long-term heat-aging data are summarized in Table 2-14 for specially stabilized grades of TPR thermoplastic rubbers. All samples were aged in an air-circulating oven in accordance with ASTM D-573. Failure was taken as the time at which either the retention of tensile strength dropped below 50% or the sample became embrittled and crazed, whichever occurred first. The accelerated failure data at higher temperatures were used to predict longer-term aging performance at lower temperatures. This extrapolation was facilitated using Arrhenius plots of the heat-aging data to failure at the experimental temperatures. The Arrhenius plots are shown in Figure 2-12 as the logarithm of the failure time vs. the reciprocal of the absolute temperature. These temperature-time relationships predict a 5-year life for TPR parts at temperatures from 220 to 225°F (93 to 107°C). A 10-year life is expected at a continuous operating temperature of 210°F (99°C).

Accelerated aging in air and oxygen at elevated pressures as required by Underwriters' Laboratories, military, and utility specifications has a minimal effect on tensile properties. The retention of tensile strength and ultimate elongation after high-pressure environmental aging are summarized in Table 2-15 for a num-

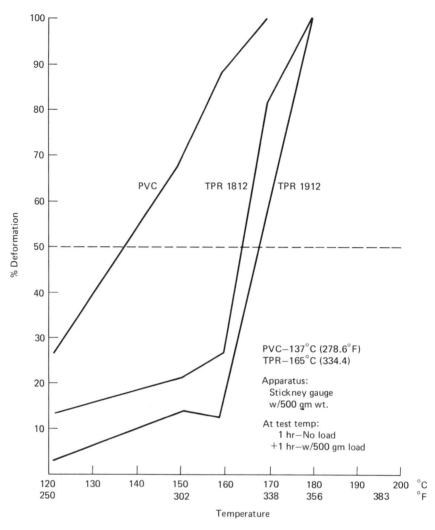

Figure 2-9. Heat deformation resistance of TPR 1812 and 1912.

ber of TPR products and ET H1100 polymer. These tensile properties are retained to a much greater extent than the 50% minimum level required for UL 62
class 1-10 rubber.

The olefinic thermoplastic elastomers have good resistance to ultraviolet light
and outdoor weathering. Retention of tensile strength and elongation after
Fade-Ometer, Weatherometer, and Florida aging are summarized in Table 2-16
for different thermoplastic elastomers. Fade-Ometer and Weatherometer aging

Table 2-11. Torsion modulus (psi) at various temperatures for polyolefin thermoplastic elastomers.

ELASTOMER	TEMPERATURE							
	−50°F −46°C	−40°F −40°C	−35°F −37°C	−10°F −23°C	0°F −17°C	50°F 10°C	73°F 23°C	100°F 38°C
TPR 1600	1430	−[a]	−	−	625	380	330	270
TPR 1700	3250	−	−	−	1100	525	420	340
TPR 1800	9020	−	−	−	3970	2100	1450	1130
TPR 1900	25,000	−	−	−	9200	3950	2910	2070
TPR 2800	9000	−	−	−	3380	1500	1080	760
TPR 4700	13,820	−	−	−	2090	950	645	360
TPR 4800	8930	−	−	−	2020	1100	850	790
TPR 4900	41,330	−	−	−	12,190	4990	3840	2670
Telcar TR 100	−	−	27,000	−	−	−	−	−
Telcar TR 101	−	−	67,000	−	−	−	−	−
Telcar TR 301	−	18,000	−	3400	−	−	−	−
Telcar TR 302	−	8000	−	1400	−	−	−	−
Telcar TR 400	−	14,000	−	−	−	−	−	−
Telcar TR 402	−	4500	−	−	−	−	−	−
Telcar TR 405	−	1450	−	−	−	−	−	−

[a]No data available.

tests were conducted in accordance with ASTM D-750. Florida aging was done on both painted and unpainted samples at a 5° angle facing south as required by automotive specifications.

Fade-Ometer and Weatherometer aging data for TPR thermoplastic elastomers show that their outdoor environmental resistance is considerably better than cross-linked polyethylene and comparable with butyl rubber. These accelerated aging data show that these products meet the automotive specifications for exterior part applications. The relatively shorter exposure times reported for ET polymers and the Telcar TR 100 series do not permit such a comparison. Florida aging tests also demonstrate the ability of TPR thermoplastic elastomers to resist the effects of prolonged sunlight and ozone present in an outdoor environment. These products exhibit good property retention after a 1-year outdoor exposure in Florida.

2.2.4 Dynamic

Dynamic mechanical data for ET polymers show the effect of grafting butyl rubber onto polyethylene. The damping factor, tan δ, is plotted against temperature in Figures 2-13 and 2-14 for graft polymers based on high-density and low-density polyethylene, respectively. The mechanical damping peak is broadened, and the value of tan δ is higher over the entire temperature range from −60 to

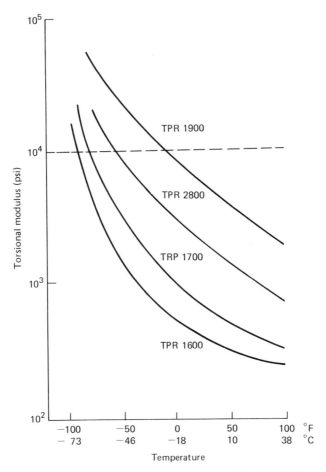

Figure 2-10. Torsion modulus vs. temperature for TPR 1000/2000 series.

140°C (-76 to 284°F) when grafting occurs. The glass transition temperature of butyl rubber is lowered from -14 to -40°C (7 to -40°F) when grafted with polyethylene. This apparent lowering of the rubber transition temperature is difficult to understand in view of the relatively higher glass transition temperature of polyethylene. These data indicate that grafting occurs randomly along the polyethylene chain resulting in a highly branched polymer network.

ET polymer composition also affects its dynamic properties. The complex Young's modulus, E*, is plotted against temperature in Figures 2-15 and 2-16 for butyl rubber grafted onto high-density and low-density polyethylene, respectively. The dynamic tensile modulus of H3100 (75/25-HDPE/BR) is slightly

Table 2-12. Flexural modulus (psi) at various temperatures for polyolefin thermoplastic elastomers.

ELASTOMER	TEMPERATURE											
	−50°F −46°C	−40°F −40°C	−20°F −29°C	0°F −17°C	50°F 10°C	72°F 23°C	100°F 38°C	120°F 49°C	150°F 66°C	160°F 71°C	200°F 93°C	250°F 121°C
TPR 1600	6500	a	—	3100	1700	1500	1100	—	820	—	640	500
TPR 1700	17,000	—	—	8500	4800	3900	3000	—	2000	—	1350	950
TPR 1800	65,000	—	—	23,000	11,000	8400	6200	—	3800	—	2500	1700
TPR 1900	—	—	—	70,000	28,000	21,000	15,000	—	8600	—	5500	3600
TPR 2800	43,000	—	—	24,000	17,300	9000	5200	—	3800	—	2500	1700
TPR 4700	57,000	—	—	17,000	7000	4600	2600	—	1400	—	690	560
TPR 4800	110,000	—	—	19,000	9000	6000	3600	—	1500	—	750	590
TPR 4900	250,000	—	—	89,000	47,000	32,000	16,000	—	10,000	—	6800	4900
Telcar TR 100	—	—	76,000	—	—	23,000	—	—	—	5800	—	—
Telcar TR 101	—	—	162,000	—	—	53,600	—	—	—	22,600	—	—
Telcar TR 301	—	—	22,000	16,000	—	4500	2750	—	—	—	—	—
Telcar TR 302	—	—	12,500	8000	—	5000	1225	—	—	—	—	—
Telcar TR 400	—	—	40,000	15,000	—	4000	2500	—	—	—	—	—
Telcar TR 402	—	—	10,150	7200	—	2450	1080	—	—	—	—	—
Telcar TR 405	—	—	3750	2300	—	900	215	—	—	—	—	—
Somel 301G	—	—	118,000	—	—	33,000	—	—	—	13,000	—	—
Somel 401T	—	—	127,000	—	—	43,000	—	—	—	13,000	—	—
Somel 402T	—	—	175,000	—	—	56,000	—	—	—	16,000	—	—
ET L1100	—	—	—	—	—	4000	—	—	—	—	—	—
ET H1100	—	—	—	—	—	6000	—	—	—	—	—	—
ET L3100	—	—	—	—	—	10,000	—	—	—	—	—	—
ET H3100	—	—	—	—	—	60,000	—	—	—	—	—	—
Profax SB 814	—	151,000	—	—	—	50,000	—	26,000	—	—	—	—

aNo data available.

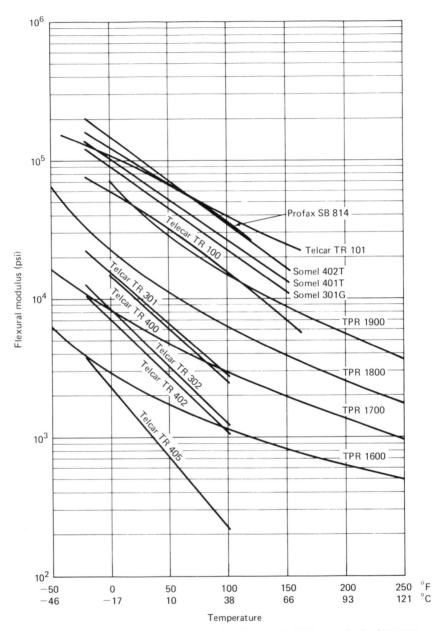

Figure 2-11. Flexural modulus vs. temperature for polyolefin thermoplastic elastomers.

Table 2-13. Air-oven aging of polyolefin thermoplastic elastomers.

AGING CONDITIONS	% TENSILE STRENGTH RETAINED/% ELONGATION RETAINED						
	TELCAR TR 100	TELCAR TR 101	TELCAR TR 301	TELCAR TR 302	TELCAR TR 400	TELCAR TR 402	TELCAR TR 405
7 days @ 100°F(38°C)	–	–	77/74	83/110	88/97	100/100	100/85
7 days @ 212°F(100°C)	102/79	110/56	–	–	–	–	–
	ET L1100	ET H1100	ET L3100	ET H3100			
4 days @ 259°F(126°C) Air pressure	70/100 –	80/92 –	83/79 –	80/85 –			
	TPR 1622	TPR 1822	TPR 1922	TPR 2822	TPR 3700		
7 days @ 250°F(121°C)	–	–	114/86	104/95	95/95		
7 days @ 275°F(135°C)	–	–	113/77	93/78	100/55		
7 days @ 300°F(149°C)	–	–	118/74	100/85	–		
7 days @ 325°F(163°C)	–	–	110/60	98/82	–		
90 days @ 207°F(97°C)	>90/90	>90/90	>90/90	–	–		

Table 2-14. Long-term heat aging of TPR 1000/2000 series.

TEMPERATURE	TIME TO FAILURE		
	TPR 1622	TPR 1922	TPR 2822
350°F (177°C)	100 hr	120 hr	240 hr
325°F (162°C)	300 hr	340 hr	740 hr
300°F (149°C)	800 hr	1000 hr	1500 hr
275°F (135°C)	2500 hr	2800 hr	4300 hr
250°F (121°C)	1.1 yr[a]	1.2 yr[a]	1.5 yr[a]
225°F (107°C)	4.3 yr[a]	4.4 yr[a]	4.7 yr[a]
200°F (93°C)	18.0 yr[a]	18.2 yr[a]	16.4 yr[a]

[a]Extrapolated from Arrhenius plot (*cf.* Figure 2-12).

lower than that of high-density polyethylene over the entire temperature range. The modulus of H1100 (50/50-HDPE/BR) is still lower and is below that of a corresponding 50/50 mechanical blend of high-density polyethylene and butyl rubber. This also confirms the presence of grafting. The same effect is found for the 50/50-LDPE/BR graft polymer, L1100, relative to low-density polyethylene.

Typical mechanical damping curves for TPR thermoplastic rubber are plotted in Figure 2-17. The dynamic mechanical properties are shown as the temperature dependence of the real shear modulus, G', the loss shear modulus, G'', and

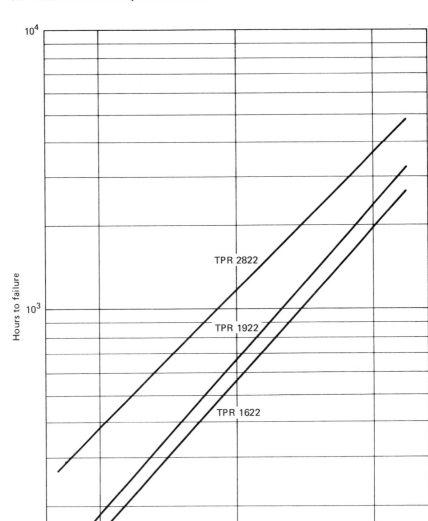

Figure 2-12. Arrhenius plots of air oven aging data.

Table 2-15. High-pressure aging of polyolefin thermoplastic elastomers.

	TPR 1822	TPR 1922	TPR 2822	TPR 3700	TPR 4700	TPR 4800	ET H1100
	% TENSILE STRENGTH RETAINED/% ELONGATION RETAINED						
AIR PRESSURE							
42 hr @ 261°F(127°C), 300 psi	81/75	117/88	97/83	102/98	88/105	99/128	—[a]
OXYGEN PRESSURE							
4 days @ 158°F(70°C), 300 psi	90/90	112/90	—	81/88	—	—	100/100
7 days @ 176°F(80°C), 300 psi	109/91	117/102	104/103	—	91/114	99/109	—

[a]No data available.

Table 2-16. Environmental aging of polyolefin thermoplastic elastomers.

AGING TEST	% TENSILE STRENGTH RETAINED/% ELONGATION RETAINED					
Fade-Ometer (hr)	ET L1100	ET H1100	ET L3100	ET H3100		
200	94/100	97/100	94/100	95/100		
	TPR 1622	TPR 1722	TPR 1922	TPR 2822	TR 100	TR 101
500	−a	116/100	100/65	108/100	−	−
1000	−	115/98	97/65	108/100	−	−
1500	−	112/95	92/50	92/95	−	−
Weatherometer (hr)						
1000	99/100	100/100	109/80	96/79	96/129	93/100
2000	80/118	100/100	109/74	86/79	−	−
3000	82/116	75/100	73/76	69/80	−	−
Florida (month)						
3	−	130/90	107/85	112/65	−	−
6	−	130/75	108/85	103/60	−	−
12	−	125/75	85/60	107/88	−	−

aNo data available.

the damping or dissipation factor, tan δ. These dynamic test data were measured using a torsion pendulum over the complete temperature range from −100 to 150°C (−148 to 302°F). The mechanical damping curves show a glass transition temperature around −50°C (−58°F), corresponding to a maximum in both the loss modulus and the damping factor and accompanied by a large decrease in the shear modulus of elasticity.

The magnitude of the dynamic modulus is dependent upon the hardness of the material at temperatures above the glass transition region. The temperature dependence of the shear modulus is shown in Figure 2-18 for Profax SB 814 and a number of ET polymers and TPR thermoplastic rubbers. For comparison purposes, the dynamic tensile modulus data reported for Profax SB 814 and ET polymers were converted to shear moduli by assuming an incompressible sample— i.e., $E = 3G$—to give the equivalent shear results shown in Figure 2-18. The modulus of ET polymer H3100 is higher than Profax SB 814, which in turn is higher than the TPR thermoplastic rubbers. The hardest TPR product commercially available, TPR 1900, has a higher shear modulus relative to softer TPR polymers such as TPR 1700 and 2800.

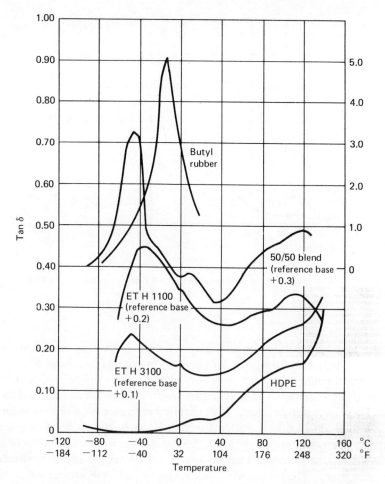

Figure 2-13. Damping factor vs. temperature for ET polymers based on HDPE.

2.2.5 Chemical

The chemical resistance of the olefinic thermoplastic elastomers is summarized in Table 2-17 for a number of chemicals, oils, and gases. Qualitative data are reported for Du Pont Somel, Uniroyal TPR, Hercules SB 814, and Allied Chemical ET polymer. No chemical resistance data are available for the Goodrich Telcar products. More quantitative data are given in Tables 2-18 and 2-19 for TPR and ET polymers, respectively. Table 2-18 summarizes the volume change of two TPR thermoplastic rubbers in various chemical environments after 1 day and 1 week. Most of the data were obtained at room temperature, although some re-

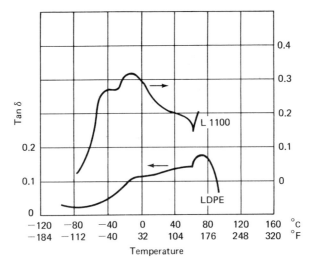

Figure 2-14. Damping factor vs. temperature for ET polymers based on LDPE.

sults at higher temperatures are also given. Table 2-19 summarizes the volume change and weight gain for all four ET polymers in a number of chemicals.

Polyolefin thermoplastic elastomers are relatively inert and are resistant to a wide variety of chemicals. They have excellent resistance to inorganic acids and bases. They are water resistant. Their chemical resistance is quite good in most low molecular weight organic solvents such as alcohols, glycols, ketones, ethers, aldehydes, esters, and carboxylic acids. Low molecular weight derivatives of hydrocarbons such as amines and amides also do not chemically affect the thermoplastic elastomers. Their resistance is not as good in higher molecular weight solvents, particularly aromatic hydrocarbons and chlorinated derivatives. Direct contact can cause appreciable swelling as well as surface attack. However, the swelling does not appear to lower the physical characteristics of molded parts so that there is little or no effect on the functionality of a finished part.

The general purpose grades have relatively poor resistance to oil and fuel. The oil resistance of TPR 1900 is sufficient to meet the Underwriters' Laboratories requirement for ASTM oil No. 2 exposure for 18 hr at 121°C (250°F). The volume swell of TPR products continues to increase with time in ASTM oils but does not change to any appreciable extent after 1 day in ASTM fuel B and JP jet fuel. Since swelling takes place in oils and fuels without any dissolution or loss in properties, it can be used to advantage in certain applications such as shaft seals. Specially formulated oil-resistant grades of thermoplastic elastomers are

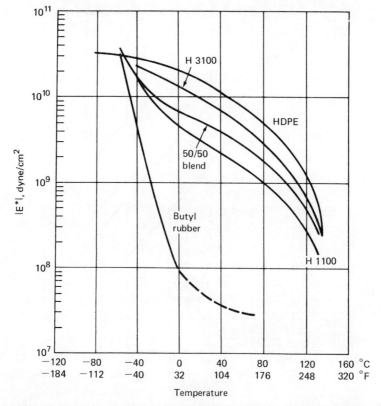

Figure 2-15. Dynamic modulus vs. temperature for ET polymers based on HDPE.

commercially available, e.g., TPR 3700 and 3812. Their oil resistance is comparable to that of specially compounded cured elastomers.

The thermoplastic elastomers have fair resistance to most gases. The air permeability of TPR 1800 and 1900 is 1.4×10^{-3} and 1.1×10^{-3} ft^3, respectively, diffusing through a 0.001-in. thickness of sample under a pressure differential of 1 atm/ft^2 of polymer per day. Water vapor permeability for these TPR polymers is 1.7×10^{-2} grain/hr/ft^2. This rate of transfer of vapor was measured at 73°F (23°C) and 50% humidity in accordance with ASTM E96.

2.2.6 Electrical

The electrical properties of a number of TPR and ET polymers are summarized in Table 2-20. Their high dielectric strength and volume resistivity are typical of

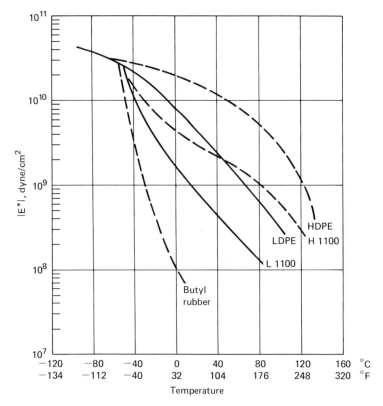

Figure 2-16. Dynamic modulus vs. temperature for ET polymers based on LDPE.

a good dielectric. The dielectric strength is somewhat higher compared to thermoplastics such as polyethylene and polyvinyl chloride and to cured rubber materials. The excellent insulating characteristics of these thermoplastic elastomers are also demonstrated by their high arc resistance. The high insulation resistance is not affected by high humidity.

Comparison with materials used in many electrical applications such as crosslinked polyethylene shows that the electrical properties of these thermoplastic elastomers are comparable. Their dielectric constant is relatively low and remains virtually constant over a wide range of frequency. The dissipation factor is also relatively low for the TPR thermoplastic rubbers, but increases with increasing frequency. The dissipation factor of ET polymers is relatively higher even at lower frequencies. Their dielectric loss factors are still lower relative to other flexible thermoplastic materials such as plasticized PVC.

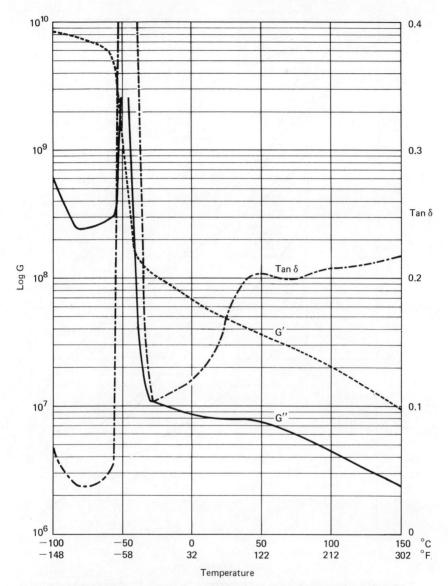

Figure 2-17. Typical dynamic mechanical curves for TPR thermoplastic rubbers.

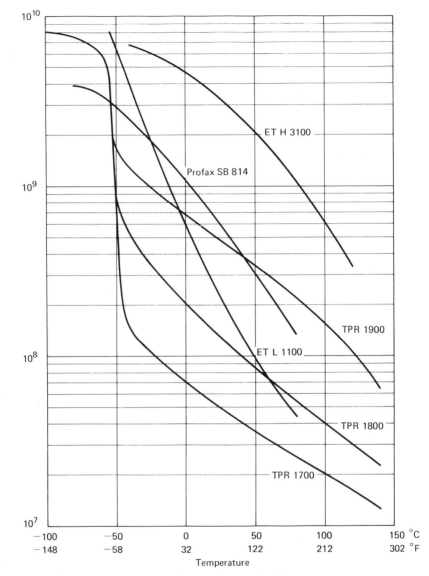

Figure 2-18. Dynamic modulus vs. temperature for polyolefin thermoplastic elastomers.

Table 2-17. Chemical resistance of polyolefin thermoplastic elastomers.

CHEMICAL ENVIRONMENT	DU PONT SOMEL	UNIROYAL TPR	HERCULES SB 814	ALLIED CHEMICAL ET
Acetaldehyde	Fair			
Acetic acid, aqueous	Good			Good
Acetic acid, glacial	Fair		Fair	
Acetone	Good	Good	Good	
Aluminum chloride, aqueous	Good			
Aluminum sulfate, aqueous	Good			
Ammonia, aqueous	Good		Good	Good
Ammonium chloride, aqueous	Good			
Ammonium sulfate, aqueous	Good			
Amyl acetate	Good			
Amyl alcohol	Good			
Aniline	Fair			
ASTM Oil No. 1	Poor	Fair		Good
ASTM Oil No. 3	Poor	Fair		Good
ASTM Fuel B		Poor		Poor
Barium hydroxide, aqueous	Good			
Benzaldehyde	Poor			
Benzene	Poor			
Benzoyl chloride	Poor			
Borax, aqueous	Good			
Boric acid, aqueous	Good			
Bromine, anhydrous	Poor	Fair		
Butane	Fair			
Butyl acetate		Good		
Butyl alcohol		Good		
Butter oil		Fair		
Butyraldehyde	Fair			
Calcium chloride, aqueous	Good			
Calcium hydroxide, aqueous	Good			
Calcium hypochlorite	Good			
Carbon tetrachloride	Poor			Poor
Castor oil	Fair			
Chlorine gas, wet	Poor			
Chloroform	Poor			
Chlorosulfonic acid	Poor			
Chlorox, aqueous		Good		
Chromic acid	Poor	Good		
Citric acid	Good			
Copper chloride, aqueous	Good			
Copper sulfate, aqueous	Good			
Cottonseed oil	Fair		Good	
Creosote oil	Poor			
Cyclohexane	Poor			
Cyclohexanone			Fair	
Detergents		Good		
Dibutyl phthalate	Fair		Good	
Diethyl sebacate	Fair			
Dioctyl phthalate	Fair			
Dowtherm A	Poor			

Table 2-17. (*Continued*)

CHEMICAL ENVIRONMENT	DU PONT SOMEL	UNIROYAL TPR	HERCULES SB 814	ALLIED CHEMICAL ET
Epichlorohydrin	Fair			
Ethyl acetate	Fair	Fair	Fair	
Ethyl alcohol	Good	Good	Good	
Ethyl chloride	Fair			
Ethylene dichloride	Fair			
Ethyl ether	Poor			
Ethylene glycol	Good	Good	Good	
Ferric chloride, aqueous	Good			
Formaldehyde, aqueous	Good	Good		
Formic acid	Good	Good		
Freon	Poor			
Furfural	Fair	Good		
Gasoline	Poor			
Genetron 113				Poor
Glycerin	Good			
n-Hexane	Poor	Poor		Poor
Hydrochloric acid	Fair	Good	Fair	
Hydrocyanic acid	Good			
Hydrofluoric acid	Fair			
Hydrogen	Good			
Hydrogen peroxide, aqueous		Good		
Hydrogen sulfate	Good			
Isooctane		Poor		
Isopropyl ether	Poor			
JP jet fuel	Poor	Poor		
Kerosene	Poor			
Lacquer solvents	Poor			
Lactic acid	Good			
Linseed oil	Fair			
Lubricating oils	Poor			
Magnesium chloride, aqueous	Good			
Magnesium hydroxide, aqueous	Good			
Mercuric chloride, aqueous	Good			
Mercury	Good			
Methyl alcohol	Good	Good		
Methylene chloride	Fair			
Methyl ethyl ketone	Fair		Good	
Methyl methacrylate		Fair		
Mineral oil	Poor			
Naphtha	Poor			
Naphthalene	Poor			
Nitric acid	Fair			Good
Nitrobenzene	Good		Good	
Oleic acid	Fair			
Oleum	Poor			
Palmitic acid	Fair			
Pentyl acetate				Fair
Perchloroethylene	Poor			
Phenol	Fair			

Table 2-17. (*Continued*)

CHEMICAL ENVIRONMENT	DU PONT SOMEL	UNIROYAL TPR	HERCULES SB 814	ALLIED CHEMICAL ET
Phosphoric acid	Good			
Pickling solution	Poor			
Picric acid	Fair			
n-Propane				Fair
Pyridine	Fair			
SAE No. 10 oil	Poor			
Sea water	Good			
Silicone grease	Good			
Skydrol 500B		Fair		
Soap solution	Good			
Sodium carbonate		Good		
Sodium dichromate	Good			
Sodium hydroxide	Good	Good	Good	
Sodium hypochlorite	Good		Good	
Soybean oil	Poor			
Stannous chloride	Fair			
Stearic acid	Fair			
Styrene	Poor			
Sulfur	Good			
Sulfur dioxide	Good			
Sulfur trioxide	Fair			
Sulfuric acid, concentrated	Fair			
Sulfuric acid, diluted		Good		Good
Sulfurous acid	Poor			
Tannic acid	Good			
Tartaric acid	Fair			
Tetrahydrofuran	Poor	Poor		
Toluene	Poor	Poor		
Tributyl phosphate	Poor			
Trichloroethylene	Poor			Poor
Triethanolamine	Good		Good	
Trisodium phosphate, aqueous	Good			
Tung oil	Poor			
Turpentine	Poor			
Water	Good	Good	Good	
Xylene	Poor			
Zinc chloride, aqueous	Good			

Table 2-18. Quantitative chemical resistance of TPR 1622/1922.

CHEMICAL ENVIRONMENT	CONCENTRATION (%)	TEMPERATURE (°F)	% VOLUME CHANGE			
			TPR 1622		TPR 1922	
			24 hr	168 hr	24 hr	168 hr
ASTM oil No. 1	100	73	8.7	–	2.9	–
ASTM oil No. 2	100	150	55	179	25	101
ASTM oil No. 3	100	73	31.8	–	10.5	–
ASTM fuel B	100	73	272	302	146	156
Acetone	100	73	–	–	1.9	3.4
Bromine	100	73	4.1	3.3	3.0	2.3
	100	158	3.3	19.1	3.6	13.9
Butter	100	73	5.7	5.2	–	–
Chromic acid	12	73	–	–	0.1	–
	60	73	–	–	0.1	–
Ethanol	100	73	0.3	0.7	–	–
Ethyl acetate	80	73	3.6	3.2	–	–
Ethylene glycol	100	280	0.1	0.1	–	–
Formaldehyde	37	73	–	–	0.2	0.4
Formic acid	90	73	–	–	0.4	1.2
Furfural	80	73	0.9	1.0	–	–
Hexane	100	73	116	116	–	–
Hydrochloric acid	30	73	0.4	0.1	0.2	0.2
	30	158	0.6	2.1	0.3	0.4
Iso-octane	100	73	183	194	100	108
JP jet fuel	100	73	276	294	141	147
Methanol	100	73	0.3	0.5	–	–
Methyl methacrylate	100	73	17	–	12	–
Skydrol 500-B	100	73	1.4	3.6	0	0.5
	100	158	3.5	6.4	4.2	6.3
Sodium carbonate	5	73	–	–	–	0
Sodium hydroxide	1	150	–	–	0	0.1
	5	150	–	–	–	1.0
Sulfuric acid	5	150	–	–	–	0.1
Tetrahydrofuran	100	73	98	98	–	–
Toluene	100	73	115	115	–	–
Water	100	73	–	–	0.1	0.2
	100	195	–	–	–	1.5

2.3 PROCESSING

Polyolefin thermoplastic elastomers can be processed under a variety of different conditions using conventional thermoplastics machinery. They are usually injection molded or extruded, but can be processed by other methods such as calendering, vacuum forming, and blow molding. Compression or press molding can also be used, but this method is not recommended for optimal properties or processing economics. The thermoplastic elastomers can be fabricated into a variety

Table 2-19. Quantitative chemical resistance of ET polymers.

CHEMICAL ENVIRONMENT	% WEIGHT GAIN AFTER 96 HR @ r.t.			
	H3100	H1100	L3100	L1100
ASTM oil No. 1	0	1.3	0.8	3.4
ASTM oil No. 2	0.5	2.0	2.1	3.2
ASTM fuel A	5	28.6	17.5	41
Ammonium hydroxide	1	1.3	1.3	2.4
Nitric acid	0	0	0	0
Sulfuric acid	0	0	0	0
	% VOLUME CHANGE AFTER 120 HR @ r.t.			
Acetic acid	0	0.15	0	0
Carbon tetrachloride	12.3	25.5	20.8	32.5
Genetron 113	4.5	20	15	54
Hexane	17	48	—[a]	—
Pentyl acetate	3.5	7.7	4.5	12.5
Propane	0.3	7	4	9
Tetrachloroethylene	29	54	63	54

[a]Not tested.

of useful shapes in the form of sheet, film, tubing, profile extrusion, jacketing, and molded goods.

Since the olefinic thermoplastic elastomers are truly thermoplastic materials, they are completely reprocessable. It is generally recommended that processed material, including scrap, be reground and blended with virgin material prior to reprocessing. For example, Hercules recommends that regrinds of Profax SB 814 should be limited to less than 25% of the total product mix for maximum retention of low temperature impact strength. Up to 50% regrind with virgin material is recommended for TPR thermoplastic elastomers, although some commercial applications have been successful using 100% regrind. The effect of reprocessing TPR 1700, 1900, and 2800 is summarized in Table 2-21 for four and seven molding cycles. The tensile strength is only slightly affected, and elongation is increased upon reprocessing 100% regrind material. In painted applications, the use of up to 20% painted regrind with unpainted virgin TPR has been successful. Above 20% painted regrind, surface imperfections on the painted parts were evident. Physical properties and paint adhesion data are summarized for TPR 1930 in Table 2-22.

Thermoplastic elastomers are heat stable in the melt state over a wide range in temperature. This provides the processor with an added safety factor since the material can remain in the processing equipment at elevated temperatures for extended periods of time without being degraded. This is particularly important

Table 2-20. Electrical properties of TPR and ET polymers.

PROPERTY	ASTM METHOD	TPR 1600	TPR 1900	TPR 2800	ET L1100	ET H1100	ET L3100	ET H3100
Dielectric strength volts/mil	D-149	600	600	640	629	737	736	803
Dielectric constant	D-150							
@ 60 Hz		2.21	2.23	2.22	2.31	2.34	2.26	2.32
@ 1 KHz		2.22	2.22	2.20	2.29	2.32	2.24	2.31
@ 1 MHz		2.20	2.20	2.19	—[a]	—	—	—
Dissipation factor	D-150							
@ 60 Hz		.0005	.0003	.0004	.0058	.0054	.0027	.0025
@ 1 KHz		.0008	.0008	.0006	.0069	.0061	.0032	.0029
@ 1 MHz		.0032	.0021	.0011	—	—	—	—
Volume resistivity @ 23°C, 50% RH-ohm cm	D-257	3×10^{16}	3×10^{16}	4×10^{16}	5.3×10^{16}	1.58×6^{17}	1.2×10^{17}	1.1×10^{16}
Insulation resistance	D-257							
40 hr @ 23°C, 50% RH-ohms		$>10^{15}$	$>10^{15}$	$>10^{15}$	—	—	—	—
96 hr @ 35°C, 90% RH-ohms		$>10^{15}$	$>10^{15}$	$>10^{15}$	—	—	—	—
Arc resistance (sec)		>180	>180	>180	—	—	—	—
SIR @ 15.6°C (60.1°F)		—	6.4×10^{5}	2.4×10^{5}	—	—	—	—
SIC - 1 day @ 75°C (167°F)		—	2.3	2.2	—	—	—	—
1-14 days, % change		—	1.9	4.3	—	—	—	—
7-14 days, % change		—	0.9	1.6	—	—	—	—

[a]No data available.

Table 2-21. Percent change in properties using 100 percent regrind for each molding cycle.

PROPERTIES	ASTM METHOD	TPR-1700		TPR-1900		TPR-2800	
		MOLD CYCLE NO.					
		4	7	4	7	4	7
Tensile strength	D-412	−2	−2	+6	−5	−1	−9
100% modulus	D-412	−17	−17	−6	−18	−1	−17
Elongation	D-412	+16	+47	+50	+77	0	+8
Elongation set (% @ Break + 1 min.)	D-412	+80	+130	+86	+124	−17	−17
Hardness (Shore A)	D-2240	+1	+3	−2	−1	−4	−4

Table 2-22. Percent change in properties using painted regrind/virgin blends.

	BLEND RATIO TPR-1930 (% PAINTED/% VIRGIN)				
	25/75	50/50	75/25	90/10	100/0
PROPERTIES					
Tensile strength	+2.5	−5	−5	−11	−17
Elongation	−39	−12.5	+16	0	−12.5
Modulus (100%)	+3.5	−6	−8	−12	−18
Elongation set (% @ Break + 1 min.)	−54	−38	0	−15	−26
Hardness (Shore A)	0	+2	+2	+1	+2
PAINT ADHESION TESTS					
Cross hatch	OK	OK	OK	OK	OK
Thermal shock	OK	OK	OK	OK	OK
Flex [−20°F (−29°C), 1 in. (25.4 mm) Mandrel]	Same as painted standard				
SLAB APPEARANCE					
Unpainted	Some paint specks	Many paint specks			
Painted	Good	Noticeable gel marks	Very noticeable gel marks		

when the processing equipment must be turned off and then started up again. The material can be left in the equipment during the entire procedure rather than having to purge and reload each time.

Mechanical cleaning or purging of equipment prior to processing a particular thermoplastic elastomer is recommended to avoid any contamination in the fabricated part. Purging materials that can be used include ABS, polypropylene, high-density polyethylene, or any other material that can withstand the higher temperatures used to process the thermoplastic elastomers.

2.3.1 Rheology

Olefinic thermoplastic elastomers have a relatively high melt viscosity and do not flow as well as other thermoplastic materials. This characteristic necessitates the use of slightly higher than usual processing temperatures and pressures for fabrication into useful articles. The flow behavior of the olefinic thermoplastic elastomers is highly non-Newtonian even at low shear rates. This non-Newtonian flow behavior results in a strong dependence of the melt viscosity on the rate of shear. Because of their extreme shear sensitivity, very high processing speeds can be used to fabricate the thermoplastic elastomers.

The melt viscosity curves of TPR thermoplastic elastomers at 400°F (204°C) are shown in Figure 2-19. These isothermal flow curves are plotted in the conventional manner as the logarithm of the apparent viscosity in poise against the rate of shear in reciprocal seconds. Comparison of the melt flow curves shows that all of the TPR thermoplastic rubbers are similar in their melt rheology behavior. The consistently lower melt viscosity of TPR 1900 over the complete range of shear rates shows that it processes more easily than any other TPR product. In contrast, TPR 1700 is less readily processible. It is the only TPR thermoplastic rubber that is not readily extrudable under normal conditions.

Telcar thermoplastic elastomers generally have a lower melt viscosity than the TPR thermoplastic rubbers. The apparent viscosity vs. shear rate curves are

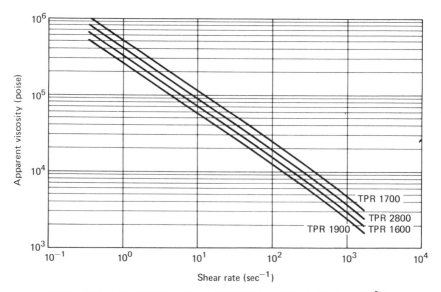

Figure 2-19. Melt viscosity curves of TPR thermoplastic rubbers at 400°F.

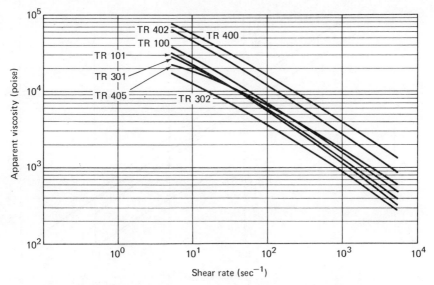

Figure 2-20. Melt viscosity curves of Telcars at 205°C.

shown for all seven Telcar products in Figure 2-20. Telcar TR 400 and 402 have the highest melt viscosity and are well suited for slot-die extrusion. TR 405 is more shear-sensitive than the other Telcar polymers, particularly at lower shear rates. Comparison of the melt rheology of Telcar vs. TPR in Figure 2-21 shows that the Telcars are generally more shear-sensitive. Only the highest and lowest viscosity polymers of each type are shown for comparative purposes.

Melt viscosity curves of ET polymers at 230°C (446°F) are shown in Figure 2-22. The melt flow data show that the melt viscosity of ET polymers depends more on their rubber content than on the type of polyethylene used. The difference in melt viscosity between low-density and high-density polyethylene is difficult to see in the melt flow curves of ET polymers based on these two types of polyethylene. The melt viscosity of the 75/25-HDPE/BR polymer is only slightly higher than that of the 75/25-LDPE/BR polymer, but this difference is minimal. The melt viscosity of the 50/50-HDPE/BR and 50/50-LDPE/BR graft polymers is virtually identical over the complete range in shear rate. The higher rubber content of the 50/50-polyethylene/butyl rubber grafts makes them more difficult to process than the corresponding 75/25-ratio graft polymers. Melt fracture was found to occur in these higher rubber grafts at relatively low shear rates, resulting in rough extrudates.

The relative magnitudes of the melt viscosity of the thermoplastic elastomers are shown in Figure 2-23 using available data at 450°F (232°C). ET polymers

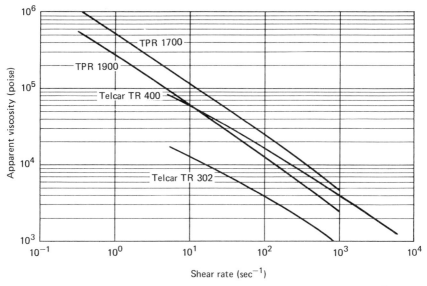

Figure 2-21. Melt viscosity curves of various thermoplastic elastomers at 400° F.

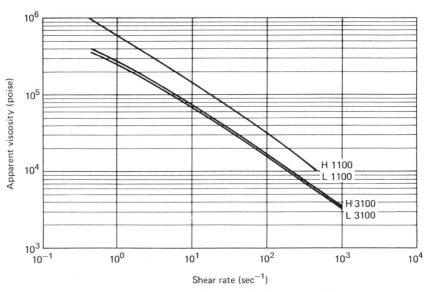

Figure 2-22. Melt viscosity curves of ET polymers at 230°C.

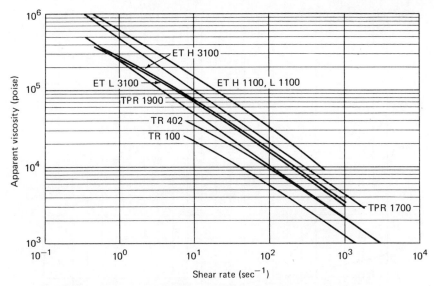

Figure 2-23. Melt viscosity curves of various thermoplastic elastomers at 450°F.

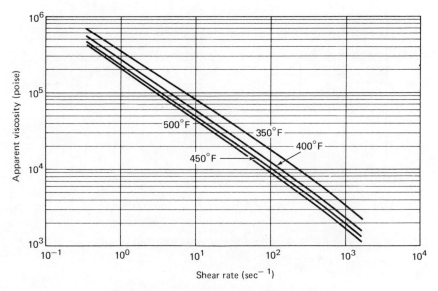

Figure 2-24. Melt viscosity curves of TPR 1900.

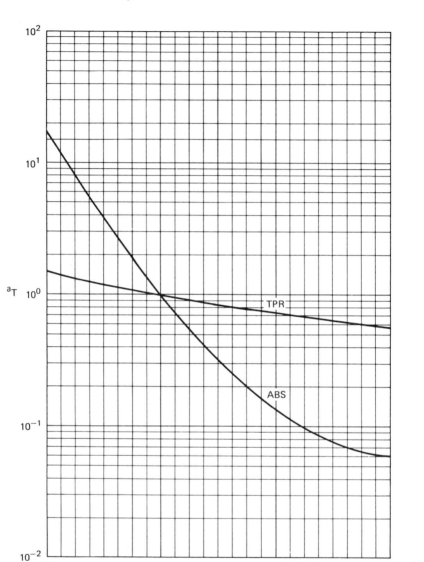

Figure 2-25. Experimental shift factors for TPR vs. ABS.

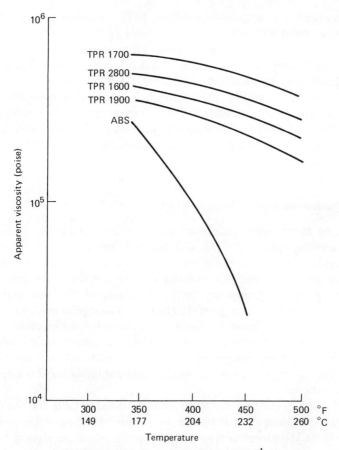

Figure 2-26. Melt viscosity vs. temperature at 1 sec^{-1} shear rate.

generally have the highest melt viscosity and are the most difficult to process. TPR thermoplastic rubbers are intermediate in their melt viscosity. Telcar thermoplastic elastomers have the lowest melt viscosity and are the easiest to process. While no melt viscosity data are available for Somel polymers or Profax SB 814, Du Pont reports that the melt viscosity of the Somels is generally higher than that of most olefinic thermoplastic elastomers.

The melt viscosity of the olefinic thermoplastic elastomers is not as dependent on temperature as are conventional thermoplastic materials. The effect of temperature on the melt viscosity curves of TPR 1900 is shown in Figure 2-24. The isothermal flow curves at 350, 400, 450, and 500°F (177, 204, 232, and 260°C) have the same shape and can be superposed by shifting horizontally along the log shear rate axis. The corresponding shift factors, a_T, are plotted in Figure 2-25 in accordance with the Williams-Landel-Ferry (WLF) equation using a reference temperature of 400°F (204°C). Comparison with the WLF-type temperature dependence for ABS polymers shows that the TPR thermoplastic rubbers are much less sensitive to temperature. The same trend is found in plots of apparent viscosity against temperature at a constant shear rate as in Figure 2-26. Because of this temperature insensitivity, the processing behavior of thermoplastic elastomers is not affected by minor fluctuations in temperature. This provides a more uniform flow and a wide safety margin in processing. However, this safety feature also limits the use of higher stock temperature as an aid to increasing polymer flow during processing.

2.3.2 Injection Molding

The olefinic thermoplastic elastomers can be processed using most types of injection-molding machines. This includes both the reciprocating-screw and plunger types of injection-molding machines designed for conventional thermoplastics as well as for injection-moldable thermoset rubber compounds. The reciprocating-screw machines are preferred because of the melt uniformity achieved and higher pressures generally available. This type of machine also provides lower power requirements. Ram-type injection-molding machines can also be used to process the lower viscosity thermoplastic elastomers. Rubber injection-molding equipment can also be used with minor modifications. Conversion of these rubber machines to allow for mold cooling and higher barrel temperatures is usually sufficient.

Typical injection-molding conditions are summarized in Table 2-23 for the different polyolefin thermoplastic elastomers. Actual injection-molding conditions will depend on the particular type of thermoplastic elastomer processed as well as the mold and part design. The processing conditions used cover a wide range and will be discussed in more detail.

The relatively high melt viscosity of the olefinic thermoplastic elastomers requires somewhat higher processing temperatures than those for conventional thermoplastic materials. A barrel temperature profile is used, which increases from rear to front. For example, the temperature profile recommended for injection molding Telcar TR 100 and TR 101 is 430°F (221°C) rear, 450°F (232°C) center, and 450°F (232°C) front. This temperature profile is shifted 50°F (28°C) higher when processing Telcar TR 400 and TR 402. Somel 301G should be injection molded using 350 to 370°F (177 to 188°C) rear, 390 to 405°F (199 to 207°C) center, and 410 to 430°F (210 to 221°C) front, but Somel 401T and 402T require 370 to 390°F (188 to 199°C) rear, 415 to 430°F (213 to 221°C) center, and 430 to 450°F (221 to 232°C) front. Higher barrel temperatures than those generally recommended can be used in molds with small

Table 2-23. Injection-molding conditions for polyolefin thermoplastic elastomers.

CONDITION	TPR	TELCAR	SOMEL	ET POLYMER	PROFAX SB 814
Barrel temperatures, °F					
Rear zone	375–410	380–430	350–390	400–440	410
Center zone	400–430	400–450	390–430	400–450	450
Front zone	400–430	400–450	410–450	400–450	470
Nozzle	400–430	400–450	400–460	440–450	480
Mold temperature, °F	30–180	125–150	50–150	70	140
Injection pressure, psi	5000–20,000	13,000–14,000	$-$[a]	–	12,000
Hold pressure, psi	4000–16,000	–	–	–	9500
Back pressure, psi	100–200	–	0–150	–	500
Screw speed, rpm	–	–	25–75	–	60
Injection speed	Fast	Moderate	–	–	Fast
Cycle time, sec					
Injection	3–15	–	–	15–25	–
Hold	15–45	–	–	75	–
Total	18–60	45–50	30–45	90–100	–
Clamp pressure, tons	–	–	2–4	–	–

[a]No data available.

gates and runners. Lower barrel temperatures should be avoided due to excessive flow orientation and part distortion.

Nozzle temperature should be controlled close to the front zone barrel temperature. However, this is not as critical with thermoplastic elastomers as with other plastic materials. The length of the nozzle should be as short as possible. Shutoff nozzles are not required since the thermoplastic elastomers do not drool easily even in hot runner systems.

Mold temperatures can range from 30°F (-1°C) up to 180°F (82°C), although 100 to 150°F (38 to 66°C) is generally recommended. The optimal mold temperature used depends on the type of thermoplastic elastomer used in addition to the mold and part design. The temperature of the mold affects cycle time, part shrinkage, surface appearance, etc. Mold temperatures below room temperature tend to exaggerate flow patterns on the surface of a part and are generally used only when molding very small parts. Higher mold temperatures are usually required for molding very large automotive parts. Temperatures above 150°F (66°C) often result in part distortion and surface imperfections. Independent temperature control of both mold halves is generally recommended to facilitate demolding parts from the moving half of the mold.

Injection pressures up to 15,000 psi (103.4 MPa) are generally recommended to minimize molding stresses and part distortion at the gate. The optimal injection pressure required to produce a filled, adequately packed part short of flash depends on the type of thermoplastic elastomer and on the mold and part design. Injection pressures as low as 5000 psi (34.5 MPa) can be used to mold lower viscosity thermoplastic elastomers. When higher injection pressures in excess of 15,000 psi (103.4 MPa) are needed to fill the higher viscosity thermoplastic elastomers, the processing temperature can be increased to lower the pressure requirements. Holding pressures of about 50 to 80% of the injection pressure are recommended. Some back pressure is generally used to increase stock temperature and aid in dispersing pigments, fillers, and color concentrates.

Screw speed is not too critical and generally ranges from 25 to 75 rpm. General purpose screws having a compression ratio between 2:1 and 3:1 with L/D ratios from 16:1 to 24:1 are generally recommended. Screws with higher compression ratios and shallow flights should not be used to injection mold the high viscosity thermoplastic elastomers. Rubber injection screws having barrel length-to-diameter ratios as low as 10:1 and compression ratios from 1.0 to 1.5 can be used provided that adequate mold cooling and barrel heating are available.

Relatively fast injection speeds are recommended for optimum mold-filling characteristics. Since the melt viscosity of the thermoplastic elastomers is highly sensitive to shear rate, they inject best at high injection speeds. Faster fill rates increase the effective shear rate through the nozzle, which lowers the apparent melt viscosity of the material. This also improves the properties of the molded part by increasing flow orientation.

Cycle times are relatively rapid and close to those achieved with thermoplastic materials such as polyvinyl chloride and polypropylene. Injection times as fast as 3 sec have been obtained for small multiple-cavity molds with an additional dwell time of 15 sec. Larger parts require longer injection and dwell times totaling as much as 1 min for the complete cycle. The minimum dwell time that can be used is determined by the part geometry and tolerance required. The fastest possible cycle is usually achieved using the lowest possible barrel temperature profile and mold temperature.

Olefinic thermoplastic elastomers can be injection-molded on a wide variety of tools designed for thermoplastic materials. The use of high injection pressure and temperatures may be employed to compensate for small gates, runners, etc. that are common to tools designed for conventional thermoplastics. Mold design changes may have to be made for the higher viscosity polymers to optimize their processing. More generous gates and larger runners and sprues are recommended for optimum mold cycles. Gates, runners, and sprues should be streamlined as much as possible when using fast injection rates. The gate land should be relatively short. Both runners and sprues should be as short as possible. Hot runner and cold runner mold designs can be used as well as conventional runner systems. Full-round runners are preferred, although half-round and trapezoidal runners can also be used. Fan, edge, flash, tunnel, tab, and direct sprue gating is generally recommended; pin and other restricted gates are unsatisfactory. Gates should be located so that the material flows the same distance from the gate to each end of the part. A vapor-honed mold finish is recommended to facilitate part ejection. Core cooling is essential. All tools should be vented to allow the release of entrapped air from the cavity.

Part design considerations are generally the same as for thermoplastic materials. Injection-molded parts with thickness ranging from 0.03 to 0.10 in. have been fabricated in a wide variety of sizes and shapes. Ribs are not recommended, but, if they must be used, they should be designed in the direction of flow. Keeping sections as thin as possible helps to eliminate sink marks. The stiffer thermoplastic elastomers generally do not require ribs for structural purposes. Small undercuts with long lands are recommended to avoid part distortion upon demolding. When several undercuts are required, manual assistance may be needed to remove the part from the mold. Ample draft angles are also recommended to facilitate removal of the molded part. The required mold draft angle is dependent on part size and dimensions, but a draft angle of at least 3° is usually sufficient. Stripper plates should be used for ejection when a molded part has little or no draft angle.

2.3.3 Extrusion

The melt viscosity characteristics of the polyolefin thermoplastic elastomers make them well suited for all extrusion processes. These thermoplastic elastomers can be extruded using conventional plastics equipment. Their relatively high coefficients of friction result in extrusion rates that are generally higher than those of conventional thermoplastic materials. The power requirements are also generally higher when extruding thermoplastic elastomers. Significantly faster extrusion rates are obtained using conventional thermoplastic extruders compared to thermoset rubber continuous vulcanization or extrusion/postcure processing. Rejection rates are also much lower when extruding thermoplastic elastomers since scrap is completely reprocessable.

The higher melt viscosity of the polyolefin thermoplastic elastomers requires some alteration of conventional extrusion conditions. Typical extrusion conditions are summarized in Table 2-24 for TPR, Telcar, Somel, and ET polymers. No information is available regarding the extrusion of Hercules Profax SB 814. A conventional temperature profile is used with temperature increasing from the rear zone to the extruder head. The optimum extrusion conditions depend on the type of thermoplastic elastomer processed and the extrusion process used. For example, the temperature profile recommended for Somel 301G is 350 to 370°F (177 to 188°C) rear, 370 to 390°F (188 to 199°C) center, 390 to 410°F (199 to 210°C) front, 400 to 420°F (204 to 216°C) adapter, and 400 to 430°F (204 to 221°C) die. These temperature ranges are shifted 20°F (11°C) higher when extruding Somel 401T and 402T. Goodrich recommends barrel temperatures of 300 to 325°F (149 to 163°C) rear, 325 to 355°F (163 to 179°C) center, and 355 to 380°F (179 to 193°C) front for the slot-die extrusion of Telcar

Table 2-24. Extrusion conditions for polyolefin thermoplastic elastomers.

CONDITION	TPR	TELCAR	SOMEL	ET POLYMER
Barrel temperatures, °F				
Rear zone	325–375	300–325	350–390	350–360
Center zone	350–400	325–355	370–410	375–390
Front zone	375–420	335–380	390–430	400–430
Adapter temperature, °F	–	335–360	400–440	425
Die temperature, °F	420–450	335–360	400–440	450–500
Melt temperature, °F	420–480	325–360	410–460	440–475
Screw speed, rpm	30–150	–	10–50	–
Screen pack, mesh	40/60/80	20/40	80/80	–

TR 400 and TR 402, but temperatures of 300 to 325°F (149 to 163°C) rear, 325 to 335°F (163 to 168°C) center, and 335 to 350°F (163 to 177°C) front in the profile extrusion of these same polymers. In each extrusion process, these temperatures are increased 25°F (14°C) when extruding the Telcar TR 100 series. In contrast to extrusion conditions for other thermoplastic elastomers, the profile extrusion of ET polymers requires a higher die temperature relative to the melt temperature to assure a smooth extrudate and to control post-extrusion die swell. Higher temperatures can be tolerated for extruding all of the olefinic thermoplastic elastomers when necessary, although temperatures in excess of 500°F (260°C) are not recommended.

Screws designed for conventional thermoplastic materials have been used to extrude polyolefin thermoplastic elastomers. Optimum extruded properties and rates of extrusion are generally obtained using screws with shallow flight depths and moderate compression ratios. The transition section of the screw should be gradual and account for at least one-fourth of the flighted screw length. Maximum screw output is obtained when the feed section is longer than the metering section. General purpose screws typically used for flexible PVC have a relatively short metering section and should be cooled to obtain a uniform extrudate. The longer, shallower metering screws typically used for polyethylene provide good melt uniformity, but output is reduced. Long metering sections with mixing rings or a fluted mixing section are recommended for extruding the higher viscosity thermoplastic elastomers. Mixing-type screws produce high output rates and good melt uniformity. Compression ratios between 2.0 and 3.5 are generally used to produce adequate melt temperature uniformity without overworking the material. Screws with L/D ratios from 16:1 to 24:1 are generally recommended, although L/D ratios of up to 30:1 can be used for extruding the lower viscosity thermoplastic elastomers.

Polyolefin thermoplastic elastomers can be extruded using a variety of sheet, tubing, profile, and crosshead dies. Dies with a wide range of land lengths have been used, but long land lengths in excess of 1 in. are generally recommended. Shorter lengths can be used with the harder, less rubbery materials. Long shallow lead-in lengths are also recommended for obtaining a high quality, smooth surface. Long lead-ins in excess of 2 in. have been used with high screw speeds of up to 150 rpm to obtain good extrusion rates with no surging. Plate dies typically used in extruding flexible PVC, which have minimal lead-in length and virtually no land length, can only be used at relatively low screw speeds. In crosshead extrusions, lead-in length should be long but land lengths should be minimized to avoid excessive back pressure during extrusion. Dies should be streamlined to assure equal pressure flow from the die. For example, coat-hanger-type dies provide a more even melt flow from the die than do T-configuration dies.

Screen packs are generally used to provide back pressure for better mixing. Two or more stainless-steel screens are normally used in combinations of 20, 40, 60, and 80 mesh, although as high as 100-mesh screens have been employed. The screen pack is usually supported by a breaker plate placed between the adapter and the end of the screw.

Standard takeoff equipment designed for conventional thermoplastics can be used to handle the polyolefin thermoplastic elastomers. A water bath is required to provide adequate cooling of the extrudates. The slight die swell that occurs upon extruding a thermoplastic elastomer can be compensated for by drawing down. Drawdown should be controlled and not too excessive because orientation effects will change the properties of the extruded material. Drawdown ratios of up to 5 usually give satisfactory results. Excessive drawdown will produce a high degree of molecular orientation, particularly at lower melt temperatures. A rapid rate of cooling as in quenching will also result in orientation. A high drawdown ratio greater than 5:1 on a cross-sectional area basis and/or rapid quench of the extrudate will generally increase the tensile strength and modulus and decrease the elongation of the extruded part.

2.3.4 Calendering

Polyolefin thermoplastic elastomers can be fabricated into sheet and film using calenders. TPR 1700 has been calendered into sheet using a four-roll calender with a 1.5:1 mill ratio. The top rolls are run at 350°F (177°C), center roll at 300°F (149°C), and bottom roll at 275°F (135°C). A minimum stock temperature of 350°F (177°C) is needed to provide a uniform melt. TPR sheet ranging in thickness from 5 to 50 mil has been calendered using these conditions. The calendered sheet can be embossed using conventional methods.

Other hot roll machines such as Zimmer and Bema equipment can also be used to process the thermoplastic elastomers. The Telcar TR 100 and TR 400 series have been processed into sheet, film, and coatings using this type of equipment.

Laboratory trials with a Zimmer coater have produced coated fabrics with 0.5 to 6 mil thick coatings. Telcar thermoplastic elastomers adhere well to cotton fabrics such as cotton duck resulting in good peel strength. Adhesion to synthetic fibers such as polyester and nylon is improved when the fabric is pretreated with a suitable primer dip coating.

The recommended melt roll temperatures for fabric coating with Telcar TR 100 and TR 101 are 375 and 400°F (191 and 204°C) for the adjustable and stationary rolls, respectively. These temperatures are lowered by 75°F (42°C) when coating fabrics with Telcar TR 400 and TR 402. The fabric pre-heat roll should be set at 212°F (100°C). The speed ratio of the stationary melt roll to the adjustable melt roll is set at 3 : 1.

2.3.5 Blow Molding

Polyolefin thermoplastic elastomers are good blow-molding materials because of their extrudability and hot extension properties. They can be blow molded using commercially available blow-molding machines. Reciprocating-screw machines are particularly well suited for these materials. The same general processing conditions used for extruding thermoplastic elastomers are recommended for blow molding. The lowest possible processing temperatures should be used to give good parison definition. Parison sag is exaggerated at higher temperatures. Melt fracture can occur if the temperature is too low.

TPR thermoplastic rubbers have been used successfully in several blow-molding applications. For example, TPR 2800 has been blow molded into balls for flue-gas filtration media. Extrusion-blown ET polymer results in a tough film, free of voids. The ET graft polymer films have better tear resistance, crease resistance, and gas-permeability resistance compared with polyethylene.

2.3.6 Foaming

TPR thermoplastic rubbers have been foamed by free extrusion and using the USM foam process. The cell structure and surface appearance are excellent, but the actual extent of expansion is limited. Some developmental work is underway using various foaming systems.

ET polymers can be blended with polyethylene to improve cell structure in chemically blown, extruded, or injection-molded foam items. Both rigid and flexible foams with uniform cell structure and smooth, tough skin can be formed depending on the amount and type of ET polymer used.

2.3.7 Thermoforming

Thermoforming of olefinic thermoplastic elastomers can be used to produce a wide variety of complex shapes. Extruded sheet can be thermoformed using vacuum, pressure, or mechanical means. Vacuum forming is the method most commonly used for thermoforming the thermoplastic elastomers. It provides even drawdown, although the depth of draw is limited. Surface definition and part fidelity are excellent. Preheat cycles are relatively fast. The use of a female mold is recommended for vacuum forming low profile parts that do not require a deep draw. Deeper draws and sharper part definition are generally obtained using air pressure instead of vacuum. Mechanical forming methods provide even deeper draws and sharper definition than pneumatic methods.

2.3.8 Compression Molding

Compression molding of polyolefinic thermoplastic elastomers is not generally recommended because of the relatively poor properties obtained and the lengthy cycle times required. This method can be quite useful for prototyping. If compression molding is used, the material should be preheated in a closed press for a few minutes at low pressure before raising the pressure. Minimum mold temperatures should be used to eliminate deformation of the sample when it is removed from the mold.

2.4 APPLICATIONS

The unique combination of elastomeric properties and thermoplastic processability have made it possible for the polyolefin thermoplastic elastomers to be used in a wide variety of applications. This versatility has enabled the olefinic thermoplastic elastomers to find applications in many markets dominated by plastics and rubbers. For example, where thermoset properties are needed and the application requirements are satisfied, the olefinic thermoplastic elastomers are replacing natural rubber, as well as such synthetic rubbers as neoprene, styrene-butadiene, and ethylene-propylene terpolymers. This has generally been based on processing economics where the number of parts produced justifies the injection-molding process. The use of conventional thermoplastic equipment results in a significantly lower cost per finished part compared to the relatively higher cost of compression-molding rubber. The olefinic thermoplastic elastomers are also replacing a number of thermoplastic materials in many applications requiring superior performance at both high and low temperatures. They are being used in place of polyethylene, polyvinyl chloride, and polyurethane in many applications requiring improved heat stability, low temperature flexibility, and rubbery properties.

2.4.1 Automotive

The largest application area for the polyolefin thermoplastic elastomers is presently in the automotive market. The excellent combination of properties, wide service temperature range, low temperature flexibility, high temperature stiffness, resiliency, and paintability of these thermoplastic elastomers have permitted them to obtain rapid acceptance by the automotive industry. The olefinic thermoplastic elastomers are replacing thermoplastic urethane, thermoplastic polyester, polyvinyl chloride, and EPDM rubber in many automotive applications. The polyolefin thermoplastic elastomers bridge the performance-vs.-price gap between polyurethane materials, which are higher priced but also have high performance, and the vinyl materials, which are lower in cost and performance. Many of the olefinic thermoplastic elastomers are designed specifically for a wide range of exterior and interior parts.

The major automotive market is in exterior body applications such as filler panels, bumper covers, fender extensions, lower fascias, flexible front and rear panels, corner panels, and sight shields. The specific application requirements of each type of part will determine which olefinic thermoplastic elastomer should be specified. For example, bumper covers must be capable of withstanding high impact so the material used should be a good energy absorber. The material requirements for the bumper filler panel are not as demanding but require good flexural recovery since the filler panel must be collapsable upon impact. Materials used for body extensions must have good compression set characteristics due to retraction of the bumper upon impact. The polyolefin thermoplastic elastomer materials used in exterior automotive-body applications must meet exacting performance standards and be compatible with commercial production methods.

These exterior body parts can be painted with commercially available primers and automotive finish topcoats. Good paint adhesion can be obtained when the flexible substrate is thoroughly cleaned and chemically pretreated before painting. The initial cleaning operation includes both degreasing and destaticizing to prevent subsequent dirt pickup. A number of pretreatment systems are commercially available but the Seibert-Oxidermo system is most widely used. This proprietary lacquer can be applied with a brush or spray and air-dries within 1 min. Other pretreatment systems include the MacDermid etchant system and the benzophenone activation process but they require special equipment. The MacDermid pretreatment consists of dipping the parts in a series of tanks containing the various chemical solutions whereas the benzophenone system requires an ultraviolet source to effect activation. TPR, Telcar, Somel, and Profax SB 814 are all paintable with the proper pretreatment.

Other exterior automotive applications include gaskets, weather stripping, and other body trim that are exposed to ultraviolet radiation. Specific applications include doorguards, body/bumper rub strips, hood gaskets, trunk gaskets, taillight gaskets, windshield gaskets, and windshield-wiper blades. The excellent weather resistance of the polyolefin thermoplastic elastomers was shown earlier by Weatherometer aging data (cf. Table 2-16), which exceed the 2000-hr automotive requirement for weatherability.

Interior automotive parts made with the olefinic thermoplastic elastomers include steering wheels, connector strips, grommets, seals, bushings, seat-belt housings, horn pads, and flexible trim. These thermoplastic elastomers have also been used in decorative applications such as dash panel, armrest, and overhead sun visors. Under-the-hood applications include sparkplug boots, electrical connectors, hose, and tubing, all of which must withstand high temperatures for long periods of time.

2.4.2 Wire and Cable

Wire and cable applications provide the largest potential nonautomotive market for thermoplastic elastomers. The polyolefin thermoplastic elastomers are used mainly as insulation and jacketing materials where environmental and heat resistance are needed. They overcome the limitations of most thermoplastic materials in wire and cable applications, which have inherently poor heat deformation and aging characteristics. The olefinic thermoplastic elastomers have excellent retention of tensile properties after accelerated aging in air and oxygen at high pressures as required by Underwriters' Laboratories, military, and utility specifications (*cf.* Table 2-15). They can be used over a wide range in temperature and in a variety of environmental conditions. They can be used in low-voltage communication cable over a wide frequency range. The olefinic thermoplastic elastomers are competitive with cross-linked polyethylene, which is widely used in the production of power and communication cable. The electrical characteristics of the polyolefin thermoplastic elastomers coupled with their abrasion resistance and low temperature flexibility provide an excellent market potential in wire and cable applications.

Some of the olefinic thermoplastic elastomers have been specially designed for applications in the wire and cable industry. For example, the TPR 1000/2000 series have been designed to replace cured elastomers such as ethylene-propylene rubber, styrene-butadiene rubber, and cross-linked polyethylene as primary insulation and jacket in wire and cable. These polymers have been designed to yield maximum extrusion production rates while meeting the electrical and physical characteristics of these cured elastomers including high temperature deformation resistance, low temperature flexibility, long-term weathering resistance, high temperature aging resistance, chemical resistance, and ozone resistance. TPR 1000/2000 types meet the requirements of primary insulation materials in UL-62, REA specifications, and many military cable specifications.

TPR 5100, 5200, and 5400 series thermoplastic rubbers are specifically designed to serve all facets of the flexible cord, portable power, and control cable markets for insulation and non-oil-resistant jackets. The TPR 5100 series polymers meet the requirements for building wire, appliance wire, power cable, and flexible cord applications. TPR 5200 types are somewhat less resistant to heat deformation but they do pass flexible cord requirements and many less demanding applications such as booster cable, welding cable, and other heavy wall construction. Both TPR 5100 and 5200 types have been successfully used as insulation in retractable cords. These products have been used in shielded coaxial inner constructions as well as in unshielded construction types. The TPR 5400 series is finding applications in molded items and less critical wire and cable uses in heavy wall construction.

The olefinic thermoplastic elastomers have also found application in a number of molded electrical components. Electrical moldings include box gaskets, transformer encapsulation, stress relief members, cable ties, sleeving, caps, plugs, grommets, and connectors.

ET polymers and TPR thermoplastic rubbers have been used in semiconductive wire and cable applications. ET polymers can accept high filler loadings of conductive carbon. Relatively low values of volume resistivity can be achieved in this manner with little loss in other properties. Several semiconductive grades of TPR have recently been developed for specific wire and cable applications. They have exceptional heat stability, cable strippability, and excellent electrical conductivity.

2.4.3 Miscellaneous

The polyolefin thermoplastic elastomers have found a number of applications in the mechanical goods market. Their abrasion resistance and flexibility have permitted them to compete with conventional thermoset rubbers in these applications. The applications include belting, hose, fabric coating, seals, gasketing, and various industrial molded goods. Belting applications include transmission belts and specialty conveyor belts.

The good chemical resistance of the polyolefin thermoplastic elastomers to hot water and detergents is very important in appliance applications. The appliance market includes parts such as hose, seals, and gaskets for washers, dryers, and refrigerators. Other areas of interest are pump impellers, molded feet, clutch parts, and wheels.

Other application areas include housewares, toys, recreational and sporting goods, medical and pharmaceutical goods, sealants, tape, and footwear. A wide variety of miscellaneous molded and extruded products include luggage handles, hammer grips, lawn-mower wheels, swim fins, shoe soles, drum covers, garden hose, spatulas, toy wheels, syringe tips, etc. The olefinic thermoplastic elastomers have also been used as impact modifiers for polyethylene and polypropylene in such items as bowling pins, tackle boxes, pool and patio decks, and tennis court installations.

2.5 REFERENCES

Uniroyal TPR

Plastics Focus 4(32), October 9, 1972.
Chemical & Engineering News 50(42): 7 (1972).
Journal of Commerce 314, November 1, 1972.
Plastics World 30(15): 102 (1972).
Rubber Age 104(11): 76 (1972).
Modern Plastics 49(11): 30 (1972).
Plastics Technology 18(11): 11 (1972).
Materials Engineering 76(6): 38 (1972).
Machine Design 44(30): 21 (1972).
Rubber & Plastics News II(9): 1 (1972).
Rubber World 167(5): 49 (1973).
Rubber & Plastics News II(18): 4 (1973).
Automotive Engineering 81(5): 54 (1973).
H. L. Morris, *TPR Thermoplastic Rubber*, 31st Annual Technical Conference of the Society of Plastics Engineers, Montreal, May 7, 1973.
J. R. Johnson and H. L. Morris, *TPR Thermoplastic Rubber*, SAE National Automobile Engineering Meeting, Detroit, May 18, 1973.
K. R. Allen, Polyolefin Thermoplastic Rubber for Electrical/Electronic Insulation, Proceedings of the International Wire and Cable Symposium, 1973.
K. R. Allen, TPR Thermoplastic Rubber in Wire and Cable Applications, Electronic Materials and Processing Symposium, September 30, 1973.
H. L. Morris, TPR Thermoplastic Rubber, *Journal of Elastomers and Plastics* 6(7): 121 (1974).
P. R. Morin and J. R. Johnson, How to Extrude TPR, *Plastics Technology* 21(9): 49 (1975).
Rubber & Plastics News V(12): 23 (1976).
Journal of Commerce 327, January 22, 1976.
Journal of Commerce 327, March 4, 1976.
Rubber Age 108(3): 51 (1976).
Rubber Age 108(4): 78 (1976).
Rubber & Plastics News V(18): 12 (1976).
K. R. Allen, *A Family of Thermoplastic Elastomers for Total Wire & Cable Coating*, 34th Annual Technical Conference of the Society of Plastics Engineers, Atlantic City, April 26, 1976.
Rubber & Plastics News V(23): 8 (1976).
Uniroyal TPR Injection Molding Design & Processing Guide, Uniroyal Chemical, Naugatuck, Connecticut.

Du Pont Somel

Journal of Commerce 325, May 12, 1975.
Rubber & Plastics News IV(22): 21 (1975).
Chemical Engineering 82(12): 34 (1975).
Plastics Technology 21(7): 25 (1975).

Du Pont Elastomers Notebook **184**: 455 (1975).
Plastics World **33**(7): 73 (1975).
Rubber Age **107**(9): 62 (1975).
Product Engineering **46**(10): 29 (1975).
Publications of E. I. du Pont de Nemours & Company, Elastomer Chemicals Department, Wilmington, Delaware:
   Types of Somel
   Injection Molding Guide
   Extrusion Guide
   Extrusion of Somel
   Thermoforming Somel
   Chemical Resistance
   Coloring Somel 402T with Cube Concentrates

Goodrich Telcar

Rubber & Plastics News **IV**(10): 12 (1974).
Plastics Technology **21**(1): 9 (1975).
Plastics World **33**(2): 70 (1975).
Elastomers News Issue No. 3, B. F. Goodrich Co., 6100 Oak Tree Boulevard, Cleveland, Ohio.
Bulletin T-1, B. F. Goodrich Chemical Co., 6100 Oak Tree Boulevard, Cleveland, Ohio.
Bulletin T-2, B. F. Goodrich Chemical Co., 6100 Oak Tree Boulevard, Cleveland, Ohio.

Allied Chemical ET Polymer

P. F. Hartman, C. L. Eddy, and G. P. Koo, *SPE Journal* **26**(5): 62 (1970).
Plastics World **28**(6): 106 (1970).
Rubber World **162**(3): 39 (1970).
P. F. Hartman, C. L. Eddy, and G. P. Koo, *Rubber World* **163**(1): 59 (1970).
ET Polymer Data Sheet, Allied Chemical Corporation, Specialty Chemicals Division, Morristown, New Jersey.

Hercules Profax

Materials Engineering **82**(5): 22 (1975).
Technical Information Report, Hercules Incorporated, Polymers Department, Wilmington, Delaware.

General

Plastics World **30**(15): 58 (1972).
Plastics Technology **19**(5): 36 (1973).
Plastics World **31**(7): 46 (1973).

Chemical Engineering **80**(19): 76 (1973).

P. A. Reismiller and F. W. Johnson, *Thermoplastic Olefin Elastomers for Exterior Body Panels*, SPE National Technical Conference, Detroit, November 12, 1974.

Materials Engineering **82**(7): 47 (1975).

H. L. Morris, Thermoplastic Elastomers, *Modern Plastics Encyclopedia* **53**(10A): 103 (1976–1977).

Specific to Rheology

M. L. Williams, R. F. Landel, and J. D. Ferry. *J. Amer. Chem. Soc.* **77**: 3701 (1955).

R. L. Bergen and H. L. Morris. *Proceedings of the Fifth International Congress on Rheology* **4**: 433 (1970).

J. D. Ferry. *Viscoelastic Properties of Polymers*, John Wiley & Sons, New York, 1970.

3

Block Polymers

J. R. Haws and R. F. Wright
Phillips Petroleum Co.
Bartlesville, Oklahoma

3.1 INTRODUCTION

Discovery and development of new polymerization initiators in recent years have led to increased versatility in the preparation of elastomers. Polymer chemists now exert considerable control over microstructure, molecular weight features, branching, and combination of comonomers. This knowledge has been applied to a number of monomers including styrene, butadiene, and isoprene. Developments worthy of note are selectively structured polyisoprenes and polybutadienes and new random copolymers containing styrene; however, some of the most interesting of the many possible variations are block polymers. Butadiene-styrene polymers with two blocks have been produced since the early 1960s—these are useful in blends to modify properties and are used for this purpose in plastics and in vulcanized rubber compounds.[1] Copolymers with multiple blocks of polystyrene connected by rubbery segments form another group, which exhibits high strength and elastomeric characteristics without chemical cross-linking. The latter group is the subject of this chapter.

3.2 STRUCTURE AND COMPOSITION

3.2.1 Structure

Block polymers are usually considered to consist of two or more segments of different composition joined end to end. As segments can be various homopolymers or copolymers, a very large number of block polymers can be prepared. However, this chapter will be primarily concerned with polymers prepared from styrene, butadiene, and isoprene. Even with this limitation, many combinations are possible. For example, segments could be polybutadiene, polystyrene, polyisoprene, or copolymers. Segments might be different isomers of a homopolymer, or segments may be arranged in various sequences. There could be two, three, or multiple blocks. Segments could be all-elastomeric or all-plastic. As this *Handbook* deals with thermoplastic rubbers, polymers that combine hard plastic-like segments with softer elastomeric segments are of particular interest. Such combinations, as exemplified by polystyrene and polybutadiene, form two separate phases and exhibit two glass-transition temperatures corresponding to each component.[2,3] The polystyrene segments tend to associate but are restricted because of attachment to the flexible polybutadiene segments, and a network is formed. The polystyrene aggregates or domains serve as both cross-linking regions and as reinforcing particles. To form an effective network, there must be two or more hard segments in each molecule. These can be situated (see Figure 3-1) at the ends of a linear rubbery central block (*a*), or at the ends of a branched rubber molecule (*c*), or a number of them can be interspersed with rubbery blocks in a linear chain (*b*).

Polymers produced by Phillips Petroleum Co. and marketed under the trademark Solprene are described as radial (branched) "teleblocks" and are called *plastomers*. Polymers marketed by Shell Chemical Company under the trademark Kraton are reportedly linear.

The polystyrene domains in these block polymers can be spherical in shape (as shown in Figure 3-2), rodlike, or lamellar. Rods and lamellae break up when the polymer is stretched, and the structure then approaches that of Figure 3-2.

When these polymers are heated, the polystyrene domains soften, and the polymer will flow under pressure and thus can be molded, extruded, or otherwise

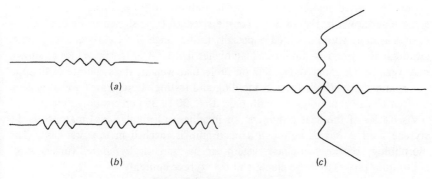

(a)

(b)

(c)

Figure 3-1. Polymer types.

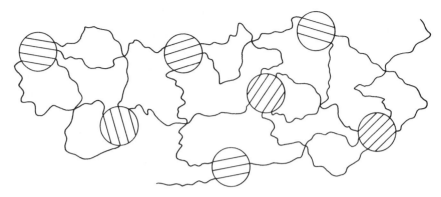

Figure 3-2. Polymer structure.

formed much like conventional thermoplastics. Upon cooling, the polystyrene segments reform into hard domains, and high strength is restored. Both polybutadiene and polyisoprene are useful as the elastomeric segment and in many respects provide similar behavior. Utilization of polyisoprene yields a softer material that shows reduced viscosity relative to polybutadiene.[4]

There are also polymers that have polystyrene end blocks and saturated elastomeric segments. These are newer versions and are more resistant to degradative effects caused by oxidation and by exposure to ultraviolet light or ozone.

3.2.2 Monomer Ratio

The monomer ratio in thermoplastic rubbers based on styrene and dienes is an important consideration and exerts a significant effect on properties. Increasing the amount of styrene will increase modulus and hardness.[4,5] Hardness (Shore A) can be varied readily from approximately 40 to 90 or higher by increasing styrene as shown in Figure 3-3. Tensile strength (also shown in Figure 3-3) increases as more styrene is used, especially in the range of 5 to 20 percent styrene, although the trend is diminished at higher levels. The tensile values as shown may vary over a range depending on molecular weight, the structure of the polymer, and the methods used in molding and testing. Cold draw upon extension is often observed in polymers with more than 30 to 35 percent polystyrene.

Viscosities of the neat polymers[6] or in adhesive formulations[7] may rise as the styrene level is raised, although a maximum is reached in the first case. The morphology of the two-phase system can be dramatically altered (inversion of continuous phase) by large changes in the styrene content.[8]

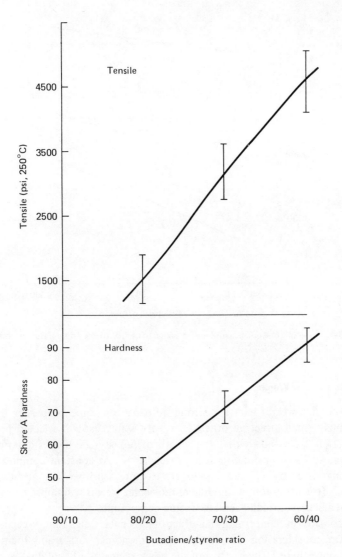

Figure 3-3. Effects of monomer ratio.

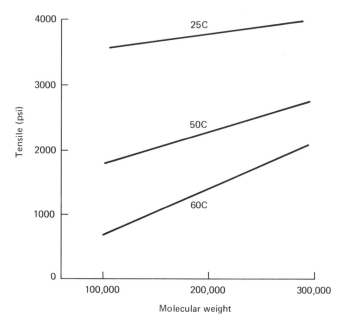

Figure 3-4. Tensile strength vs. molecular weight for 60/40 butadiene/styrene radial block polymer.

3.2.3 Molecular Weight

The molecular weight exerts a strong influence on some properties but has a surprisingly small effect on others. At least with regard to selected properties, investigators have shown that the length of polystyrene blocks determines behavior more than the total molecular weight.[6,9] At constant composition and branching, viscosity of these polymers is quite sensitive to molecular weight changes. It is often found that higher molecular weight will improve some properties in adhesive, molding, and extrusion compounds.[5,7]

Any conclusions concerning the effect of molecular weight on properties should take into consideration the composition (monomer ratio) and branching involved, since these influence size of the block segments. Trend lines as shown in Figure 3-4 have been noted.

3.2.4 Linear and Branched Polymers

As indicated in Figure 3-1, the basic molecule can be linear or branched; if nonlinear, the number of branches can be predominantly three, four, and more or may be a mixture of various numbers of branches.[10-15] It has been shown that

Table 3-1. Comparison of teleblock polymers at equal formulation viscosities.

30/70 STYRENE/BUTADIENE POLYMER	MOLECULAR WEIGHT	FORMULATION VISCOSITY (cps)	SHEAR RESISTANCE (Hr to Fail at 90°C)
Linear	84,000	1,520	1.0
Trichain	136,000	1,580	2.4
Tetrachain	182,000	1,820	2.8

this aspect of structure has a considerable effect on solution and melt viscosities. Increasing the degree of branching results in lower viscosity at constant molecular weight.[16] In certain uses, a higher-molecular-weight branched polymer can be used to obtain better properties without loss in processability. Examples are improved shear resistance in adhesives or better tensile strength at elevated temperature in molded compounds. An illustration of a 70/30 butadiene/styrene block polymer in an adhesive formulation is shown in Table 3-1.[17]

3.3 AVAILABILITY OF POLYMER

Block polymers are commercially available as (1) neat (i.e., noncompounded and nonextended), (2) oil-extended, or (3) fully compounded products with either saturated or unsaturated center blocks. Examples of commercial polymers and compounds are listed in Tables 3-2 through 3-5. As can be seen, a wide range of properties is possible. A number of other products based on these elastomers are also available, and additional grades are in developmental stages. Commercial products are produced in a variety of forms including bale, crumb, pellet, and ground particles. Optimum choice of product and product form is dependent on the consumer's process equipment and intended application.

3.4 PROPERTIES OF NEAT POLYMERS

Typical properties of nonextended rubbers are listed in this section. The polymers are identified only by styrene content, elastomeric midblock monomer, and melt flow range. Actual property values could vary somewhat, depending on additional polymer variables such as molecular weight, degree of branching, or other structural differences.

3.4.1 Mechanical Properties

The subject polymers do not require vulcanization, but have excellent green strength and elastomeric properties (Table 3-6). Unlike plastics, these materials

Table 3-2. Nonextended polymers with unsaturated center block.

POLYMER[a]	SOLPRENE					KRATON		
	406	414	411	416	418	1101	1102	1107
Diolefin/ styrene ratio	60/40	60/40	70/30	70/30	85/15[b]	70/30	72/28	86/14[b]
Molecular weight	High	Low	High	Low	–	–	–	–
Type structure	Radial	Radial	Radial	Radial	Radial	Linear	Linear	Linear
Specific gravity	0.95	0.95	0.94	0.94	0.92	0.94	0.94	0.92
Melt flow, 200°C/5 kg[c]	0	4	0	3	3	<1	6	9
300% modulus, psi	600	600	300	420	140	400	400	100
Tensile, psi	3900	4000	2800[d]	2900	2400	4600	4600	3100
Elongation, %	700	750	700	720	1050	880	880	1300
Shore A hardness	93	90	78	68	34	71	62	37

[a]Partial listing only.
[b]Isoprene/styrene; others are butadiene/styrene.
[c]ASTM D 1238.
[d]Resin additives result in higher tensile strength—retains tensile better than polymer of lower molecular weight on extension.

Table 3-3. Nonextended polymers with saturated center block.

POLYMER[a]	SOLPRENE 512	KRATON G 1650	KRATON G 1652
Olefin/styrene ratio	70/30	70/30	70/30
Specific gravity	0.91	0.91	0.91
Melt flow, 190°C/21.6 kg[b]	0.3	0 (nil)	2.5
300% modulus, psi	730	550	800
Tensile, psi	4300	3700	3850
Elongation, %	540	560	520
Shore A hardness	85	72	77

[a]Partial listing only.
[b]ASTM D 1238.

Table 3-4. Oil-extended unsaturated polymers.

POLYMER[a]	475	SOLPRENE 478	480	481	4113	KRATON 4124	4122
Butadiene/ styrene ratio	60/40	60/40	70/30	52/48	67/33	67/33	52/48
Type structure	Radial	Radial	Radial	Radial	Linear	Linear	Linear
Extractable, % (oil)	33	44	33	37	31	33	35
Specific gravity	0.94	0.93	0.93	0.95	0.94	0.93	0.95
Melt flow, 200 C/5 kg[b]	5	35	3	5	26	16	22
300% modulus, psi	300	160	200	220	300	200	230
Tensile, psi	2700	2000	1300	2500	1700	1700	2250
Elongation, %	1000	1300	1100	1100	1150	1350	1150
Shore A hardness	67	48	45	68	46	43	62

[a] Partial listing only.
[b] ASTM D 1238.

exhibit low permanent set after extension and are highly flexible and resilient. Surface friction is high, with coefficient-of-friction values similar to those of conventional vulcanized rubbers.[18]   Due to their thermoplastic nature, block polymers exhibit a loss in tensile strength and hardness as temperature increases. Thermoplasticity also contributes to increased flow and ease of processing at elevated temperatures.

3.4.2 Thermal Characteristics

Block polymers remain flexible at very low temperatures as indicated by the data in Table 3-7. Indicative of a two-phase nature, two glass-transition points are exhibited by the elastomers. The upper transition temperature is dependent on the styrenic block, and the lower transition temperature on the elastomeric block. Distortion characteristics can be altered somewhat by varying structure (molecular weight, branching, etc.), or more so by compounding. Maximum service temperature can vary widely, depending on formulation and specific requirements.

3.4.3 Environmental and Chemical Resistance

Unsaturated block polymers are similar to SBR rubber in resistance to ozone, oxidation, and ultraviolet radiation; these can be used in many applications

Table 3-5. Examples of commercially available compounds.

COMPOUNDS DESIGNED FOR	SPECIFIC GRAVITY	TENSILE (psi)	ELONGATION (%)	SHORE A HARDNESS	OTHER FEATURES
Footwear					
Slipper soling	1.10	970	410	81	Economical, easily fabricated, highly flexible, slip- and abrasion-resistant
Sneaker soling	1.14	850	520	44	
Unit soling	1.02	910	450	67	
"Earth" shoe	1.02	860	480	59	
General purpose extruded products					
Cove base	1.68	750	210	86	Good extrusion
Rubber band	1.02	2900	960	59	High resilience, elastomeric
Garden hose	1.26	1100	800	65	Flexible at low temperature
Gasket (appliance)	1.27	2020	910	69	Good sealing qualities
Milk tubing	1.26	1590	1040	49	High purity, disposable
General purpose molded products					
Flexible toys	1.00	810	870	46	Soft, pliable, good color
Swim fins	0.98	1800	780	76	Flexible, water-resistant
Crutch tips	0.99	1050	630	48	Slip and abrasion resistance
Golf-club grip	0.98	1250	880	62	High friction, rubbery feel
Pharmaceutical, medical					
Tubing, packaging	0.93	900–1900	800–1300	45–55	High purity, good clarity
Automotive					
Sight shields	1.16	2000	900	84	Impact- and weather-resistant
Bumper fillers					

TYPICAL PROPERTIES[a]

[a]Representative data for some of Phillips Petroleum Co. (Solprene LR, Live Rubber) compounds or Shell Chemical Company (Kraton) products. Some specific products are listed in Table 3-17.

Table 3-6. Typical mechanical properties of various polymer compositions.[a]

POLYMER COMPOSITION

TYPE CENTER BLOCK	BUTADIENE	BUTADIENE	SATURATED-OLEFINIC	ISOPRENE
Styrene content, %	30	40	30	ca. 15
Melt flow range, 200 °C/5 kg[b]	2-10 <1	2-10 <1	<1	5
Properties				
300% modulus, psi	400	600	550-800	150
Tensile, psi	2500-3500	4000	4000	2500-3000
Elongation, %	750	750	550	1000
Shore D Hardness	27	41	30	–
Shore A Hardness at 25 C	70-75	92	72-85	35
at 70 C	42 70	65 79	68	–
at 100 C	15 55	25 55	48	–
Tensile, psi				700-1000
at 50 C	550 1100	1800 2500	1800	1000
at 60 C	350 –	600 1900	1200	200-400
at 70 C	200 800	450 1700	700	–
Set, % (after 300% elongation)	5-10	15-20	10-30	<5
Yerzley resilience, %	70 –	55 80	75-80	85

[a]Determined on compression molded samples. Test values may be varied to some extent by method of processing (injection molded, extruded, solvent cast, etc.).
[b]ASTM D 1238.

without special stabilization. Additives can markedly improve aging characteristics under more demanding conditions (see Section 3.5.6). Polymers with saturated rubber sections are inherently resistant to effects of ozone, oxidation, and ultraviolet radiation.

Block polymers can be used in contact with water, alcohols, weak acids, or bases with little change in properties (Table 3-8). However, many hydrocarbons, esters and ketones dissolve or cause excessive swelling of the rubbers. Solubility characteristics of block polymers make them well suited for solvent-based formulations (adhesives, sealants, caulks, etc.), but limit their use in applications requiring resistance to many chemicals.

3.4.4 Electrical Properties

Plastomers are good electrical insulators as indicated by data in Table 3-9. Properly compounded materials exhibit properties attractive for various electrical and wire and cable applications.

Table 3-7. Thermal characteristics.

POLYMER VARIABLES

TYPE CENTER BLOCK	BUTADIENE	SATURATED-OLEFINIC	ISOPRENE
Styrene content, %	30–40	30	15
Melt flow range, 200 C/5 kg[a]	2–10 <1	<1	5
Properties, °C			
Tg			
lower	-90	-52	-55
upper	100	100	100
Gehman freeze point	-90	-60	-60
Brittleness temperature	<-60	<-60	<-60
Vicat softening point	60–75	60–70	–
Distortion temperature[b]	50–55	45–55	–
% Distortion at 100 C[c]	80 0	0	100
Thermal conductivity[d]	3.6[e]	–	3.6[e]
Specific heat, cal/°C/gm	0.45–0.50[e]	–	0.45–0.50[e]
Thermal expansion, 10^{-5} in./in./°C	13–13.7[e]	–	13–13.7[e]

[a]ASTM D 1238.
[b]ASTM D 648, 66 psi.
[c]ASTM D 2633.
[d]10^{-4} cal/sec/cm^2/1(°C/cm).
[e]Value from *Modern Plastics Encyclopedia* (1974–1975).

Table 3-8. Chemical resistance.

POLYMER VARIABLES

TYPE CENTER BLOCK	BUTADIENE	BUTADIENE	SATURATED-OLEFINIC
Styrene content, %	30	40	30
Volume swell (%), after 22 hours at 25°C in:			
10% sodium hydroxide	0	1	0.4
10% sulfuric acid	0.2	0.7	0.3
Diethylene glycol	0.1	0.5	0.4
Ethyl alcohol	2	2	1
Vegetable oil (Wesson)	27	5	4
Bath oil (Avon)	26	9	61
Acetone	41	57	19
ASTM Oil No. 1	10	3	8
ASTM Oil No. 3	67	38	46
ASTM fuel A	a	114	a
ASTM fuel C	a	a	a
Normal hexane	a	a	a
Carbon tetrachloride	a	a	a

[a]Dissolves.

Table 3-9. Electrical properties.

POLYMER VARIABLES

TYPE CENTER BLOCK	BUTADIENE	BUTADIENE	SATURATED-OLEFINIC
Styrene content, %	30	40	30
Dielectric constant			
1 kHz	2.51	2.53	2.30
1 MHz	2.50	2.53	2.30
Dissipation factor			
1 kHz	4×10^{-4}	1×10^{-4}	13×10^{-5}
1 MHz	8×10^{-4}	7×10^{-4}	23×10^{-5}
Volume resistivity, ohm-cm			
1 min	3×10^{16}	2×10^{16}	9×10^{16}
5 min	1×10^{17}	2×10^{16}	2×10^{17}

3.4.5 Permeability

The highly permeable nature of block polymers (Table 3-10) suggests their use in breathable-type packaging. Permeability is much greater than that of Saran wrap or polyethylene.

3.4.6 Viscosity and Rheological Properties

Solution viscosity of plastomers depends on a number of factors. The block structure in itself contributes to low solution viscosity. At 10% solids, solutions of block polymers may display a viscosity that is about one-tenth that of SBR or natural rubber.[18] Other factors exerting strong effects are monomer ratio, block styrene content, molecular weight and structure of the elastomer molecule, and, of course, solids concentration. Some typical solution viscosities for branched polymers are noted in Table 3-11.

Trends observed in solution viscosity with changes in molecular structure (linear vs. branched) and in molecular weight are illustrated in Figure 3-5. These are generalized data for solutions in solvents such as toluene or naphtha-toluene blends.

Melt viscosity of block polymers depends on monomer type and ratio,[18] molecular structure,[16,17] and molecular weight as well as temperature and shear rate. Overall, it would appear that one of the most important considerations in melt behavior is the length of the polystyrene terminal blocks.[9] Butadiene leads to higher viscosity than isoprene. Increasing styrene in copolymers with butadiene appears to increase viscosity up to approximately 30% styrene followed by a decrease in viscosity at higher styrene levels. Branching reduces viscosity if total molecular weight is constant.

Table 3-10. Gas permeability.

POLYMER VARIABLES				SARAN[a]	HIGH-DENSITY POLY-ETHYLENE
TYPE CENTER BLOCK	BUTADIENE	BUTADIENE	SATURATED-OLEFINIC	_[b]	–
Styrene content, %	30	40	30	–	–
Permeation, cm^3/100 in.^{2}/mil thickness/24 hr					
Oxygen	3600	700	2000	0.1–0.2	110
Carbon dioxide	13,000	2800	8500	0.3	350
Nitrogen	1300	180	700	0.025	50
Mositure-vapor transmission[c]	36	17	8	1.8	–

[a]Vinylidene chloride.
[b]Not applicable.
[c]Gm/100 in.^{2}/24 hr/mil.

As noted in Table 3-11, some neat polymers are low in melt flow. Response of these polymers to changes in pressure and temperature may vary but the apparent viscosity generally decreases with an increase in shear rate. Two examples of neat polymers are shown in Figure 3-6. Quite often, the subject polymers are blended with other polymers, or compounded with oils and resins, which may alter flow properties. Melt viscosities and response to shear rate of compounds and blends will often be similar to that displayed by thermoplastics such as polyethylene or polystyrene. A polymer with two levels of added oil

Table 3-11. Melt viscosities of typical polymer solutions.

Polymer Description						
Solprene	417	416	411	414	406	418
Type center block	Butadiene	Butadiene	Butadiene	Butadiene	Butadiene	Isoprene
Styrene content, %	20	30	30	40	40	15
Type structure	Radial	Radial	Radial	Radial	Radial	Radial
Toluene solution viscosity						
5 wt%, cst	14	10	30	7	18	15
25 wt%, cP	3500	1400	17,000	600	7800	2300
Melt flow, gram/10 min[a]						
180 C, 5 kg	1	1	0	2	0	2
200 C, 5 kg	2	2	0	5	0	–

[a]ASTM D 1238.

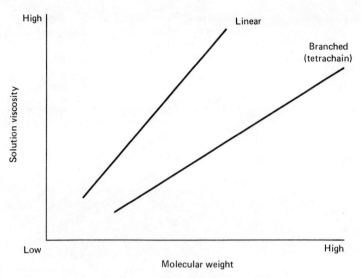

Figure 3-5. Molecular weight and structure effects.

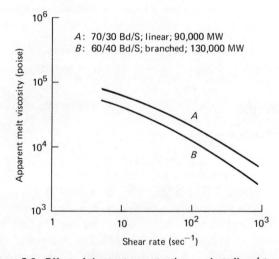

A: 70/30 Bd/S; linear; 90,000 MW
B: 60/40 Bd/S; branched; 130,000 MW

Figure 3-6. Effect of shear rate—neat polymers, butadiene/styrene.

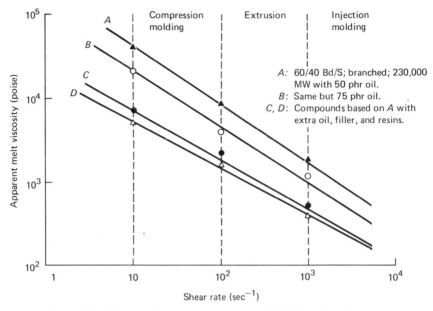

Figure 3-7. Effect of shear rate—compounds of 60/40 butadiene/styrene.

and compounds based on the same polymer were used to obtain the data in Figure 3-7, which is rather typical of the behavior to be expected.

3.5 COMPOUNDING

3.5.1 General Comments

The plastomers (or block polymers) described previously display an interesting balance of properties and can be used as manufactured in various applications, including products formed by heat and pressure as well as those deposited from solvents. Also, these polymers can be used to modify properties of other polymers—polyolefins, polystyrene, etc.—without the need for other added ingredients. For many uses, however, such as adhesives, hot melts, extrusions, and moldings, the addition of minor or major amounts of other materials may prove advantageous. Thermoplastic elastomers display good strength and can be compounded to provide a very wide range of properties.[5, 21–24] The polymers are easily mixed with compounding ingredients either as a melt or as a solution. These rubbers respond well to compounding, which can be useful to adjust cost, viscosity and flow, hardness, flexibility, tack, deformation resistance, oxidation and ozone resistance, flammability, and other properties.

Various materials are useful in compounding block polymers—fillers, plasticizers, resins, and antidegradants. Choice of ingredients will often depend on the composition of the neat polymer as well as the effect desired. Another factor to be kept in mind is the two-phase nature of these polymers. Ingredients may be miscible or compatible with the hard segments, the soft segment, both, or neither. The morphology can be affected, i.e., the addition of a sizable amount of some polymer or resin may cause inversion of the continuous phase.

3.5.2 Plasticizers

Various oils and waxes serve as plasticizers for block polymers. In most cases, it is desired to use a material that will soften and plasticize the elastomeric portion and not the polystyrene segment. Oils that are generally most useful are those classified as paraffinic, naphthenic, or white mineral oils. Aromatic content of the oil should be low to avoid softening of polystyrene blocks and the resultant excessive decreases in strength and hardness. Of course, all oils reduce tensile and abrasion resistance but serve to regulate hardness and modulus as well as increasing melt flow. Oils may provide benefits in resistance to crack growth during flexing.

Materials other than oils may serve as plasticizers, especially at elevated processing temperatures. Some of the resins and process aids discussed in following sections serve in this capacity.

Plasticizers or other compounding ingredients may reduce the stability of compounds compared to the neat polymer upon exposure to ultraviolet radiation. In such cases, addition of pigments or other ultraviolet stabilizers may be necessary.

3.5.3 Fillers

Large quantities of inexpensive fillers can be added to block polymers, usually in combination with plasticizers and/or resins to reduce cost and modify properties. The effect of a few fillers at several loadings is shown in Table 3-12.

In general, fillers decrease melt flow and tensile strength; however, strength at elevated temperatures may be increased. Other changes to be expected include an increase in tear strength, flex life, and abrasion resistance imparted by fine-particle-size silicas, carbon blacks, and hard clays. These fillers also increase modulus and hardness. Calcium carbonates have less effect on properties, but improve flex life with only a slight increase in hardness or stiffness. Fillers such as titanium dioxide, zinc oxide, or carbon black are sometimes added to improve resistance to ultraviolet radiation. Glass beads, talc, or other materials may also be useful as fillers for some applications.

Table 3-12. Effect of fillers on compound properties.

Polymer (60/40 butadiene/styrene)	100	100	100	100	100	100	100	100	100	100
Calcium carbonate	0	40	80	120	0	0	0	0	0	0
Hard clay	0	0	0	0	40	80	120	0	0	0
Fine silica	0	0	0	0	0	0	0	10	20	40
Melt flow, 180 C/5 kg[a]	3	1.5	0.9	0.5	1.4	0.5	0	1	0.3	0
300% modulus, psi	590	580	560	570	1300	1720	2000	800	910	1300
Tensile, psi	4000	2800	1950	1400	2600	2150	2000	3900	3750	2700
Elongation, %	780	750	700	630	700	470	300	760	750	660
Crescent tear, lb/in.	220	210	220	190	350	380	420	280	400	560
Shore D hardness	36	38	42	46	42	48	52	38	41	48
NBS abrasion index, % of RMA standard	52	39	34	30	67	64	63	75	80	81
Ross flex, M flexures to 0.5-in. cut growth	3.5	23	40	13	>200	>200	30	50	>200	>200

[a] ASTM D 1238.

3.5.4 Resins and Plastic Polymer Additives

A number of resins and plastic polymers can be used to advantage in developing specific properties in block copolymer adhesive and thermoformed compounds. These materials tend to decrease elasticity or "rubbery feel" and are generally used in combination with plasticizers (and fillers). In adhesives, resins are used to improve tack, adhesion, peel strength, and shear strength. In extruded or molded goods, resins and plastics can be added to adjust hardness and improve a variety of physical properties including distortion resistance. These materials also often reduce viscosity at elevated temperatures, thus permitting easier processing. Different resins affect the ratio of properties in different ways—some increase melt flow with small effect on hardness while others have the reverse effect. Resins that are more compatible with the styrenic end-block are likely to produce a hard, nontacky material; a sticky, soft, flexible composition is likely to result from resins that are more compatible with the rubbery central block. Some useful resins or plastics and effects of primary interest are:

- Polystyrene (e.g., Styron 678). Increases tear strength, abrasion resistance, flex life, and hardness.
- Polyethylene (e.g., Marlex TR-885). Increases abrasion resistance, hardness, and distortion resistance.
- Ethylene vinyl acetate (e.g., Ultrathene UE 631). Improves ozone resistance.
- Polypropylene (e.g., Marlex HGZ-120-03). Increases modulus, hardness, and distortion resistance.
- Vinyl toluene copolymer (e.g., Piccotex 100). Increases melt flow and adhesion.
- Polyindene (e.g., Picco 6100). Increases melt flow, hardness, tensile, and adhesion.
- Coumarone-indene (e.g., Cumar LX-509). Increases distortion resistance, melt flow, tensile, and tear strength.
- Pentaerythritol ester of hydrogenated rosin (e.g., Pentalyn H). Increases melt flow, adhesion, and flex life.

Care should be exercised to adequately disperse the resin or plastic in block polymer rubber goods by fluxing at sufficiently high temperature (see p. 94). One should also be aware that morphology of blends can be altered to some extent by various conditions of molding or extrusion, causing some differences in physical properties. This latter effect is especially evident in blends with polystyrene. For example, compression molding below the softening point of polystyrene ($<220°$F) can result in considerably higher hardness than molding at higher temperature (see Figure 3-8). Extruded or injection-molded specimens containing polystyrene usually have properties more similar to those obtained by compression molding at the lower temperature.

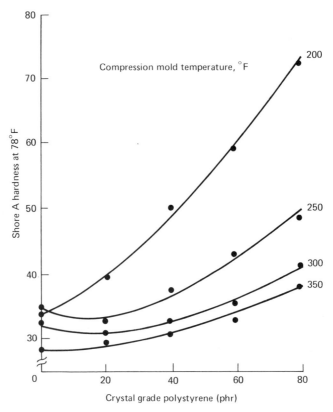

Figure 3-8. Effect of mold temperature on hardness of blends with polystyrene.

3.5.5 Blends with Other Rubbers

Block polymers are compatible with most conventional rubbers, and many types of blends are possible. Green strength and processing characteristics of conventional rubbers may be improved by the addition of block polymer. Or, conversely, block polymer properties such as solvent resistance or ozone resistance can be upgraded by blending with minor amounts of some rubbers including neoprene, nitrile, polyurethane, propylene oxide, or ethylene-propylene-diene (EPDM). High green-strength rubbers are best suited for these blends in order to maintain optimum physical properties. Probably of most commercial significance at present are blends composed of unsaturated block polymers with 15 to 30 percent of a high green-strength EPDM. Such compositions exhibit good thermoplastic properties and a high degree of ozone resistance. Examples of such blends are shown in Table 3-13. Process conditions can affect the degree of

Table 3-13. Ozone resistance of blends.

Polymer Composition				
Polymer (60/40 butadiene/styrene)	100	80	75	0
High green strength EPDM	0	20	25	100
Blend Properties				
300% modulus, psi	650	620	580	—[a]
Tensile, psi	4000	3350	2600	1030
Elongation, %	750	670	630	1010
Ozone resistance	Poor	Fair-good	Good	Good

[a]Not determined.

ozone resistance obtained, with high-shear operations (such as injection molding) or relatively low temperature in compression molding ($<290°F$) thought to be most favorable.

3.5.6 Stabilizers

A number of factors should be considered in choosing stabilizers for block polymers and their compounds. Of primary importance are type of central block in the polymer, compounding ingredients to be added, and process and application requirements. In general, block polymers with a butadiene or isoprene segment are similar in stability to SBR rubber or natural rubber, respectively. A polymer with a saturated elastomeric block is inherently more stable.

Sufficient stabilizer is added by the manufacturer to prevent degradation during normal finishing operations and storage of polymer. For many applications, additional stabilizer may not be required. However, under some conditions deterioration can occur due to oxidation, ultraviolet radiation, or ozone attack. Nonstaining stabilizers are preferred for most applications utilizing these elastomers. FDA acceptance of stabilizers is also required for many uses.

Oxidative conditions such as encountered in air at elevated temperatures may cause polymer with a butadiene block to cross-link, increasing in hardness and viscosity; an isoprene segment will undergo scission when oxidized, becoming softer and less viscous. Polymer with a saturated center segment can also be affected by high temperature exposure, usually resulting in reduced viscosity. Combinations of phenolic antioxidants or dithiocarbamates with dilauryl thiodipropionate effectively increase oxidative stability.

Ultraviolet radiation can cause surface embrittlement of neat, unsaturated polymers and, depending on formulation ingredients, can cause discoloration and embrittlement of compounded stocks regardless of the chemical composition of the polymer center block. Only stable plasticizers and resins should be included in compounds intended for outdoor use where direct exposure to ultraviolet light might cause objectionable property changes. Certain chemical additives such as nickel dibutyldithiocarbamate, benzophenones, or benzotriazoles will increase resistance to ultraviolet light. Also, fillers which absorb or reflect ultraviolet radiation (carbon black, zinc oxide, titanium dioxide) can be added to increase ultraviolet stability.

When under stress, unsaturated block polymers are susceptible to attack by ozone. However, ozone protection is easily attained by blending with minor amounts of EPDM or ethylene vinyl acetate polymers (see Blends with Other Rubbers, pp. 90–91). Also, chemical antiozonants including nickel dibutyldithiocarbamate, dibutyl thiourea, or certain waxes offer some ozone protection.

3.5.7 Miscellaneous Additives

Process aids or lubricants may be added to reduce viscosity, decrease tackiness, increase flow, and/or improve surface gloss of finished articles. Stearic acid (0.5 to 2 phr) and some metallic stearates are excellent process aids. Certain waxes, polyamides, polyethylene glycols, and low-density polyethylenes are also effective.

Pigments, dyes, or color concentrates are often added to obtain various shades of color. Colorants may be dispersed during initial mixing, or dry blended and subsequently dispersed during fabrication. Stability (durability) and ease of incorporation should be considered in choosing colorants. Inorganic pigments generally possess good stability and are easy to disperse. Organic pigments often produce brighter colors and are more soluble in organic solvents and polymers. Dyes also produce bright colors but many are relatively poor in stability and tend to bleed or migrate.

Other additives that are sometimes utilized include antistatic or antiblocking agents, flame retardants, fungicides, and blowing agents. Although added for specific effects, additives often cause some change in general characteristics—their effect on all properties of interest should be determined.

3.6 PROCESSING

3.6.1 Mixing

As noted, the high-strength plastomers may be used alone or in admixture with other ingredients. When mixing or compounding is desired, several methods may be considered—solution (or liquid) mixing (including emulsions and plastisol-type mixes), melt processing, and dry blending.

3.6.2 Solution Mixing

The solution-mixing method is useful for preparation of solvent-based adhesives, sealants, and coatings. Plastomers are soluble in a wide range of common, inex-

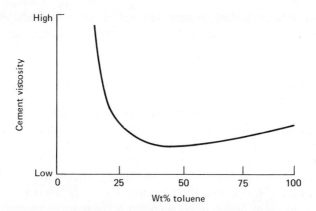

Figure 3-9. Solution viscosities in hexane-toluene blends.

pensive solvents. The polymers dissolve quickly and display fast solvent release. Since two phases are present, a hard segment of polystyrene and an elastomeric segment, both must be considered in the selection of solvents and additives. Both segments must be dissolved if the polymer is to be considered truly in solution. Dissolution of the polystyrene domains temporarily destroys the network, which reforms on subsequent solvent release, restoring strength to the polymer or compound.

The morphology of the polymer can differ if deposited from different solvents, and this can affect properties of coatings or adhesives.[25] Plastomers often display lower solution viscosity than SBR random copolymers or natural rubber (depending on molecular weight). The structure of the polymer (linear or branched) must be considered as this will affect viscosity; branched polymers give lower viscosity than linear at the same molecular weight (see Properties, p. 76).

Good solvents for elastomeric block copolymers of styrene with polybutadiene or polyisoprene include cyclohexane, toluene, methyl ethyl ketone, diethyl ether, and styrene. Mixtures of solvents are often found practical; for example: naphtha-toluene, hexane-toluene, or hexane-toluene-ketone. The viscosity is sensitive to the solvent-blend composition as broadly indicated in Figure 3-9.

The thermoplastic elastomers can be converted to emulsions by suitable methods. Films and coatings can then be prepared by evaporation of water. Since the polystyrene will tend to be deposited in discrete particles, higher strength will be developed if the film or coating is heated after drying.

Block copolymers based on styrene and butadiene can absorb large quantities of oil and still provide some useful properties. Another useful processing method involves the combination of oil and ground polymer to make a fluid mixture, which can then be formed into a product by compression molding, injection molding, rotational molding, casting, and perhaps other methods. As the mixture is heated, the oil is incorporated into the polymer forming a solid (usually soft) product.

3.6.3 Melt Mixing

Block copolymers soften on heating and can be processed easily using equipment designed either for rubber or for plastics. Internal mixers of various types are preferred for addition of compound ingredients, but conventional roll mills are also suitable. Proper temperature control is necessary in order to achieve maximum efficiency in melt mixing. Block polymers can be fluxed at 200 to 250°F; however, higher temperatures are often required to disperse high-softening-point resins, fillers, or other additives. Banbury dump temperatures of 280 to 320°F are usually adequate; a few additives, such as polypropylene, may increase requirements to 350°F or more.

Dispersion of resins and fillers is best accomplished by early addition in the mix cycle and fluxing with rubber before addition of plasticizers or softeners. Block polymers will build up heat during mastication, readily softening and mixing with moderate amounts of added materials. If a high plasticizer level is required, addition should be in several increments to prevent the mix from becoming lubricated, with resultant slipping on rotors. Compounds to be mixed with high levels of filler and oil may require addition of part of the oil initially in order to flux the dry mixture.

A typical Banbury mix schedule follows:

Formulation

Polymer (60/40 butadiene/styrene)	100
Calcium carbonate	150
Polystyrene	40
Naphthenic oil	60

"B" Banbury, 158°F, 118-rpm rotor speed
0 min: add polymer, polystyrene, and calcium carbonate.
280°F (approximately 2 min): add ½ oil.
Power-up: add remaining oil.
280 to 320°F (approximately 4.5 min): dump. Sheet off on roll mill at 240°F.

A roll mill temperature of 200 to 250°F is generally satisfactory for banding stocks. If a temperature differential exists between rolls, compounds will tend to band on the hotter roll; for this reason, it may be advantageous to operate with the front (preferred) roll 15 to 25°F hotter than the back roll.

Hot-melt adhesive formulations containing plastomers are readily mixed in either a sigma-blade-equipped mixer or by simple stirring in a heated vessel. Mixer temperatures of 330 to 380°F are common.

3.6.4 Dry Blending

Dry blends can be prepared by mechanically mixing ground or powdered block polymer with other components at a temperature less than that required to flux.[19] In most formulations, added oil tends to bind an even coating of filler and other ingredients to polymer particles, resulting in a homogeneous, free-flowing mixture. This mixture can be fed directly to fabrication equipment capable of handling powder forms. Here the material is fluxed prior to formation of finished articles. Energy requirements may be reduced by this method of mixing compared to melt mixing and subsequent finishing operations.

Intensive mixers (of the Henschel type) or ribbon blenders are suitable for dry blending. Typical mix procedures are shown below. Dump temperature should be kept below the point (depending on formulation) at which ingredients tend to stick together, losing their free-flowing characteristics. Components should be fairly uniform in particle size. If large differences exist, the mixture may tend to segregate or layer during storage or finishing operations.

High-Intensity Mix Procedure—Dry Blending

Use cooling water on jacket; 625-rpm rotor speed.*
　0 min: Add all dry ingredients
　0.5 min: Begin addition of oil. If oil used is of high viscosity, it should be heated to about 120°F. Addition time is dependent on the batch size and polymer particle size. Mix until compound appears to be free-flowing.
　2–5 min: Dump. Temperature is usually less than 150°F.

Ribbon-Blender Mix Procedure—Dry Blending

　0 min: Add all ingredients except oil, other liquids, and small amount of filler.
　0.5 min: Add liquids slowly, preferably through a spray head. Mix until ingredients are dispersed; add remainder of filler.
　5–15 min: Dump.

3.6.5 Extrusion

Extrusion techniques similar to those established with other thermoplastics can be used to form film, tubing, and other cross-sections from block polymers and their compounds. Low die swell is exhibited by these materials, permitting the use of relatively simple dies to produce rather complex sections.

---

*Rotor speed required will vary with capacity of mixer; it is generally reduced with increasing mixer capacity.

A temperature gradient should be maintained between feed zone and die, with the following ranges typical:

Barrel temperature
Feed zone	240–270°F
Intermediate zone	250–300°F
Final zone	270–340°F
Die temperature	280–340°F
Melt temperature	270–380°F

Adjustments may be required to optimize rates and prevent excessive melt temperatures, depending on formulation. Excessive heat increases the possibility of degradation and also weakens the extrudate, increasing the chance for distortion before cooling.

Extruder size can vary considerably; satisfactory results have been demonstrated with L:D ratios of 10:1 to 25:1. The longer barrel may be preferred for cold feed, and a shorter barrel for hot feed (direct from internal mixer or sheet-off mill). In either case, low compression screws are recommended.

3.6.6 Molding

Thermoplastic block polymers can be molded by most conventional methods including injection, compression, rotational, or blow molding. A wide selection of equipment exists.[20] A brief discussion and general guidelines applicable to the subject rubbers follow.

Injection molding of block polymer compositions can generally be accomplished quite easily with melt temperature in the 300 to 400°F range and mold temperatures of 60 to 150°F. Melt fracture or excessive orientation can occur if melt temperature is too low (producing insufficient flow); degradation is possible if temperature is too high. Injection time should be kept to a minimum to avoid appreciable cooling before mold is completely filled, possibly causing skin formation or layering. Relatively large gates, short sprues, and short runners are desirable. Due to low shrinkage (usually less than 1%) and high friction characteristics, ejection of molded parts may be difficult compared to that encountered with plastics. This problem can be alleviated by tapering and/or rounding mold-cavity corners and edges or by use of additives.

To obtain satisfactory specimens by compression molding, it is recommended that copolymers or their compounds be placed in a hot mold and allowed to soften before applying enough pressure to initiate flow into the cavity. Mold temperatures are usually 250 to 350°F. The ideal temperature should provide good flow under pressure but cause little deformation of specimens during removal from the mold. In practice, it is sometimes necessary to cool the mold (below softening point of the composition) before opening, to prevent distortion of the sample. The use of mold release agents and/or molding between sheets of foil is also helpful.

Blow-molding techniques are similar to those established for polyethylene. In general, imperfections in mold finish are less critical with block polymer compositions than with polyethylene or other crystalline thermoplastics. However, tearing of the parison could be more of a problem because block polymers are usually lower in melt strength. If tearing occurs, corrective steps suggested are (1) reduce melt temperature as low as possible (near 300°F), (2) reduce mold closure rate, and (3) round off corners at point of "pinch-off."

3.6.7 Sealing, Bonding

Articles prepared from block polymers and their compositions can be sealed or bonded by a number of procedures. Methods include sealing by heat, solvent, microwave, ultrasonic treatment, adhesive bonding, or thermoplastic welding. These processes,[20] can also be employed to form laminates with plastic or metallic materials. Equipment can range from very simple to highly sophisticated systems, permitting quick and easy assembly of parts and efficient sealing of films. Block polymers remain elastomeric at point of sealing or welding.

3.7 APPLICATIONS

The properties or combination of properties of elastomeric materials determine to a great extent the ultimate uses. For the thermoplastic elastomers or plastomers, three general areas of use have developed. These are (1) adhesives, sealants, and coatings; (2) plastics modification; and (3) molded and extruded elastomeric items.

Some of the more notable features of thermoplastic elastomers based on polystyrene blocks connected with polydiene or polyolefin-type segments are listed in Table 3-14, and the general areas where these properties should be of interest are indicated.

Characteristics of the neat polymers considered with the effects of compounding ingredients serve as a guide to the properties that can be achieved in compounded stocks. As an additional aid, Table 3-15 shows some of the variations in important properties that can be obtained. Other typical properties available for molded and extruded goods were shown in Table 3-5.

The thermoplasticity, solubility, high strength (without vulcanization), and elasticity of thermoplastic rubbers make these ideal candidates for adhesives and sealants. Thermoplastic block polymers described in this chapter can be formulated to provide excellent quality of tack, quick stick, peel strength, and resistance to shear. Examples are shown in References 7, 17, and 22 through 24.

Table 3-14. Features of block polymers.

CHARACTERISTIC	APPLICATION AREAS		
	ADHESIVES, SEALANTS, COATINGS	MOLDED AND EXTRUDED ITEMS	PLASTICS MODIFICATION
Soluble in many organic solvents	X[a]		
Fast solvent release	X		
High strength	X	X	X
Compatible with numerous resins	X	X	
Compatible with many other elastomers		X	
Compatible with many plastics		X	X
Good tear resistance	X	X	X
Good abrasion resistance		X	
Resistant to crack growth		X	
Resistant to shear	X		
Low brittle point	X	X	X
High elongation	X	X	X
High coefficient of friction		X	
Good resilience		X	
Hardness can be varied over wide range		X	
Low specific gravity	X	X	X
High purity	X	X	X
Light color	X	X	X
Thermoplastic	X	X	X
Available in various forms	X	X	X
Does not need vulcanization	X	X	
Easy mixing	X	X	
Fast, smooth extrusion		X	X
Easy molding		X	X
Low mold shrinkage		X	
Scrap can be recycled		X	X
High permeability			X
High oil levels can be used	X	X	
Good electrical properties		X	X
Resistant to bases, weak acids, water, alcohol		X	
Ozone and oxidation resistant (Special grades or compounds)	X	X	X

[a]Denotes applications where features are especially attractive.

Block polymers based on styrene and dienes are used to modify properties of plastics in both polymerization and mechanical melt-blending systems. Polystyrene can be toughened considerably by the addition of block copolymers. An example of impact improvement in polystyrene is illustrated in Table 3-16. Resistance to both impact and stress cracking have been improved in polyolefins by incorporation of thermoplastic block polymer.

Several specific applications where styrenic-type thermoplastic rubbers are currently used, or where there is now consideration of their use, include:

Table 3-15. Typical property ranges for block polymers.

PROPERTY	RANGE
Hardness, Shore A	25 to 95
Flexural modulus, psi	500 to 20,000
300% modulus, psi	100 to 1800
Elongation at break, %	100 to 1200
Tensile strength, 80°F, psi	500 to 5000
Resilience, %	20 to 85
Specific gravity	0.9 to 1.2[a]
Deformation temperature, °F	100 to 270
Tear strength, lb/in.	Up to 500
Brittleness temperature	Down to <−100F
Volume resistivity, ohm-cm	Up to 10^{16}
Dielectric constant, 60 Hz to 1 MHz	2.4 to 3.4
Dissipation (power) factor, 60 Hz to 1 MHz	0.001 to 0.009

[a]Most common range; can be wider for special compounds.

Table 3-16. Modification of polystyrene.

	MELT INDEX	TENSILE (psi)	ELONGATION (%)	NOTCHED IZOD IMPACT (ft-lb/in.)
General purpose polystyrene	3.5	9170	9	0.4
General purpose polystyrene blended with 19% Solprene 417[a]	4.0	5550	38	1.8

[a]80/20 butadiene/styrene plastomer.

Adhesives or hot melts (pressure-sensitive, contact, construction, product assembly)
Auto parts
Coatings (for chemical milling, paper, fabrics)
Flooring products
Footwear
Gaskets, seals, weather strip
High-impact plastics
Hose and tubing
Modifier for asphalt
Pharmaceutical items
Plastics resistant to stress cracks
Sealants
Sound insulators
Sporting goods
Toys
Wire covering

3.8 PROPERTIES OF COMMERCIAL BLOCK POLYMER TPEs

A comparison of the properties of commercially available TPE compounds is given in Table 3-17.

Table 3-17. Compounds Based on Styrene Block Copolymers[a]

COMPOUND	SPECIFIC GRAVITY	MELT FLOW CONDITION E	300% MODULUS (psi)[b]	TENSILE (psi)[b]	ELONGATION (%)[b]	SHORE A HARDNESS[b]
Soling for canvas footwear						
Live Rubber 601[c]	1.12	40	–	680	280	49
Kraton 5119	1.14	30	550	600	350	47–57
Live Rubber 601A[c]	1.08	57	–	950	280	75
Kraton 5122	1.08	30	720	830	380	60
Unit soling						
Live Rubber 602A[c]	1.01	22	490	800	510	64
Live Rubber 606[c]	1.01	24	490	780	560	64
Live Rubber 606B[c]	0.99	21	400	660	600	49
Live Rubber 607[c]	1.02	5	–	1220	250	81
Kraton 5148	1.02	6	–	1700	300	
Kraton 5152[c]	1.00	30	450	600	450	52
Kraton 5239[c]	0.98	20	310	610	610	58
Injection-molded grades						
Live Rubber 801A[c]	0.99	4	880	2080	770	80
Kraton 3202[c]	1.01	14	600	850	300–500	67
Kraton 3204[d]	1.01	22[e]	970	1350	400–700	73
Kraton 3226[c]	1.00	21	300–500	700	640	45
Live Rubber 804BC,[f]	0.98	1	400	600	500	47

Live Rubber 807c,f	1.02	35g	–	400	550	35
Kraton 7720Gf	1.21	0.4e	400	800	800	60
Kraton 7820Gf	1.16	0.3e	1200	2200	750	84
Extrusion grades						
Kraton 2104d	0.93	7	200	1700	1350	43
Kraton 2109d	0.94	13e	300	950	800	47
Kraton 2705Gb,f	0.90	–	–	1650	800	57
Wire and cable gradesh						
Elexar 8421	0.94		1200i	2100	650	88
Elexar 8431	0.87		600i	1500	700	66
Elexar 8613	1.16		1400i	1600	430	95
Elexar 8614	1.20		1400i	1700	430	95

aIncludes many of the available compounds; however, suppliers should be contacted for latest information. Live Rubber compounds are based on Solprene plastomers made by Phillips Petroleum. Kraton and Elexar products are made by Shell Chemical Company.

bThese properties may vary depending on how sample is formed.

cProperties typical for injection-molded samples.

dProperties typical for compression-molded samples.

eCondition G.

fGrades that have improved weather resistance.

gMelt flow at 180°C, 5 kg.

hExact composition not disclosed.

i400% modulus.

3.9 REFERENCES

1. Kraus, G. and Railsback, H. E. *Recent Advances in Polymer Blends, Grafts and Blocks* (Sperling, L. H., Editor), Plenum Publishing Corp. (1974).
2. Angelo, R. J., Ikeda, R. M., and Wallach, M. L. *Polymer* 6: 141 (1965).
3. Kraus, G., Childers, C. W., and Gruver, J. T. *J. Applied Polym. Sci.* 11: 1581 (1967).
4. Holden, G. *J. Elastoplastics* 2: 234 (1970).
5. Haws, J. R. and Middlebrook, T. C. *Rubber World* 167: 27 (1963).
6. Holden, G., Bishop, E. T., and Legge, N. R. *J. Polym. Sci.*, C, 26: 37 (1969).
7. Marrs, O. L., Naylor, F. E., and Edmonds, L. O. *J. Adhesion* 4: 211 (1972).
8. Matsuo, M., Ueno, T., Horino, H., Chujo, S., and Asai, H. *Polymer* 9: 425 (1968).
9. Kraus, G., Naylor, F. E., and Rollmann, K. W. *J. Polym. Sci.*, A-2, 9: 1839 (1971).
10. Zelinski, R. P. and Wofford, C. F. *J. Polym. Sci.*, A, 3: 93 (1965).
11. Zelinski, R. P. and Hsieh, H. L. U.S. Patents 3,078, 254 (Feb. 19, 1963), 3,280,084 (Oct. 18, 1966), and 3,281,383 (Oct. 25, 1966).
12. Holden, G. and Milkovich, R., U.S. Patent 3,265,765 (1966).
13. Morton, M., McGrath, J. E., and Juliano, P. C. *J. Polym. Sci.*, C, 26: 99 (1969).
14. Fetters, L. J. *J. Polym. Sci.*, C, 26: 1 (1969).
15. Hsieh, H. L. Paper presented at ACS Rubber Division Meeting, Minneapolis, April 27-30, 1976.
16. Railsback, H. E. and Zelinski, R. P. *Kautchuk und Gummi Kunststoffe* 25: 254 (1972).
17. Marrs, O. L., Zelinski, R. P., and Doss, R. C. *J. Elast. and Plastics* 6: 246 (1974).
18. Holden, G., Chapter 6 in *Block and Graft Polymerization*, Vol. 1 (R. J. Ceresa, Editor), John Wiley & Sons (1973).
19. Cornell, W. H., Kliever, L. B., and Dearmont, D. D. Paper presented at ACS Rubber Division Meeting, New Orleans, October 7-10, 1975.
20. Gross, S., Editor, *Modern Plastics Encyclopedia*, Vol. 50, McGraw-Hill Inc. (1973).
21. Holden, G. *New Developments in Block Copolymer Applications* (Sperling, L. H., Editor), Plenum Publishing Corp. (1974).
22. Marrs, O. L. and Edmonds, L. O. *Adhesives Age* 14: 15 (1971).
23. Jurrens, L. D. and Marrs, O. L. *Adhesives Age* 18: 31 (1975).
24. Gray, R. A. and Marrs, O. L. *Adhesives Age* 19: 51 (1976).
25. Beecher, J. F., Marker, L., Bradford, R. D., and Aggarwal, S. L., *J. Poly. Sci.*, C, 26: 117 (1969).

4

Polyester Thermoplastic Elastomers

Stanley C. Wells
Engineering Group Leader for Research & Development
NDM Corporation
Dayton, Ohio

4.1 INTRODUCTION

A family of novel segmented copolyesters has been developed by E. I. du Pont de Nemours & Company and introduced to the marketplace under the trademark Hytrel®. These elastomeric polymers provide design materials that fill the gaps between conventional synthetic rubbers and flexible plastics. These polymers have many of the characteristics of rubbers, but are designed for processing on thermoplastic equipment such as extruders, injection-molding, and blow-molding machines.

These materials, developed by Du Pont's Elastomeric Chemical Department, are fully polymerized and require no postcuring or annealing to attain their full strength. Most of the conventional processing and postforming operations associated with other thermoplastics are applicable to the Hytrel elastomers.

Because of their combination of good melt flow properties, melt stability, low mold shrinkage, and rapid crystallization rate, polymers of Hytrel can be formed into a variety of high-performance products using the low-cost, short-cycle methods of the plastics industry.

Hytrel elastomers, in either pellet or powder form, are available in several hardness grades from 92 Shore A to 72 Shore D. For most applications, polymers are used in their natural form. However, when requirements exist for weather resistance, ultraviolet radiation, or flame resistance, selective additives are necessary. The polymers may also be blended with other resins, such as polyvinyl chloride, for certain end-use applications.

In addition to offering fabricators easy processing methods, and many marketing opportunities, Hytrel polyester elastomers offer broad design application options and assure the users exceptional value-in-use performance. They are structurally strong, yet resilient, and resistant to impact and flex fatigue. This combination has made possible their use for such diverse applications as rotationally molded tires, hydraulic hoses, drive belts, gears, flexible couplings, retractable telephone cords, automotive parts, and segmented tracks for recreational and military use.

4.1.1 Chemistry

The Hytrel copolyesters are prepared by transesterification from readily available starting materials such as dimethyl terephthalate polytetramethylene ether glycol—i.e., PTMEG (molecular weight 600 to 3000) and 1,4-butanediol (4GT). A typical structure is shown below.

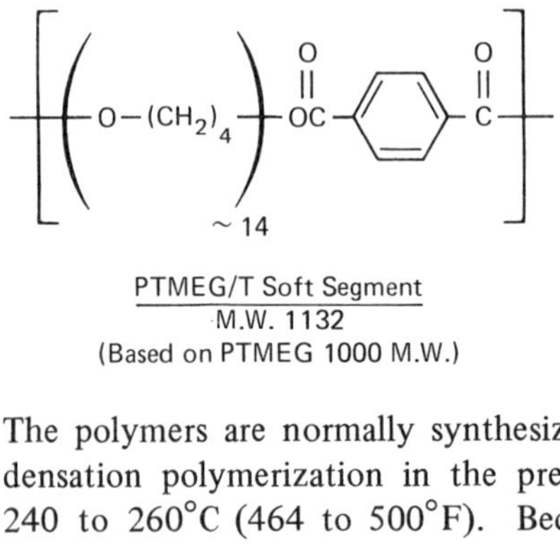

PTMEG/T Soft Segment
M.W. 1132
(Based on PTMEG 1000 M.W.)

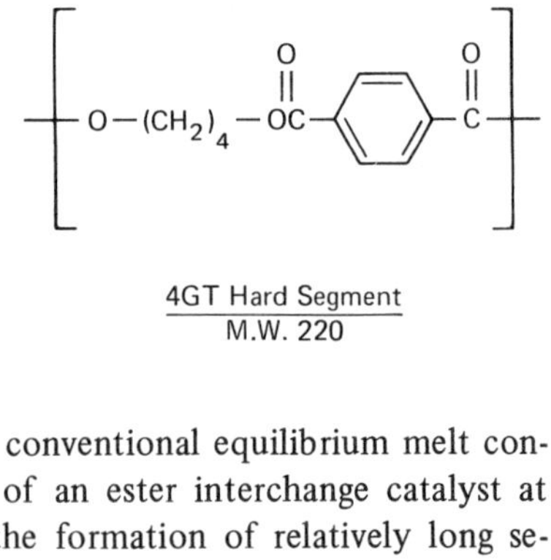

4GT Hard Segment
M.W. 220

The polymers are normally synthesized by conventional equilibrium melt condensation polymerization in the presence of an ester interchange catalyst at 240 to 260°C (464 to 500°F). Because the formation of relatively long sequences of tetramethylene terephthalate (4-GT units) is greatly favored by the stoichiometry, the resulting condensation products are random block copolymers that consist of crystalline 4GT hard segments and amorphous elastomeric polyalkylene ether terephthalate (PTMEG/T) soft segments.

These materials are thermoplastic and exhibit a continuous two-phase domain structure. The crystalline phase serves as thermally reversible chemical crosslinks. The amorphous phase (PTMEG/T) contributes the elastomeric character to the polymer series. Varying the relative proportions of the two phases determines the hardness, modulus, melting point, chemical resistance, and permeability. Obviously, the higher the crystalline segment content, the higher the hardness.

A thermogram, by differential scanning calorimetry, for a copolyester of 55

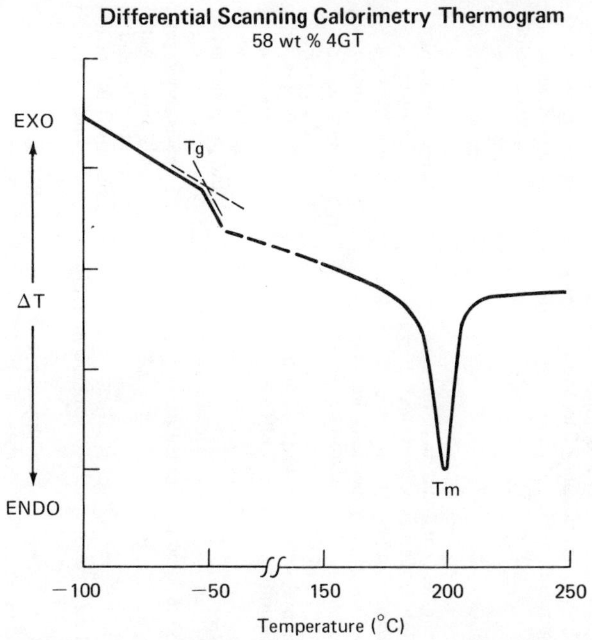

Differential Scanning Calorimetry Thermogram
58 wt % 4GT

Figure 4-1. DSC thermogram for the 55D hardness of 58% 4 GT. T_g (amorphous) is at −50°C, while the crystalline melt point is at 200°C.

Durometer D hardness that contains 58 weight percent of 4-GT hard segments, is shown in Figure 4-1. The scan reveals two transitions: a glass transition (T_g) of the amorphous phase at about −50°C (−58°F), and a well-defined crystalline melting point at about 200°C (392°F). This combination of a low glass-transition temperature and a high crystalline melting point is characteristic of the polyesters and is in part responsible for the broad service temperature range of this class.

Gel-permeation data indicate that the polymers prepared under these conditions have the expected geometric molecular weight distribution. A number average molecular weight in the range of about 25,000 to 30,000 is normally required to achieve optimum physical properties.

Hytrel polymer properties can be varied widely, ranging from highly resilient elastomers to tough elastoplastics having high load-bearing capacity. Copolyesters containing significantly less than 30% 4-GT hard segment have relatively low strength, particularly at elevated temperature. The soft segment homopolymer itself, PTMEG/T, is a soft gum that flows readily under stress.

Because of their combination of unique morphology, polarity, and melt rheology, Hytrel copolyesters have been found to fulfill certain unusual industrial applications, which will be described later in this chapter.

Table 4-1. Commercial Hytrel polymers available.[a]

TYPE	HARDNESS	DESCRIPTION	CHARACTERISTICS	USES
4055	40D	General purpose molding and extrusion resin.	Low temperature stability and impact resistance, good resilience, flex fatigue, oil and solvent resistance at moderate temperatures. Temperature range: −60 to 225°F (−51 to 107°C).	Tubing, hose, film, sheeting, belting, auto trim, seals, gears, other molded parts.
4056	40D	Nondiscoloring molding and extrusion grade.	Same as above.	Same as above.
5526	55D	General purpose, nondiscoloring, molding grade, and some extrusion applications.	Exhibits the best combination of high and low temperature properties such as flexibility, impact resistance, and creep resistance. Good flex fatigue and abrasion properties. Good oil and solvent resistance. Temperature range: −60 to 300°F (−51 to 149°C).	Tubing, hose, film, sheet, belting, segmented tracks, seals, packings, fuel tanks, roto-molded tire, molded parts.
5555HS	55D	Heat-stabilized grade for prolonged exposure to temperatures exceeding 250°F, including oils.	Same as above, with improved service use at elevated temperatures in air and oils.	Hydraulic hose and tubing, matching parts, belts in ovens and other hot areas.
5556	55D	Nondiscoloring extrusion grade. Adequate for some molding applications.	Same as 5526, used for painted parts.	Same as above, primarily in tubing and hose, profiles and other extrusions.
HTX-4275	55D	A variation of the 5556 type.	Increased melt viscosity to provide blow-molding parison stability.	Containers, other blow-molded items.
6345	63D	General purpose molding and extrusion grade.	Excellent resistance to gas and liquid permeation. Very good oil and solvent resistance. Excellent abrasion, impact, and creep resistance. Temperature range: −60 to 325°F (−51 to 163°C). Compounding recommendations available for prolonged exposure at temperatures above 250°F.	Tubing, hose, film, extruded profiles, gears, fuel tanks.
6346	63D	Nondiscoloring molding and extrusion grade.	Same as above.	Same as above.

7246	72D	Nondiscoloring general purpose molding and extrusion grade.	Nondiscoloring resin demonstrating lowest permeability, best oil/solvent resistance. Temperature range: −60 to 325°F (−51 to 163°C). Compounding recommendations are available for prolonged exposure over 250°F (131°C).	Tubing, wire and cable jacketing, molded shapes.
HTG-4450 (additive)		Flame-retardant master-batch.	To be used with all grades, contains 67% by weight of flame-retardant material, recommended at 25 parts HTG-4450 per 75 parts of Hytrel.	
HTG-3539 (additive)		Master batch to increase heat and oil aging.	To be melt-blended with Hytrel to provide improved heat aging resistance for prolonged exposure at temperatures exceeding 250°F.	
10MS		Hydrolytic stabilizer master batch	Let down at 10 to 1 in other grades for hot, moist environments.	

[a]Several grades of Hytrel are available, covering the hardness range of 92 Shore A to 72 Shore D. There are also other additive blends for property enhancement.

4.1.2 Hytrel Grades

Hytrel is available in compositions from 92 Shore A (40 Shore D) to 72 Shore D hardness. Several grades of each of the four hardnesses—40D, 55D, 63D, and 72D—can be obtained, depending on end use. The standard polymers contain a phenolic-based antioxidant for color stability. Some hardness grades have adjusted melt viscosity to accommodate certain processing methods, and other grades are available for use as master-batch additive for characteristics such as flame retardancy and improved hydraulic stability.

Table 4-1 shows the various grades and additives available, each with its characteristics and some of the end uses the various grades have found.

4.2 MECHANICAL PROPERTIES

The Hytrel elastomers possess a set of physical properties that qualify them for a number of demanding applications. These copolyester thermoplastics combine such features as resilience, high resistance to deformation under moderate strain conditions, outstanding flex fatigue resistance, good abrasion resistance, retention of flexibility at low temperatures, and good retention of properties at elevated temperatures (Table 4-2).

In addition to good mechanical properties, Hytrel elastomers demonstrate good resistance to chemicals, oils, and solvents, and exhibit good weatherability.

4.2.1 Hardness and Resilience

Hytrel spans a broad middle ground between the contrasting yielding nature of rubber and the rigidity of plastics. The softer members of the series resemble elastomers more than plastics; the converse is true of the harder members.

The change in hardness of the four basic grades of Hytrel, with temperature, is shown in Figure 4-2. As can be seen, the higher hardness grades have an essentially linear change in Shore D Durometer over the polymer's useful working range. The 40D through 72D notations indicate each grade's hardness at 24°C (75°F, room temperature).

Bashore resilience exceeds 60 percent for the 40D hardness grade. As Hytrel approaches the hardness of plastics (63D), it still has a resilience exceeding 40 percent. The 72D grade possesses enough resilience to make it tough, in addition to being hard and able to withstand moderate impact and to bend without fracture.

4.2.2 Tension

The tensile stress-strain relationships of Hytrel at 24°C (75°F) are shown in Figure 4-3 at a rate of change in strain of 20 in./min (ASTM D-412). Figure 4-4

Table 4-2. Mechanical properties of Hytrel[1].

PROPERTY	UNITS	ASTM METHOD	HARDNESS GRADES			
			40D	55D	63D	72D
Tensile strength	psi	D-638	3700	5500	5700	5700
Ultimate elongation	%	D-638	450	450	350	350
Stress @ 25% strain, 1 in./min. (or at yield point)	psi	D-638	1100	2000	2500 (yield)	3800 (yield)
Modulus @ 100%, 20 in./min.	psi	D-412	925	2100	2700[b]	4100
Stress @ 25% compression	psi	D-695	2000	4350	N.D.	N.D.
Flexural modulus @ 72°F	psi	D-790	7000	30,000	50,000	75,000
Tensile set @ 100% strain	%	D-412	18	38	50	N.D.
Compression set @ 1350 psi (22 hr @ 158°F, after annealing)	%	D-395A	27	4	2	2
Compression set @ 25% deflection (22 hr @ 158°F, no annealing)	%	D-395B	60	56	N.A.[c]	N.A.
Compression set @ 25% deflection (22 hr @ 158°F, after annealing)	%	D-395B	36 (16 hr @ 212°F)	38 (16 hr @ 250°F)	N.A.	N.A.
Resilience, Bashore	%	—	62	53	43	N.A.
Tear strength, split	lb/in.	D-470	170	200	N.D.	N.D.
Tear strength, Die B	lb/in.	D-624	631	935	1055	N.A.
Tear strength, Die C	lb/in.	D-624	700	900	850	N.A.
Resistance to flex cut growth						
Ross (pierced)	cycles to failure	D-1052	$>3 \times 10^5$	$>3 \times 10^5$	2.8×10^5	N.A.
DeMattia (pierced)	cycles to failure	D-813	$>2 \times 10^5$	$>7 \times 10^4$	N.A.	N.A.
Notched impact, Izod						
@ 75°F (24°C)	ft-lb/in.	D-256A	>20 N.B.[d]	>20 N.B.	>20 N.B.	3.9
@ -40°F (-40°C)	ft-lb/in.	D-256A	>20 N.B.	>20 N.B.	0.5	0.8
Tabor abrasion						
(CS-17 wheel, 1000-g load)	mg loss per 1000 cycles	D-1044	3	5	8	13
(H-18 wheel, 1000-g load)	mg loss per 1000 cycles	D-1044	100	64	160	N.D.
N.B.S. abrasion	% of standard	D-1630	800	3540	2300	N.D.

Table 4-2. (Continued)

PROPERTY	UNITS	ASTM METHOD	HARDNESS GRADES			
			40D	55D	63D	72D
Brittleness temperature	°F	D-746	<-94	<-94	<-94	<-94
Softening point, Vicat	°F	D-1525	234	356	363	397
Heat distortion temperature						
@ 66 psi	°F	D-648	N.D.	315	N.D.	330
@ 264 psi	°F	D-648	N.D.	110	N.D.	155
Coefficient of linear expansion	in./in./°C	D-696	20×10^{-5}	18×10^{-5}	17×10^{-5}	21×10^{-5}
Water absorption, 24 hr	%	D-570	0.6	0.5	0.3	0.3
Specific gravity	—	D-720	1.17	1.20	1.22	1.25

[a]Physical properties of the four hardness grades indicate high modulus coupled with good flexural properties.
[b]N.D., No data.
[c]N.A., Not applicable.
[d]N.B., No break.

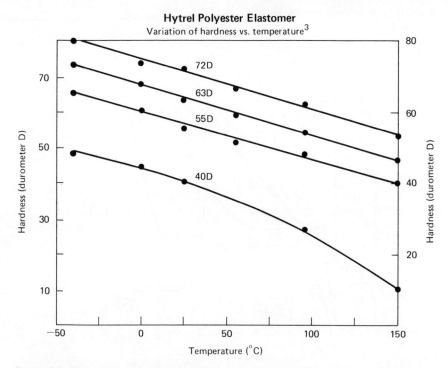

Figure 4-2. The change in hardness of the four basic grades with temperature shows a relatively linear relation for all but the 40D resin.

shows an expansion of the curves of Figure 4-3 through an elongation of 20 percent using a strain rate of 1 in./min (ASTM D-638). At low strain, the tensile stress shows higher modulus values than other thermoplastic elastomers of comparable hardness. Therefore, when modulus is an important design criterion, thinner cross sections of Hytrel are possible.

Tensile strength values at elevated temperatures are shown in Figures 4-5 through 4-9. Particularly at low strain values, these polymers retain excellent tensile properties, rendering them very useful over a considerable temperature range.

Allied with the stress-strain relation is the hysteresis loss of a material. When stressed *below the yield point*, Hytrel demonstrates very little hysteresis loss in dynamic applications. Parts functioning at low strain levels can usually be expected to exhibit complete recovery, and to continue to do so in cyclic applications with little heat buildup. Resistance to cut growth during flexing, as measured by either the Ross or DeMattia flex tests, is outstanding due to high resilience (i.e., less energy stored) and low heat buildup (see Table 4-3).

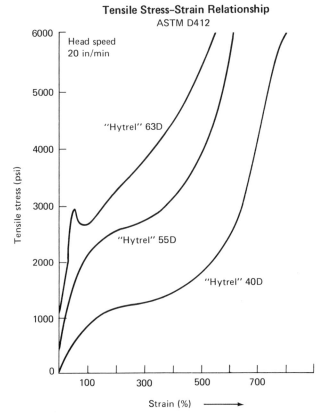

Figure 4-3. The ASTM D-412 tensile curves for the three softest Hytrel grades show a broad yield point for 40D and a sharp yield with the 63D grade.

4.2.3 Flexural Modulus and Modulus of Rigidity

The flexural modulus (ASTM D-790) is shown in Figure 4-10. In comparison to other thermoplastic elastomers, Hytrel has a high flexural modulus, which again indicates that less material has to be used to cantilever beam- or torque-type applications, particularly at elevated temperatures.

Comparisons of the apparent modulus of rigidity ASTM D-1043 (Clash-Berg) of Hytrel is shown for all Hytrel polymers by Figures 4-11 and 4-12. It can be seen by these graphs that Hytrel has a higher rigidity above 35°F (1°C) and is far less stiff at -40°F (-40°C). In many applications, this is a desirable feature, particularly in the low temperature range. Table 4-3 indicates that in a comparison with urethane, the flex fatigue resistance is equal to or better for Hytrel, particularly at elevated temperatures.

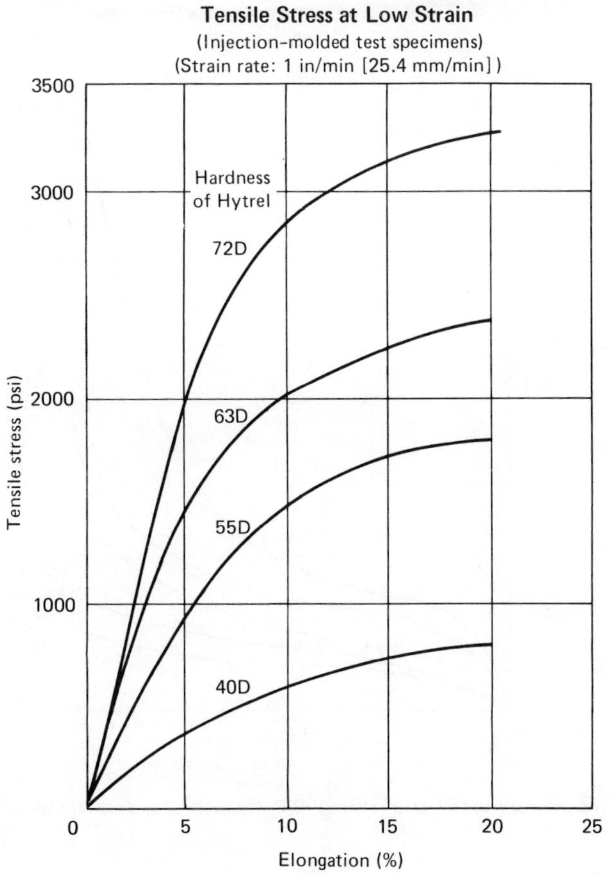

Tensile Stress at Low Strain
(Injection-molded test specimens)
(Strain rate: 1 in/min [25.4 mm/min])

Figure 4-4. The tensile stress at low strain is among the highest of all thermoplastic elastomers.

4.2.4 Compression

At comparable hardnesses, Hytrel elastomers are superior to commercial thermoplastic urethane rubbers in load-bearing capacity. They can be used in smaller, thinner cross sections to give equivalent performance. Table 4-4 and Figure 4-13 illustrate the compressive strength of Hytrel in comparison with urethanes of the same hardness.

4.2.5 Compression Set

Because of the high modulus characteristics of Hytrel, compression set measurements by ASTM D-395, method B, require extremely high stress levels to deflect

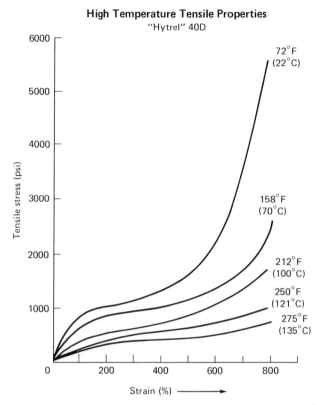

Figure 4-5. The tensile properties of Hytrel 40D through a temperature of 275°F (135°C).

the material to the required 25%, as can be seen in Figure 4-13. The majority of applications for high modulus elastomers involve constant load rather than constant deflection. Therefore, compression set measurements by ASTM D-395, method A, are more meaningful. Table 4-5 gives compression set values for the various grades at three different temperatures. At 23°C (75°F), the specimen is deformed about 11% with the applied stress of 1350 psi.

It has been found that compression set values of these elastomers may be greatly improved by annealing the article prior to use. The optimum temperature required is quite specific and varies according to hardness. Figures 4-14 and 4-15 show compression set by method B, after annealing at various temperatures. As the figures indicate, the optimum temperature for the 40D polymer is 100°C (212°F), and for the 55D material, it is 121°C (250°F).

It is believed that annealing relieves molded-in strains, and promotes the growth of crystallites, which control the modulus characteristics. Excessively high annealing temperatures will melt some of the crystallites, resulting in poorer compression set resistance.

4.2.6 Tensile Creep Characteristics

Creep strain is defined as *the additional strain recorded after the initial elastic strain takes place in the first minute when stress is applied.* The incremental strain, at contact stress, is plotted vs. time to give typical creep strain curves for 55D Hytrel (Figures 4-16 and 4-17). Figure 4-16 relates creep strain with temperature at various stresses, while Figure 4-17 shows creep strain vs. stress for various temperatures.

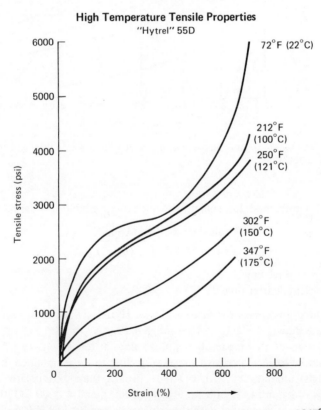

Figure 4-6. The tensile properties of Hytrel 55D through a temperature of 347°F (175°C).

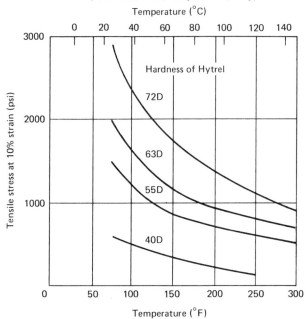

Figure 4-7. The tensile stress of all hardness grades at 10% extension through a temperature range of 75 to 300°F.

Apparent tensile modulus, sometimes called *creep modulus*, is defined as

$$\frac{\text{Applied stress}}{\text{Total strain at time } T} = \frac{\text{Applied stress}}{(L_T - L_o)/L_o}$$

where L_o = original length
L_T = length after time T.

Apparent modulus curves for three grades of Hytrel at various stresses and temperatures are shown in Figures 4-18 through 4-20.

Extrapolation of the apparent modulus values at low strains to 10^{-2} hr (0.6 min.) would be expected to give values very close to those obtained for the tensile (Young's) modulus by ASTM D-638. In fact, these extrapolated values of 7000 psi (490 kg/cm^2), 27,000 psi (1894 kg/cm^2), and 48,000 (3370 kg/cm^2) psi are in excellent agreement with the values obtained by ASTM D-638.

Tensile Stress at 20% Strain vs Temperature
(Injection–molded test specimens)
(Strain rate: 1 in/min [25.4 mm/min])

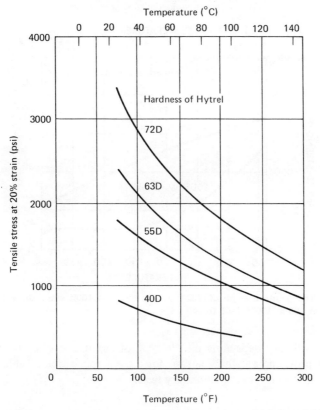

Figure 4-8. The tensile stress of all hardness grades at 20% extension through a temperature range of 75 to 300° F.

4.2.7 Impact Strength

The greater flexibility of Hytrel at low temperature results in improved impact strength at -40°F (-40°C), as shown in Table 4-6. The notch sensitivity, particularly at room temperature, is greatly improved over other elastomers.

4.2.8 Abrasion Resistance

The resistance to abrasion is a complicated function of tear strength, surface coefficient of friction, resilience, heat dissipation, and other properties. Compara-

Tensile Strength and 100% Modulus
vs Temperature

(Injection-molded test specimens)

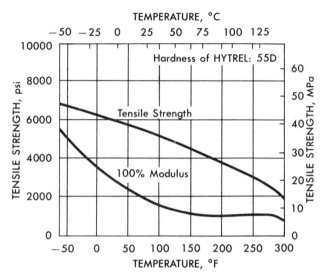

Figure 4-9. The tensile strength of 55D hardness Hytrel at 100% strain through a temperature range of –50 to 300° F (–46 to 149° C).

tive values will vary depending on the type of test run: end use testing is the method of providing a definite answer for a given application. Table 4-7 gives the results of several types of laboratory tests.

4.2.9 Dynamic Properties

Hytrel elastomers appear to have unusual, if not unique, dynamic properties. Its resistance to fatigue in cyclic load-bearing applications is outstanding. This is particularly true in deformation at low strain ranges where it may be considered to act like a perfect spring with no or very little hysteresis. This means that a part made of Hytrel, engineered to operate in low strain levels, can be expected to exhibit complete recovery from deformation and to continue to do so under repeated cycling for extremely long periods without heat buildup or distortion. This, coupled with the high load-carrying capabilities of Hytrel and its unusual resiliency characteristics, makes it an ideal candidate for doing useful work in many cyclic load-bearing applications. These uses include gears, timing belts, rolls, flexible couplings, belts, seals, and diaphragms. Fields such as materials handling, large and small appliances, hand and stationary power tools, low horse-

Table 4-3. The flex fatigue resistance of Hytrel in comparison to urethane, as measured by DeMattia and Ross flex tests.[a]

	HARDNESS (ASTM D-2240)	DeMATTIA FLEX, PIERCED (ASTM D-813) KILOCYCLES TO FAILURE		ROSS FLEX, PIERCED (ASTM D-1052) KILOCYCLES TO 5X CUT GROWTH	
		73°F [23°C]	250°F [121°C]	73°F [23°C]	-40°F [-40°C]
HYTREL	40D (92A)	216	108	>300[b]	>12[c]
TPU-ESTER	80A	1.5	1.5	30[b]	Immediate
TPU-ESTER	91A	216	18	>300[b]	Immediate
TPU-ETHER	90A	3	Immediate	144	Immediate
HYTREL	55D	72	18	>300[b]	>12[d]
TPU-ESTER	55D	1.5	Immediate	84	Immediate
HYTREL	63D	–	–	280	Immediate

[a]Pierced samples.
[b]No change in the length of the pierced area after 300,000 cycles.
[c]Test terminated after 3× cut growth.
[d]Test terminated after 4× cut growth.
Note: Properties were measured on injection-molded test specimens.

Flexural Modulus vs Temperature

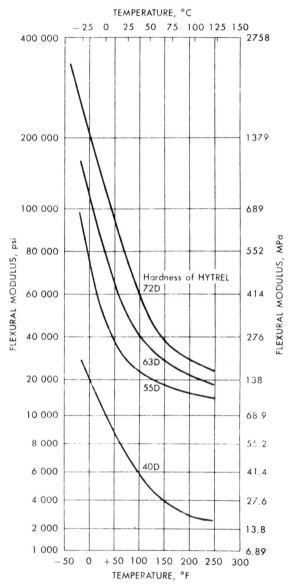

Figure 4-10. The flexural modulus of Hytrel is relatively high above room temperature and yet is less stiff than urethanes below 0°F (−18°C).

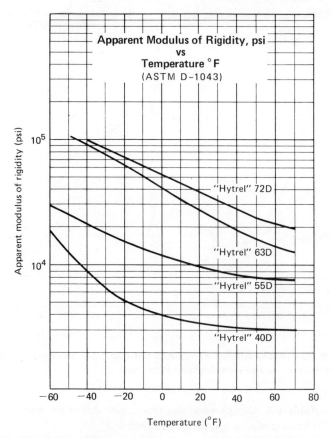

Figure 4-11. The relative stiffness of the four grades of Hytrel at the low-temperature range shows a general plateau near room temperature.

power transmission, gear reduction, and recreational items should all benefit from Hytrel's dynamic properties.

A dynamic shear test, which reveals the unique hysteresis properties of Hytrel in the form of a double shear sandwich (Figure 4-21), was deformed to strain levels of 0.5 and 2.5 percent. In each case, the sandwich was dynamically cycled to a nominal 1 percent peak-to-peak amplitude at 45 cycle/sec. The data thus generated are shown in Table 4-8.

It can be seen from these figures that at low strain levels, Hytrel returns all, or nearly all, of the energy of deformation. Virtually no heat buildup, therefore, will be experienced in such dynamic applications. The high elastic moduli indicate that parts have a very good capability for performing useful work in spite of

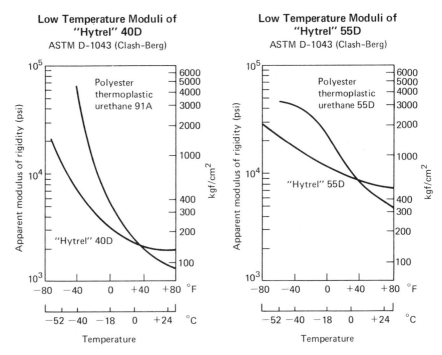

Figure 4-12. The relative stiffness of the 40D and 55D grades show lesser rigidity below –40°F (–40°C) than the equivalent hardness of urethane.

Table 4-4. Compression and tensile modulus of the four Hytrel grades in comparison to urethane.[5]

		Hardness (ASTM D-2240)	Compression Modulus, psi [MPa] (ASTM D-695)	Tensile Modulus, psi [MPa] (ASTM D-638)
TENSILE STRESS, MPa	HYTREL	40D (92A)	7 400 [51.0]	7 800 [53.8]
	TPU-ESTER	91A	4 000 [27.6]	5 600 [38.6]
	TPU-ETHER	90A	4 800 [33.1]	5 600 [38.6]
	HYTREL	55D	12 500 [86.2]	20 000 [138]
	TPU-ESTER	55D	8 800 [60.7]	–
	TPU-ETHER	55D	–	–
	HYTREL	63D	20 000 [138]	50 000 [345]
	HYTREL	72D	–	75 000 [517]

Note: Properties were measured on injection-molded test specimens.

Compressive Strength vs. Deformation

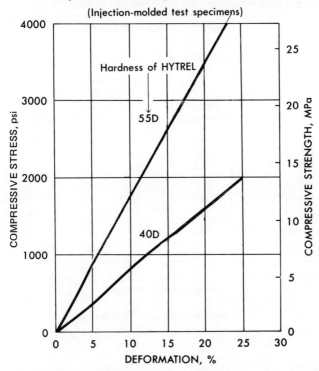

Figure 4-13. The compressive stress of 40D and 55D Hytrel with low deformation.

their relatively low hardnesses. In general, Hytrel has 30 to 40 percent greater stiffness than competitive materials in the same hardness range. The results of a study on the effect of frequency on the dynamic Young's modulus of Hytrel are summarized in Table 4-9.

4.3 ELECTRICAL PROPERTIES

Measurements show that Hytrel elastomers have electrical properties that are relatively insensitive to moisture. These electrical data indicate that they are suitable for low voltage applications, as well as jacketing where mechanical toughness, oil, solvent, or chemical resistance is required. Table 4-10 shows the common electrical information for all the Hytrel Durometers. The change in properties with temperature is indicated in Table 4-11.

Table 4-5. Method A compression set for all grades of Hytrel in comparison with urethane and nylon.[4]

Compression Set Resistance (Measured by ASTM D-395, Method A, 1350 psi [9.3 MPa] load)				
	Hardness (ASTM D-2240)	Compression Set, % after 22 hours at:		
		73°F [23°C]	158°F [70°C]	212°F [100°C]
HYTREL	40D (92A)	11	27	33
TPU-ESTER	91A	15	27	44
TPU-ETHER	90A	8	24	33
HYTREL	55D	<1	4	8
TPU-ESTER	55D	3	9	28
HYTREL	63D	<1	2	4
Plasticized Nylon 11	65D	1	3	5
HYTREL	72D	<1	2	5

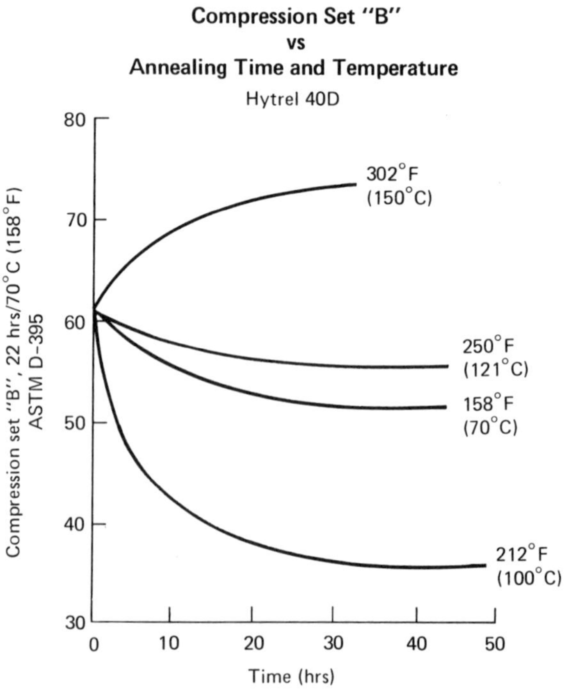

Compression Set "B"
vs
Annealing Time and Temperature

Hytrel 40D

Figure 4-14. Method B compression set vs. time at various temperatures for the 40D grade.

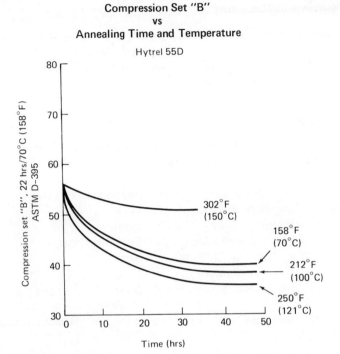

Figure 4-15. Method B compression set vs. time at various temperatures for the 55D.

4.4 ENVIRONMENTAL AND CHEMICAL PROPERTIES

4.4.1 Heat Resistance

The Hytrel elastomers, particularly the harder polymers, possess exceptional "hot strength." Above 250°F (121°C), their tensile strengths far exceed those of competitive polyurethanes. For example, the 55D polymer at 347°F (121°C) still retains a tensile strength of nearly 2000 psi (140 kg/cm^2).

4.4.2 Cold Resistance

All Hytrel polymers have solenoid brittle points below −94°F (−70°C). However, as would be expected, the softer materials exhibit the better low temperature flexibility. Thus, an appropriate design choice can be made, regardless of the anticipated thermal conditions, between the extremes of −65 and 300°F.

4.4.3 Resistance to Weathering

For resistance to ultraviolet radiation, pigments or screening agents are required. Properly stabilized, these elastomers will provide satisfactory service under all climatic conditions. Results of 2-year weathering tests in Florida and 4000-hr Fade-Ometer exposure confirm this.

4.4.4 Microbiological Resistance

The resistance of Hytrel 40D elastomer to certain fungi was determined according to ASTM D-1924 using the following cultures.[11]

CULTURE	OBSERVED GROWTH
Aspergillus niger	None
Aspergillus flavus	None
Aspergillus versicolor	Very slight, sparse
Penicillium funiculosum	None
Pullularia pullulans	None
Trichloderma sp.	None

Samples of 40D were also buried for 1 year in Panama. Tensile test results, before and after, follow.

PROPERTY	ORIGINAL	AFTER 1 YR
Shore A hardness	92	90
Tensile strength, psi	4600	3850
Elongation at break, %	830	680
100% modulus, psi	1000	990
300% modulus, psi	1280	1250

The harder durometers were not included in these tests but should show at least equivalent resistance, since they are based on the same raw materials.

4.4.5 Radiation Resistance

The increasing use of nuclear energy in power plants, military areas, medicine, and other fields places new requirements on many rubber compounds as well as other materials. Some factors that are important to market-development activities in this field include, for example: (1) the maximum dosage to which the material can be subjected without damaging effects, (2) the possible use of additives to provide additional stabilization to radiation, and (3) the effect of radiation on physical properties.[12]

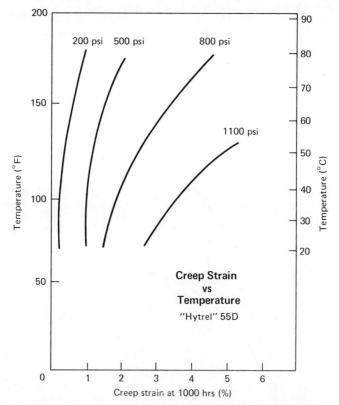

Figure 4-16. Creep strain vs. temperature, in %, for 55D Hytrel at a 1000-hr strain.

Uncompounded Hytrel polyester elastomers of all four hardness grades have excellent retention of physical properties after irradiation at 23°C (73.4°F) in air.

Injection-molded 3-by-5-by-0.075-in. slabs were exposed to a 2-MeV electron beam at a dose rate of 10^5 rad/hr. The slabs were then tested by ASTM methods. For the most part, radiations of prime interest from the standpoint of insulation damage have energies of the order of 1 MeV. These are principally gamma photons and fast neutrons. Damage is caused by collisions of this radiation with electrons and nuclei in the elastomer, where the energy input from such collisions may be greater than the bond energies in the elastomer.

Most elastomers are embrittled by radiation exposure, which induces cross-links between molecules. This eventually gives a three-dimensional network, such as seen in hard rubber or phenolic resins. A few polymers, notably butyl rubber, degrade by reversion to low molecular weight tars and oils.

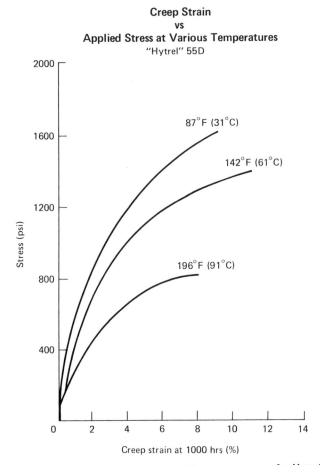

Figure 4-17. Creep stress vs. creep strain at three temperatures for Hytrel 55D.

Although upgrading changes can occur under controlled low dosage (radiation cross-linked polyolefins), long exposures normally produce degradation. Thus, the amount of change is dependent on radiation flux rate, total radiation dose, energy of radiation, chemical composition of the polymer, environment (ambient temperature, air vs. inert gas, steam exposure, etc.), and the initial properties of the elastomer compound. The amount of change is independent of the type of radiation at equal energy whether alpha, beta, or gamma rays or neutrons. This is known as the equal-energy, equal-damage concept.

Table 4-12 summarizes the effect of radiation on three hardness grades of Hytrel. It will be seen that the exposure to 10^7 rad produces very little change

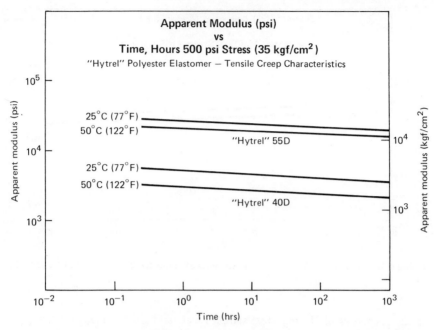

Figure 4-18. Apparent modulus at various stress and temperatures for Hytrel 55D and 40D.

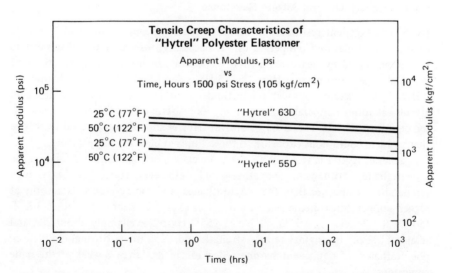

Figure 4-19. Apparent modulus at various stress and temperatures for Hytrel 63D and 55D.

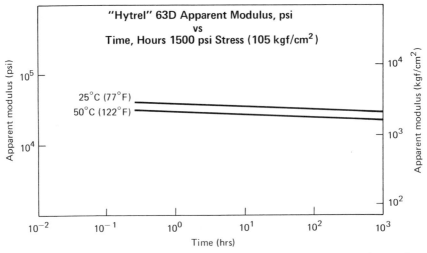

Figure 4-20. Apparent modulus vs. time for 63D at room temperature and 50°C (122°F).

in the properties of Hytrel. Test samples were still glossy, highly resilient, and flexible after this exposure.

4.4.6 Chemical, Oil, and Solvent Resistance

Hytrel has excellent resistance to nonpolar materials such as oils and hydraulic fluids, even at elevated temperatures. If necessary, resistance to hot oils can be further enhanced by heat-stabilization. The superior hot-oil aging resistance of heat-stabilized types such as Hytrel 5555 HS is described later in this chapter.

Hytrel is resistant to most polar fluids—such as acids, bases, amines, and glycols—at room temperature. However, its resistance to polar fluids is poor at temperatures of 158°F (70°C) or above. Hytrel should not be used in service that requires continuous exposure to these fluids at elevated temperatures.

In general, Hytrel is resistant to the same classes of chemicals and fluids as are polyurethanes, both ester- and ether-based. However, Hytrel has better high temperature properties than the polyurethanes, and can be used satisfactorily at higher temperatures in the same fluids. For example, after exposure at 302°F (50°C) for 7 days in ASTM oil No. 1, 55D Hytrel swells only about 2%, and retains 60% of its original tensile strength and 90% of its original elongation; polyurethanes of equivalent hardness degrade in less than a week at the same conditions.

Table 4-6. The impact resistance of the three hardest grades of Hytrel at two temperatures in comparison to urethane and plasticized nylon 11.[5]

Impact Resistance

| | Hardness (ASTM D-2240) | Izod Impact Strength, (ASTM D-256, Method A) ft-lb/in [J/cm] | | | | Gardner Impact Strength[e] in-lb [J] |
| | | Unnotched | | Notched | | |
		73°F [23°C]	−40°F [−40°C]	73°F [23°C]	−40°F [−40°C]	−40°F [−40°C]
HYTREL	55D	>20 [10.6] No break	>20 [10.6] No break	>20 [10.6] No break	>20 [10.6] No break	158 [17.9]
TPU-ESTER	55D	>19 [10.1] No break	>20 [10.6] No break	>17 [9.0] No break	0.7 [0.4]	No data
HYTREL	63D	>20 [10.6] No break	>20 [10.6] No break	>20 [10.6] No break	0.5 [0.3]	98 [11.1]
Plasticized Nylon 11	65D	>19 [10.1] No break	15 [8.0]	0.5 [0.3]	0.6 [0.3]	60 [6.8]
HYTREL	72D	40 [21] No break	40 [21] No break	3.9 [2.1]	0.8 [0.4]	82 [9.3]

Note: Properties were measured on injection-molded test specimens.
[e] Measured on a 75-mil [1.91 mm] slab.

Table 4-7. The comparison of three abrasion tests for Hytrel and urethane of comparable durometer.[5]

		Taber Abrasion, (ASTM D-1044)		NBS Index (ASTM D-1630)	Pico Abrasion (ASTM D-2228)
Abrasion Resistance					
	Hardness (ASTM D-2240)	CS-17 Wheel mg/1000 rev	H-18 Wheel mg/1000 rev	%	Weight loss, mg
HYTREL	40D (92A)	3	100	800	5.5
TPU-ETHER	90A	6	No data	395	6.5
HYTREL	55D	5	64	3540	3.7
TPU-ESTER	55D	2	80	1200	No data
HYTREL	63D	8	160	2300	No data
HYTREL	72D	13	66	4900	No data

Note: Properties were measured on injection-molded test specimens.

Hytrel polyester elastomers do not contain an extractable plasticizer, as do flexible vinyls, certain grades of nylon, and many rubber compounds. Many fluids and chemicals will extract the plasticizer from these materials, causing a significant increase in stiffness (modulus) and volume shrinkage. For example, a plasticized nylon of approximately 63D hardness undergoes a twofold increase in modulus and shrinks about 10% when exposed to ASTM oil No. 1 for 7 days at 250°F (121°C). Hytrel of the same hardness shows no change in modulus and swells approximately 0.3% under the same exposure conditions.

Table 4-13 shows a generalized rating of these polymers to various solvents, oils, and chemicals. It should serve as a guideline only, as hardness and other variables have an influence on these data. Physical property changes for the four grades are shown in Tables 4-14 through 4-17.

4.4.7 Hot Oil Resistance

Tables 4-14 through 4-17 summarize data on the resistance of Hytrel polyester elastomers to hot ASTM oils, automatic transmission fluids, phosphate ester hydraulic fluids (Skydrol, Pydraul), and waterglycol fluids (Houghto-Safe 620).

4.4.8 Fuel Permeability

A number of potential applications for Hytrel polyester elastomers require low permeability to standard fuels. These markets include fuel lines, seals, diaphragms, coated fabrics for fuel cells, and molded high-impact fuel tanks and

DYNAMIC SHEAR TEST

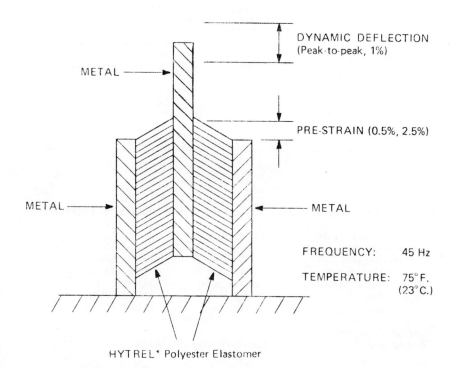

- COMPLEX MODULUS, $E^\dagger$ = K
  Where K is Dynamic Spring Rate
- LOSS MODULUS, E'' = $E^\dagger$ SIN ϕ
  Where ϕ is loss angle
- ELASTIC MODULUS, E' = $\sqrt{(E^\dagger)^2 - (E'')^2}$

Figure 4-21. Dynamic shear sandwich for testing of the complex and elastic modulus of Hytrel.

filler necks. The 55D and 63D Hytrel are compared in permeability to ASTM reference fuels by ASTM D-814.

It should be noted that all these permeability values are very low compared to common fuel-resistant elastomers such as neoprene, Hypalon* synthetic rubber, and nitrile rubber. Table 4-18 compares these three common elastomers. At a

*Registered U.S. trademark of the Du Pont Company.

Table 4-8.   Values of the complex, elastic, and loss modulus for the two softest grades of Hytrel at two prestrain levels.[6]

MATERIAL	PRESTRAIN %	% TOTAL AMPLITUDE PEAK-TO-PEAK	COMPLEX MODULUS PSI	ELASTIC MODULUS PSI	LOSS MODULUS PSI
HYTREL 40D	0.5	0.98	18,000	18,000	0
		0.90	19,800	19,800	0
	2.5	1.0	37,500	35,600	1800
		0.85	41,200	41,100	1235
HYTREL 55D	0.5	1.05	32,400	32,400	0
		0.95	33,700	33,700	0
	2.5	0.95	51,400	51,300	1335
		0.70	55,400	55,400	990

Table 4-9.   The dynamic Young's modulus by several methods for 55D Hytrel.[9]

METHOD	FREQUENCY, HZ	E, PSI (kg/cm^2)
Impact	980–1390	38,000 (2660)
Cantilever Beam[a]	42–2493	34,000 (2380)
Sound Velocity	approx. 2000	34,000 (2380)
Instron	Very Low	29,000 (2030)
Creep	Very Low	25,000[b] (1750)

[a]Loss tangent approx. 0.09
[b]Modulus at strain of approx. 4% (1 minute after applying stress).

thickness of 0.025 in. (0.64 mm), the family of Hytrel polymers is less permeable to these fuels by factors ranging from approximately 3X at the lowest, to almost 300X at the highest.

Figures 4-22 and 4-23 illustrate the smooth log-log relationship of permeability and film thickness. In the case of reference fuel B, which is a blend of 70% isooctane and 30% toluene, 63D Hytrel shows a very strong relationship between permeability and film thickness. Doubling thickness reduces permeability by a factor of slightly more than 10. Permeability of 55D Hytrel is less dependent on thickness; a 2X increase in thickness decreases permeability by a factor of 2.

In the case of reference fuel C (1:1 isooctane-toluene), shown in Figure 4-23, similar relationships hold. The slopes of the log-log relationships for fuel C are approximately the same as for fuel B, although shifted to slightly high permeability levels, particularly in the case of 55D Hytrel.

Table 4-10. The common electrical properties of the Hytrel polymers at room temperature.[10]

Electrical Properties at Room Temperature

	ASTM Test	40D HYTREL	55D HYTREL	63D HYTREL	72D HYTREL
Dielectric Strength, volts/mil [MV/m]	D-149				
72°F, [22°C] 50% R.H.		900 [35.4]	845 [33.3]	815 [32.1]	645 [25.4]
72°F, [22°C] 100% R.H.		865 [34.0]	750 [29.5]	785 [30.9]	—
Power Factor, 1 kHz, %	D-150				
72°F, [22°C] 50% R.H.		0.66	0.82	0.80	—
72°F, [22°C] 100% R.H.		0.77	0.87	0.91	—
SIC, 1 kHz	D-150				
72°F, [22°C] 50% R.H.		5.97	4.6	4.84	4.16
72°F, [22°C] 100% R.H.		6.01	4.9	4.96	—
Volume Resistivity, ohm-cm	D-257				
72°F, [22°C] 50% R.H.		2.25×10^{13}	5.6×10^{13}	1.43×10^{13}	4.45×10^{15}
72°F, [22°C] 100% R.H.		1.11×10^{13}	3.0×10^{13}	1.01×10^{12}	—

Table 4-11. Electrical properties of the 55 and 63D Hytrel at five temperatures.[10]

Electrical Properties as a Function of Temperature			
(Ambient Humidity)			
55D HYTREL	Vol. Resistivity ohm-cm, ASTM D-257	SIC, 1 kHz ASTM D-150	Power Factor, % ASTM D-150
73°F [23°C]	3.0×10^{13}	4.97	0.84
212°F [100°C]	9.3×10^{9}	5.91	5.82
257°F [125°C]	6.0×10^{9}	5.76	9.56
302°F [150°C]	2.6×10^{9}	6.16	24.11
447°F [175°C]	1.0×10^{9}	6.70	53.82
63D HYTREL			
73°F [23°C]	1.43×10^{13}	4.84	1.02
212°F [100°C]	1.15×10^{10}	5.88	5.26
257°F [125°C]	1.19×10^{10}	5.92	11.59
302°F [150°C]	3.93×10^{9}	6.94	43.72
447°F [175°C]	1.8×10^{9}	8.53	81.06

4.4.9 Gas Permeability

Hytrel polyester elastomers have an unusual combination of polarity, crystallinity, and morphology. Thus, they have a high degree of permeability toward polar molecules such as water, but provide considerable resistance to permeation by nonpolar hydrocarbons and refrigerant gases (see Table 4-19).[15]

In degree of permeability to moisture, Hytrel is comparable to the polyether-based urethanes and therefore is useful in coating fabrics for apparel applications. Its low permeability toward refrigerant gases makes Hytrel of interest for evaluation for use in refrigerant hose. Their impermeability to propane gas makes the polymers of interest for use in flexible hose or tubing that transmits propane gas for heating or cooking.[15]

4.4.10 Aging Resistance

Hytrel polyesters are very resistant to oxidation, which means that they are substantially unaffected by the passage of time at room temperature under normal stress conditions. Accelerated, dry heat aging tests show these polymers to be more resistant than polyurethanes. Table 4-20 shows the effect of heat on physical properties for three grades. Incorporation of special heat-stabilizing additives can further improve the aging resistance of Hytrel.

Table 4-12. Stability of Hytrel polyester elastomers to radiation electron beam, 2 MeV, 30°C (86°F)/50% RH, radiation dosage in rads.[12]

Stability of HYTREL Polyester Elastomers to Radiation Electron Beam, 2 Mev., 30°C. (86°F)/50% RH, Radiation Dosage in Rads		
	HYTREL 40D	HYTREL 55D	HYTREL 63D
ORIGINAL			
Tensile Strength, psi (kgf/cm^2)	3500 (246.0)	5090 (357.8)	5225 (367.3)
Elongation at Break, %	610	570	450
100% Modulus, psi (kgf/cm^2)	1275 (89.6)	2025 (142.4)	2790 (196.1)
300% Modulus, psi (kgf/cm^2)	1620 (113.9)	2660 (187.0)	3750 (263.6)
10^5 RADS			
Tensile Strength, psi (kgf/cm^2)	3315 (233.0)	4415 (310.4)	5270 (370.5)
Elongation at Break, %	595	525	425
100% Modulus, psi (kgf/cm^2)	1185 (83.3)	1980 (139.2)	2750 (193.3)
300% Modulus, psi (kgf/cm^2)	1620 (113.9)	2525 (117.5)	3830 (269.2)
10^6 RADS			
Tensile Strength, psi (kgf/cm^2)	3500 (246.0)	4280 (300.9)	4910 (345.2)
Elongation at Break, %	600	530	430
100% Modulus, psi (kgf/cm^2)	1285 (90.3)	1980 (139.2)	2680 (188.4)
300% Modulus, psi (kgf/cm^2)	1700 (119.5)	2500 (175.8)	3900 (274.2)
10^7 RADS			
Tensile Strength, psi (kgf/cm^2)	3380 (237.6)	4220 (296.7)	5120 (359.9)
Elongation at Break, %	535	450	415
100% Modulus, psi (kgf/cm^2)	1230 (86.5)	2150 (151.1)	2840 (199.7)
300% Modulus, psi (kgf/cm^2)	1760 (123.7)	2680 (188.4)	4000 (281.2)

Heat aging characteristics of Hytrel in air or hot oil may be improved by the incorporation of an aromatic amine antioxidant or a polymeric dihydroquinoline antioxidant. However, the resulting blend will no longer be color-stable due to the yellowing tendencies of the antioxidant. The improvement in heat aging resistance is greatest at temperatures of 250°F (121°C) and above. The dihydroquinoline type produces better hot-oil aging characteristics than the aromatic amine type. The antioxidant can be dry blended with the Hytrel pellets, and the blend can be injection molded or extruded directly into the final product. Adhesion of the powdered antioxidant to Hytrel, and uniformity of the final melt-blended product, are improved by the use of 0.1 to 0.2% Sandozin D-100 to pre-wet the surface of the pellets. Alternatively, plasticizers such as Santicizer 711 or Benzoflex 9-88 may be used to wet the pellet surfaces. To blend the antioxi-

Table 4-13. The general rating of chemical resistance of Hytrel elastomers.

The data tabulated below summarize the effects of a broad variety of fluids on HYTREL polyester elastomers. As a general rule the resistance of HYTREL elastomers to fluids and chemicals increases as the polymer hardness increases. Unless otherwise noted the ratings shown in the table apply to all hardness grades.

Rating Key: A–Fluid has little or no effect
B–Fluid has minor to moderate effect
C–Fluid has severe effect
T–No data–likely to have minor effect
X–No data–likely to have severe effect

Ratings are at 72°F [22°C] unless otherwise specified. Concentrations of aqueous solutions are saturated, except where noted.

CHEMICAL	RATING	CHEMICAL	RATING
Acetic Acid, 20%	A	ASTM Reference Fuel C (158°F) [70°C]	B (40, 55D)
Acetic Acid, 30%	A	ASTM Reference Fuel C (158°F) [70°C]	A (63, 72D)
Acetic Acid, Glacial	A	Asphalt	T
Acetic Acid, Glacial (100°F) [38°C]	B	Barium Hydroxide Solutions	T
Acetic Anhydride	T	Beer	A
Acetone	B	Benzene	B (40, 55D)
Acetylene	A	Benzene	A (63, 72D)
Aluminum Chloride Solutions	T	Borax Solutions	A
Aluminum Sulfate Solutions	T	Boric Acid Solutions	A
Ammonium Chloride Solutions	A	Bromine, Anhydrous Liquid	X
Ammonium Hydroxide Solutions	T	Butane	A
Ammonium Sulfate Solutions	B (40, 55, 63D)	Butyl Acetate	B (40, 55D)
Ammonium Sulfate Solutions	A (72D)	Butyl Acetate	A (63, 72D)
Amyl Acetate	B	Calcium Chloride Solutions	A
Amyl Alcohol	A	Calcium Hydroxide Solutions	T
Aniline	C	Calcium Hypochlorite, 5%	A
ASTM Oil No. 1 (300°F) [149°C]	A	Carbon Bisulfide	B (40, 55D)
ASTM Oil No. 3 (300°F) [149°C]	A	Carbon Bisulfide	A (63, 72D)
ASTM Reference Fuel A (158°F) [70°C]	A	Carbon Dioxide	A
ASTM Reference Fuel B (158°F) [70°C]	A	Carbon Monoxide	A
ASTM Reference Fuel C	A	Carbon Tetrachloride	C (40D)

Chemical	Rating
Carbon Tetrachloride	B (55, 63D)
Carbon Tetrachloride	A (72D)
Castor Oil	B (40, 55D)
Castor Oil	A (63, 72D)
Chlorine Gas, Dry	X
Chlorine Gas, Wet	X
Chloroacetic Acid	X
Chlorobenzene	X
Chloroform	C (40, 55D)
Chloroform	B (63, 72D)
Chlorosulfonic Acid	C
Citric Acid Solutions	A
Copper Chloride Solutions	A
Copper Sulfate Solutions	A
Cottonseed Oil	A
Cyclohexane	A
Dibutyl Phthalate	A
Diethyl Sebacate	A
Dioctyl Phthalate	X
Epichlorohydrin	B (40, 55, 63D)
Ethyl Acetate	A (72D)
Ethyl Alcohol	A
Ethyl Chloride	C (40, 55D)
Ethyl Chloride	B (63, 72D)
Ethylene Dichloride	C (40, 55D)
Ethylene Dichloride	B (63, 72D)
Ethylene Glycol	A
Ethylene Oxide	A
Ferric Chloride Solutions	T
Fluosilicic Acid	T
Formaldehyde, 40%	B
Formic Acid	B
FREON-11(5)	A
FREON-12	A
FREON 113 (130°F) [55°C]	A
FREON 114	A
Gasoline	A
Glue	A
Glycerin	A
n-Hexane	C
Hydrazine	B
Hydrochloric Acid, 20%	C
Hydrochloric Acid, 37%	T
Hydrocyanic Acid	X
Hydrofluoric Acid, 48%	X
Hydrofluoric Acid, 75%	X
Hydrofluoric Acid, Anhydrous	A
Hydrogen	A
Hydrogen Sulfide	A
Isooctane	A
Isopropyl Alcohol	T
JP-4 Jet Fuel	T
Kerosene	T
Lacquer Solvents	B (40, 55D)
Lacquer Solvents	A (63, 72D)
Lactic Acid	A
Linseed Oil	T
Lubricating Oils	T
Magnesium Chloride Solutions	A
Magnesium Hydroxide Solutions	A
Mercuric Chloride Solutions	C
Mercury	A
Methyl Alcohol	T
Methyl Ethyl Ketone	B (40, 55D)
Methyl Ethyl Ketone	A (63, 72D)
Methylene Chloride	T
Mineral Oil	A
Naphtha	A
Naphthalene	B (40, 55D)
Naphthalene	A (63, 72D)
Nitric Acid, 10%	B

Table 4-13. The general rating of chemical resistance of Hytrel elastomers.

CHEMICAL	RATING	CHEMICAL	RATING
Nitric Acid, 30%	C	Stannous Chloride, 15%	T
Nitric Acid, 60%	C	Steam (212°F) [100°C]	B
Nitric Acid, 70%	C	Steam (230°F) [110°C]	C
Nitric Acid, Red Fuming	C	Stearic Acid	T
Nitrobenzene	C	Styrene	X
Oleic Acid	A	Sulfur, Molten	T
Oleum, 20–25%	C	Sulfur Dioxide, Liquid	T
Palmitic Acid	A	Sulfur Dioxide, Gas	T
Perchloroethylene	C (40, 55D)	Sulfuric Acid, up to 50%	A
Perchloroethylene	B (63, 72D)	Sulfuric Acid, above 50%	C
Phenol	C	Sulfuric Acid, Fuming (20% Oleum)	C
Pickling Solution (20% Nitric Acid, 4% HF)	X	Sulfurous Acid	B
Pickling Solution (17% Nitric Acid, 4% HF)	X	Tannic Acid, 10%	A
Potassium Dichromate Solutions	T	Tartaric Acid	T
Potassium Hydroxide Solutions	A	Tetrahydrofuran	B (40, 55D)
PYDRAUL 312[a]	A	Tetrahydrofuran	A (63, 72D)
Pyridine	X	Toluene	B (40, 55D)
SAE 10 Oil	A	Toluene	A (63, 72D)
Sea Water	A	Trichloroethylene	C (40, 55D)
Silicone Grease	A	Trichloroethylene	B (63, 72D)
SKYDROL 500[b]	A	Triethanolamine	C
Soap Solutions	A	Trisodium Phosphate Solution	A
Sodium Chloride Solutions	A	Tung Oil	T
Sodium Dichromate, 20%	T	Water (158°F) [70°C]	A
Sodium Hydroxide, 20%	A	Water (212°F) [100°C]	B
Sodium Hydroxide, 46½%	B	Xylene	B (40, 55D)
Sodium Hypochlorite, 5%	A	Xylene	A (63, 72D)
Soybean Oil	T	Zinc Chloride Solutions	A

Table 4-13. (Continued)

FLUID	IMMERSION TIME, DAYS	IMMERSION TEMPERATURE °F [°C]	VOLUME INCREASE, %			
			40D HYTREL	55D HYTREL	63D HYTREL	72D HYTREL
Oils and Hydraulic Fluids						
ASTM Oil No. 1	7	212 [100]	2	2	<1	<1
ASTM Oil No. 3	7	212 [100]	23	11	6	4
Ethylene Glycol	7	72 [22]	<1	<1	<1	<1
PYDRAUL 312[a]	7	212 [100]	110	31	20	15
SKYDROL 500[b]	7	212 [100]	–	22	15	–
Solvents and Fuels						
ASTM Ref. Fuel C	7	72 [22]	50	24	15	9
n-Butyl Alcohol	7	72 [22]	18	11	5	2
CELLOSOLVE Acetate[c]	7	72 [22]	40	19	13	6
Iso-octane	7	72 [22]	8	5	<1	<1
Methyl Isobutyl Ketone	7	72 [22]	42	19	14	6
Xylene	7	72 [22]	88	36	20	13
Halocarbons						
FREON 113[d]	7	72 [22]	19	7	2	<1
Perchloroethylene	7	72 [22]	81	32	19	10
Trichloroethylene	7	72 [22]	Dissolved	67	41	25
Acids and Bases						
Acetic acid, glacial	7	100 [38]	No data	39	22	16
Acetic acid, 5%	7	100 [38]	No data	<1	<1	<1
Formic acid, conc.	7	72 [22]	57	31	No data	No data
Formic acid, 50%	7	72 [22]	11	8	No data	No data
Sodium Hydroxide, 20%	7	72 [22]	<1	<1	<1	<1
Sulfuric acid, 20%	7	72 [22]	<1	<1	<1	<1

[a]PYDRAUL 312, hydraulic fluid. Disiloxane fluid. Chevron Chemical Co. Ornate Division, San Francisco, CA.
[b]SKYDROL 500B. Phosphate ester. Monsanto Chemical Co., St. Louis, MO.
[c]CELLOSOLVE Acetate. Ethylene glycolmonethyl ether acetate. Union Carbide Corp., New York, NY.
[d]FREON 113. Trichlorotrifluorethane. E. I. du Pont de Nemours & Company, Wilmington, DE.

Table 4-14. The changes in physical properties of 40D Hytrel with various chemical exposures.

Original Properties[a] at 72°F [22°C]:
Tensile Strength . . . . . . 3700 psi [25.5 MPa]
Elongation 450%
100% Modulus . . . . . . 1100 psi [7.6 MPa]

FLUID	IMMERSION TIME, DAYS	IMMERSION TEMPERATURE, °F [°C]	TENSILE STRENGTH, % OF ORIGINAL RETAINED AFTER IMMERSION[a]	ELONGATION, % OF ORIGINAL RETAINED AFTER IMMERSION[a]	100% MODULUS, % OF ORIGINAL RETAINED AFTER IMMERSION[a]	VOLUME INCREASE, %
Oils and Hydraulic Fluids						
ASTM Oil No. 1	7	72 [22]	100	101	99	<1
ASTM Oil No. 1	7	212 [100]	83	103	111	2
ASTM Oil No. 3	7	72 [22]	99	107	95	8
ASTM Oil No. 3	7	212 [100]	78	96	100	23
Crude oil, Algerian	3	158 [70]	108	101	No data	21
PYDRAUL 312(9)	7	72 [22]	90	112	78	40
PYDRAUL 312(9)	7	212 [100]	50	104	44	110
URSA oil(11)	7	72 [22]	112	110	100	1
URSA oil(11)	7	212 [100]	93	104	110	5
Solvents and Fuels						
ASTM Reference Fuel B	7	72 [22]	100	104	84	28
ASTM Reference Fuel B	7	158 [70]	78	96	93	36
ASTM Reference Fuel C	7	72 [22]	62	110	67	50
ASTM Reference Fuel C	7	158 [70]	47	89	53	88
n-Butyl alcohol	7	72 [22]	82	113	91	18
CELLOSOLVE Acetate(4)	7	72 [22]	83	110	78	40
Isooctane	7	72 [22]	106	104	101	8
Methyl isobutyl ketone	7	72 [22]	57	81	81	42
Xylene	7	72 [22]	57	74	75	88
Halocarbons						
FREON 113(5)	7	72 [22]	99	107	67	19
Perchloroethylene	7	72 [22]	73	98	58	81
Trichloroethylene	7	72 [22]	Dissolved	—		
Acids and Bases						
Formic acid, conc.	7	72 [22]	47	94	49	57
Formic acid, 50%	7	72 [22]	58	108	66	11
Formic acid, 25%	7	72 [22]	72	110	85	5
Formic acid, 10%	7	72 [22]	71	114	86	2
Sodium hydroxide, 20%	7	72 [22]	100	103	77	<1
Sulfuric acid, 20%	7	72 [22]	91	100	74	<1
Miscellaneous						
Dimethyl formamide	7	72 [22]	85	111	82	39
Ethylene glycol	7	72 [22]	76	102	82	<1
Nitromethane	7	72 [22]	65	103	59	33
WESSON oil[b]	7	72 [22]	90	102	102	<1

[a]These properties were measured at room temperature at a strain rate of 2 in/min (51 mm/min) on dumbbells died from slabs injection-molded under

Table 4-15. The changes in physical properties of 55D Hytrel with various chemical exposures.

Original Properties[a] at 72°F [22°C]
Tensile Strength . . . . . . 5700 psi [39.3 MPa]
Elongation 350%
100% Modulus . . . . . . 2500 psi [17.2 MPa]

FLUID	IMMERSION TIME, DAYS	IMMERSION TEMPERATURE, °F [°C]	TENSILE STRENGTH, % OF ORIGINAL RETAINED AFTER IMMERSION[a,b]	ELONGATION, % OF ORIGINAL RETAINED AFTER IMMERSION[a,b]	100% MODULUS, % OF ORIGINAL RETAINED AFTER IMMERSION[a,b]	VOLUME INCREASE, %
Oils and Hydraulic Fluids						
ASTM Oil No. 1	7	212 [100]	94	100	No data	2
ASTM Oil No. 1	7	250 [121]	100	109	No data	2
ASTM Oil No. 1	7	302 [150]	97	125	No data	2
ASTM Oil No. 2	7	212 [100]	108	105	No data	7
ASTM Oil No. 2	7	250 [121]	105	109	No data	8
ASTM Oil No. 2	7	302 [150]	95	118	No data	11
ASTM Oil No. 3	7	212 [100]	104	107	101	11
ASTM Oil No. 3	7	250 [121]	102	109	102	13
ASTM Oil No. 3	7	302 [150]	61	86	103	18
Automatic transmission fluid,						
Type A	7	212 [100]	109	130	No data	5
Type A	7	250 [121]	110	109	No data	6
Type A	7	302 [150]	105	123	No data	8
Type A	14	302 [150]	60	89	No data	9
Automatic transmission fluid,						
Type F	7	212 [100]	104	100	No data	5
Type F	7	250 [121]	101	103	No data	6
Type F	7	302 [150]	92	131	No data	8
HARMONY Oil No. 41	7	212 [100]	101	98	No data	3
HARMONY Oil No. 41	7	250 [121]	104	103	No data	4
HARMONY Oil No. 41	7	302 [150]	35	8	No data	-3
HOUGHTO-SAFE 620	7	158 [70]	95	96	No data	<1
HOUGHTO-SAFE 620	14	158 [70]	95	103	No data	<1
PYDRAUL 312	7	212 [100]	90	91	98	31
PYDRAUL 312	7	250 [121]	77	91	93	40
PYDRAUL 312	14	250 [121]	80	101	No data	41
SKYDROL 500B	7	212 [100]	72	80	95	22
SKYDROL 500B	7	250 [121]	<10	<10	–	32
Solvents and Fuels						
ASTM Reference Fuel C	7	,72 [22]	93	94	91	24

Table 4-15. (Continued)

FLUID	IMMERSION TIME, DAYS	IMMERSION TEMPERATURE, °F [°C]	TENSILE STRENGTH, % OF ORIGINAL RETAINED AFTER IMMERSION[b,c]	ELONGATION, % OF ORIGINAL RETAINED AFTER IMMERSION[b,c]	100% MODULUS, % OF ORIGINAL RETAINED AFTER IMMERSION[b,c]	VOLUME INCREASE, %
ASTM Reference Fuel C	7	158 [70]	105	102	92	31
n-Butyl alcohol	7	72 [22]	116	100	80	11
CELLOSOLVE Acetate	7	72 [22]	95	94	80	19
Isooctane	7	72 [22]	106	94	86	5
Methyl isobutyl ketone	7	72 [22]	108	97	80	19
Xylene	7	72 [22]	108	97	77	36
Halocarbons						
Carbon tetrachloride	7	72 [22]	94	94	69	32
FREON 113	7	72 [22]	102	106	91	7
Perchloroethylene	7	72 [22]	96	100	84	32
Trichloroethylene	7	72 [22]	99	106	77	67
Acids and Bases						
Acetic acid, glacial	7	100 [38]	85	88	74	39
Acetic acid, 5%	7	100 [38]	128	112	96	<1
Formic acid, conc.	7	72 [22]	82	89	74	31
Formic acid, 50%	7	72 [22]	84	111	70	8
Formic acid, 25%	7	72 [22]	95	105	86	4
Formic acid, 10%	7	72 [22]	100	109	88	2
Sodium hydroxide, 20%	7	72 [22]	95	106	95	<1
Sulfuric acid, 20%	7	72 [22]	92	106	100	<1
Miscellaneous						
Aniline	7	72 [22]	51	64	44	93
Dibutyl phthalate	7	72 [22]	110	97	83	12
Diethylene glycol	7	72 [22]	101	97	79	1
Dimethyl formamide	7	72 [22]	98	94	76	19
Dioctyl phthalate	7	72 [22]	121	112	91	3
Ethylene glycol	7	72 [22]	101	94	86	<1
Nitromethane	7	72 [22]	100	109	89	17
Toluene diisocyanate (mixed isomers)	7	72 [22]	97	90	67	41
WESSON oil	7	72 [22]	98	94	87	<1

[a]These properties were measured at room temperature at a strain rate of 2 in/min [51 mm/min] on dumbbells died from slabs injection-molded under standard conditions.

[b]These values are based on unmodified HYTREL; the superior hot oil aging of heat-stabilized types such as HYTREL 5555 HS is covered in other literature.

Table 4-16. The changes in physical properties of 63D Hytrel with various chemical exposures.

Original Properties[a] at 72°F [22°C]

Tensile Strength . . . . . . 5500 psi [37.9 MPa]
Elongation 450%
100% Modulus . . . . 2000 psi [13.8 MPa]

FLUID	IMMERSION TIME, DAYS	IMMERSION TEMPERATURE, °F [°C]	TENSILE STRENGTH, % OF ORIGINAL RETAINED AFTER IMMERSION[d]	ELONGATION, % OF ORIGINAL RETAINED AFTER IMMERSION[d]	100% MODULUS, % OF ORIGINAL RETAINED AFTER IMMERSION[d]	VOLUME INCREASE, %
Oils and Hydraulic Fluids						
ASTM Oil No. 1	7	212 [100]	86	101	No data	<1
ASTM Oil No. 1	7	250 [121]	79	107	97	<1
ASTM Oil No. 1	7	302 [150]	83	104	94	<1
ASTM Oil No. 1	14	250 [121]	82	90	No data	<1
ASTM Oil No. 1	14	302 [150]	70	119	No data	<1
ASTM Oil No. 2	7	212 [100]	90	99	No data	3
ASTM Oil No. 2	7	250 [121]	88	101	No data	4
ASTM Oil No. 2	7	302 [150]	81	99	No data	5
ASTM Oil No. 3	7	212 [100]	89	112	No data	6
ASTM Oil No. 3	7	250 [121]	93	106	128	7
ASTM Oil No. 3	7	302 [150]	56	57	94	10
ASTM Oil No. 3	14	250 [121]	56	18	No data	7
ASTM Oil No. 3	14	302 [150]	17	1	No data	9
Automatic transmission fluid,						
Type A	7	212 [100]	100	101	No data	3
Type A	7	250 [121]	97	99	111	3
Type A	7	302 [150]	78	114	109	4
Type A	14	302 [150]	55	91	No data	5
Automatic transmission fluid,						
Type F	7	212 [100]	94	101	No data	2
Type F	7	250 [121]	92	103	94	3
Type F	7	302 [150]	76	111	97	3
HARMONY Oil No. 41	7	212 [100]	88	106	No data	1
HARMONY Oil No. 41	7	250 [121]	96	103	No data	2
HARMONY Oil No. 41	7	302 [150]	Failed	Failed	Failed	—
HOUGHTO-SAFE 620	7	158 [70]	101	105	No data	<1
HOUGHTO-SAFE 620	14	158 [70]	74	114	No data	<1
ORONITE 8200	7	250 [121]	86	91	No data	1
ORONITE 8200	14	250 [121]	76	88	No data	2
ORONITE 8200	7	302 [150]	67	77	No data	2
ORONITE 8200	14	302 [150]	49	67	No data	4

Table 4-16. (Continued)

FLUID	IMMERSION TIME, DAYS	IMMERSION TEMPERATURE, °F [°C]	TENSILE STRENGTH, % OF ORIGINAL RETAINED AFTER IMMERSION[d]	ELONGATION, % OF ORIGINAL RETAINED AFTER IMMERSION[d]	100% MODULUS, % OF ORIGINAL RETAINED AFTER IMMERSION[d]	VOLUME INCREASE, %
PYDRAUL 312	7	212 [100]	88	110	No data	20
PYDRAUL 312	7	250 [121]	79	101	No data	23
PYDRAUL 312	14	250 [121]	94	111	No data	24
SKYDROL 500B	7	212 [100]	82	91	97	15
SKYDROL 500B	7	250 [121]	17	<10	—	21
Solvents and Fuels						
ASTM Reference Fuel B	7	72 [22]	96	94	97	6
ASTM Reference Fuel B	7	122 [50]	88	92	91	12
ASTM Reference Fuel C	7	72 [22]	84	92	89	15
ASTM Reference Fuel C	7	122 [50]	80	85	83	18
N-Butyl alcohol	7	72 [22]	112	104	86	5
CELLOSOLVE Acetate	7	72 [22]	107	96	79	13
Isooctane	7	72 [22]	103	100	100	<1
JP-4 jet fuel	7	72 [22]	111	94	90	2
JP-4 jet fuel	7	100 [38]	109	86	92	4
Methyl isobutyl ketone	7	72 [22]	103	95	89	14
Xylene	7	72 [22]	106	95	84	20
Halocarbons						
Carbon tetrachloride	7	72 [22]	109	92	81	23
FREON 113	7	72 [22]	100	89	83	2
Perchloroethylene	7	72 [22]	101	88	80	19
Trichloroethylene	7	72 [22]	88	82	66	41
Acids and Bases						
Acetic acid, glacial	7	100 [38]	105	95	79	22
Acetic acid, 5%	7	100 [38]	103	90	81	1
Sodium hydroxide, 20%	7	72 [22]	75	68	94	<1
Sodium hydroxide, 10%	7	72 [22]	69	67	97	<1
Sulfuric acid, 20%	7	72 [22]	104	99	94	<1
Sulfuric acid, 10%	7	72 [22]	106	97	94	<1
Miscellaneous						
Aniline	7	72 [22]	75	78	61	52
Dibutyl phthalate	7	72 [22]	110	89	88	1
Dimethyl formamide	7	72 [22]	102	96	80	16
Ethylene glycol	7	72 [22]	109	104	95	<1
Toluene diisocyanate (mixed isomers)	7	72 [22]	110	97	87	16
WESSON oil	7	72 [22]	102	102	93	<1

[a] These properties were measured at room temperature at a strain rate of 2 in/min [51 mm/min] on dumbbells died from slabs injection-molded under standard conditions.

Table 4-17. The changes in physical properties of 72D Hytrel with various chemical exposures.

	Original Properties[a] at 72°F [22°C]	Tensile Strength . . . . . .5700 psi [39.3 MPa] Elongation . . . . .350% 100% Modulus . . . . . .2500 psi [17.2 MPa]			
FLUID	IMMERSION TIME, DAYS	IMMERSION TEMPERATURE, °F [°C]	TENSILE STRENGTH, % OF ORIGINAL RETAINED AFTER IMMERSION[e]	ELONGATION, % OF ORIGINAL RETAINED AFTER IMMERSION[e]	VOLUME INCREASE, %
Oils and Hydraulic Fluids					
ASTM Oil No. 1	7	250 [121]	83	62	<1
ASTM Oil No. 1	7	302 [150]	98	88	1
ASTM Oil No. 3	7	250 [121]	92	62	5
ASTM Oil No. 3	7	302 [150]	83	31	6
Automatic transmission fluid,					
Type A	7	250 [121]	97	70	1
Type A	7	302 [150]	101	96	2
Automatic transmission fluid,					
Type F	7	250 [121]	98	74	2
Type F	7	302 [150]	99	94	2
PYDRAUL 312	7	250 [121]	97	112	15
Solvents and Fuels					
ASTM Reference Fuel B	7	72 [22]	102	104	4
ASTM Reference Fuel B	7	122 [50]	94	101	9
ASTM Reference Fuel C	7	72 [22]	99	104	9
ASTM Reference Fuel C	7	122 [50]	104	103	12
n-Butyl alcohol	7	72 [22]	108	112	2
CELLOSOLVE Acetate	7	72 [22]	104	112	6
Isoöctane	7	72 [22]	98	112	<1
JP-4 jet fuel	7	72 [22]	107	103	<1
JP-4 jet fuel	7	100 [38]	112	106	<1
Methyl isobutyl ketone	7	72 [22]	109	112	6
Xylene	7	72 [22]	99	101	13

Table 4-17. (Continued)

Original Properties[a] at 72°F [22°C]
Tensile Strength.....5700 psi [39.3 MPa]
Elongation.......350%
100% Modulus.....2500 psi [17.2 MPa]

FLUID	IMMERSION TIME, DAYS	IMMERSION TEMPERATURE, °F [°C]	TENSILE STRENGTH, % OF ORIGINAL RETAINED AFTER IMMERSION[e]	ELONGATION, % OF ORIGINAL RETAINED AFTER IMMERSION[e]	VOLUME INCREASE, %
Halocarbons					
Carbon tetrachloride	7	72 [22]	109	109	7
FREON 113	7	72 [22]	106	110	<1
Perchloroethylene	7	72 [22]	102	104	10
Trichloroethylene	7	72 [22]	98	93	25
Acids and Bases					
Acetic acid, glacial	7	100 [38]	93	100	16
Acetic acid, 5%	7	100 [38]	107	113	<1
Sodium hydroxide, 20%	7	72 [22]	90	104	<1
Sodium hydroxide, 10%	7	72 [22]	109	110	<1
Sulfuric acid, 20%	7	72 [22]	110	117	<1
Sulfuric acid, 10%	7	72 [22]	102	110	<1
Miscellaneous					
Aniline	7	72 [22]	82	88	31
Dibutyl phthalate	7	72 [22]	98	112	<1
Ethylene glycol	7	72 [22]	100	114	<1
Toluene diisocyanate (2,4 isomers)	7	72 [22]	110	104	6
WESSON oil	7	72 [22]	101	110	<1

[a]These properties were measured at room temperature at a strain rate of 2 in/min [51 mm/min] on dumbbells died from slabs injection-molded under standard conditions.

Table 4-18. The fuel permeability of Hytrel is superior to several types of rubber, which makes it suitable for fuel lines, gaskets, etc.[14]

	PERMEABILITY[a] OF FUEL-RESISTANT ELASTOMERS (ASTM D-814)				
FUEL	55D HYTREL	63D HYTREL	NEOPRENE[b] WHV	HYPALON[b] 48	NITRILE RUBBER MED. HIGH NITRILE
Reference Fuel B	0.43 [1.6]	0.024 [0.088]	6.9 [25]	2.7 [9.9]	1.2 [4.4]
Reference Fuel C	0.74 [2.7]	0.060 [0.22]	17.4 [64]	8.2 [30]	2.9 [11]

[a]Units of permeability: Fluid oz/24 hr · ft^2 at 73°F, 25 mil film thickness
[mm^3/s · m^2 at 23°C, 0.64 mm film thickness]
[b]Reg U.S. Trademark of the Du Pont Company.

dant with pellets of Hytrel 5556, first tumble the wetting agent with the pellets for 10 to 15 min.; then add the powdered antioxidant, and tumble the mixture for an additional 10 to 15 min. Data demonstrating the improvement are presented in Tables 4-21 and 4-22. The data are based on Hytrel 5556. Similar improvement with other grades has been achieved.

4.5 SPECIAL HYTREL COMPOSITIONS

4.5.1 Hytrel 10MS

The hydraulic stability of all grades of Hytrel can be improved substantially with the addition of a master batch containing polycardobiimide (PCD).* The latter is sold as Hytrel 10MS, a 20% concentrate of polycardodiimide in 40D Hytrel.

Hytrel 63D and 72D are less stable in boiling water in an unstabilized condition than are Hytrel 40D and 55D. Failure occurs in the former grades in about 2 weeks, compared with failure times of 5 to 6 weeks for the latter two. Addition of the stabilizer increases the service life of the 63D and 72D polymers to approximately 6 weeks in 100°C water and 6 months for the 40D and 55D materials. Both stabilized and unstabilized 63D and 72D types show little, if any, degradation after 2 months at 70°C.

Table 4-23 shows a comparison of physical properties of unstabilized and hydrolytically stabilized Hytrel. It is obvious that the 10MS additive enhances the physical properties severalfold in hot water.

*Stabaxol P, Mobay Chemical Corp., Division of Baychem Corp., Pittsburgh, PA.

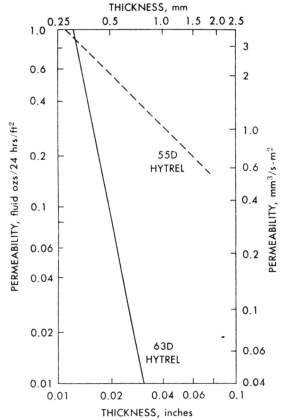

Figure 4-22. ASTM test D-814 shows the permeability of 55D and 63D to Reference Fuel B.

4.5.2 Flame Retardancy and Combustion Products

In all current hardness types, Hytrel, without added flame retardant, passes the 4 in./min. maximum allowable rate when tested according to Federal Motor Vehicle Safety Standard FMVSS-302, sometimes referred to as DOT-302. Twenty-mil-thick (0.51 mm) film specimens of the four hardnesses were tested, and the data are shown in Table 4-24.[18]

The products of combustion, when Hytrel is burned, are listed in Table 4-25. Data are presented under two different conditions. The first is for good combustion in an excess of air; the second is for poor combustion in a deficiency of air.

Permeability to
Reference Fuel C, 23°C (73°F)
(ASTM D-814)

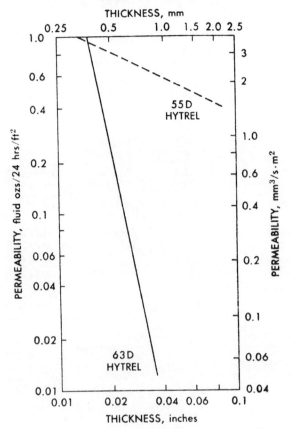

Figure 4-23. ASTM test D-814 shows the permeability of 55D and 63D to Reference Fuel C.

4.5.3 Hytrel 5555 HS

4.5.3.1 Description

Hytrel 5555 HS polyester elastomer is a specially stabilized version of Hytrel 5556. It is designed to provide superior resistance to heat and/or oil aging (Table 4-26). It is processible by the same thermoplastic techniques, temperatures, and pressures that are used with Hytrel 5556. Since it contains a yellowing antioxidant, it is not recommended for applications where color stability is critical.

Table 4-19. The low permeability of Hytrel to gases makes it suitable for diaphragms, fuel gases, and laboratories.[15]

	Permeability[a] of HYTREL to Gases			
Gas	40D HYTREL	55D HYTREL	63D HYTREL	72D HYTREL
Air	2.4×10^{-8} [2.4×10^{-3}]	1.8×10^{-8} [1.8×10^{-3}]	– –	– –
Nitrogen	1.7×10^{-8} [1.7×10^{-3}]	1.4×10^{-8} [1.4×10^{-3}]	– –	– –
Carbon dioxide	3.5×10^{-7} [3.5×10^{-2}]	1.8×10^{-7} [1.8×10^{-2}]	– –	– –
Helium	15.7×10^{-8} [15.5×10^{-3}]	9.9×10^{-8} [9.8×10^{-3}]	– –	3.2×10^{-8} [3.2×10^{-3}]
Propane	$<0.2 \times 10^{-8}$ [$<0.2 \times 10^{-3}$]	$<0.2 \times 10^{-8}$ [$<0.2 \times 10^{-3}$]	$<0.2 \times 10^{-8}$ [$<0.2 \times 10^{-3}$]	–
Water[b]	3.1×10^{-5} [3.1]	2.4×10^{-5} [2.4]	–	–
FREON† 12 fluorocarbon	1.4×10^{-8} [1.4×10^{-3}]	1.2×10^{-8} [1.2×10^{-3}]	1.2×10^{-8} [1.2×10^{-3}]	0.82×10^{-8} [0.81×10^{-3}]
FREON 22 fluorocarbon	0.47×10^{-8} [0.46×10^{-3}]	0.59×10^{-8} [0.58×10^{-3}]	$<0.2 \times 10^{-8}$ [$<0.2 \times 10^{-3}$]	–
FREON 114 fluorocarbon	41×10^{-8} [40×10^{-3}]	28×10^{-8} [28×10^{-3}]	4.6×10^{-8} [4.5×10^{-3}]	2.7×10^{-8} [2.7×10^{-3}]

[a]Units of permeability: cm^3 (at STP)·cm/atm·sec·cm² at 71°F and ΔP = 5psi
[cm^3 (at STP)·mm/Pa·s·m² at 21.5°C and ΔP = 34.5 kPa]
[b]Values obtained at 90% relative humidity, 77°F [25°C], assuming that permeability laws hold for water.

†FREON is a registered trademark of DuPont.

4.5.3.2 Properties

In addition to having the physical properties of Hytrel 5556, Hytrel 5555 HS resists dry heat aging at temperatures of 302°F (150°C) and above by a factor of 8 to 10X better than Hytrel 5556 and 3 to 5X better than Hytrel 5556 containing post-added amine antioxidant. Similar performance improvements are attained in hot hydrocarbon oils (see Figure 4-24). Superior weatherability, hydrolytic stability, and flame retardance can be obtained by the incorporation of special additives.[20]

4.5.3.3 Processing

Hytrel 5555 HS can be extruded, injection molded, and melt cast at melt temperatures ranging from 410 to 465°F (210 to 241°C). Temperature settings on

Heat Aging of HYTREL 5555 HS

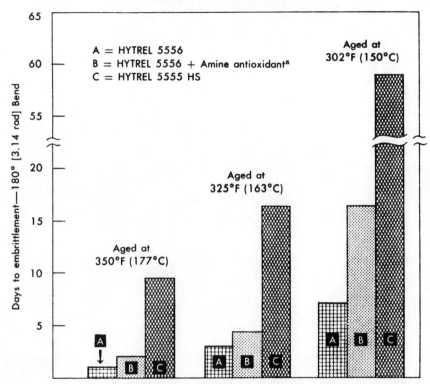

Figure 4-24. Heat aging of Hytrel 5555 HS.

process equipment should be similar to those used for processing Hytrel 5556. Scrap can be reprocessed. The polymer is available as $\frac{1}{8}$-in. (3.2-mm) diameter right regular cylindrical pellets.

4.5.3.4 Applications

Hytrel 5555 HS is useful for such products as tubing, hose, wire and cable jacketing, seals, packings, and gaskets that require a higher level of heat and/or oil-aging resistance than is provided by Hytrel 5556.

4.5.4 Hytrel HTG-4450

HTG-4450 is a concentrate containing 67% by weight of a flame retardant based on a halogen-containing mixture plus antimony trioxide dispersed in 40D Hytrel

Table 4-20. The dry heat aging properties show good retention of properties for as long as 6 weeks at 300° F.[9]

Dry Heat Aging of HYTREL

Properties Measured at Room Temperature

	92A HYTREL	55D HYTREL	63D HYTREL
Original Properties, 72°F. (22°C.)			
Tensile strength, psi	5,900	6,400	6,300
kg./cm.²	414.8	449.9	442.9
Ultimate elongation, %	805	750	530
100% modulus, psi	925	2,100	2,500
kg./cm.²	65.0	147.6	175.7
300% modulus, psi	1,200	2,325	3,530
kg./cm.²	84.4	163.4	248.2
After 4 Weeks at 250°F. (121°C.)			
Tensile strength, psi	4,000 (67)*	5,350 (83)	4,400 (70)
kg./cm.²	281.2	376.1	309.3
Ultimate elongation, %	760 (94)	700 (93)	440 (83)
100% modulus, psi	930 (100)	2,375 (113)	2,790 (112)
kg./cm.²	65.4	166.9	196.1
300% modulus, psi	1,280 (107)	2,400 (103)	2,825 (80)
kg./cm.²	90.0	168.7	198.6
After 2 Weeks at 302°F. (150°C.)			
Tensile strength, psi	—	2,150 (33)	3,350 (53)
kg./cm.²	—	151.1	235.5
Ultimate elongation, %	—	110 (14)	420 (80)
100% modulus, psi	—	2,050 (98)	2,600 (104)
kg./cm.²	—	144.1	182.8

| | 300% modulus, psi
kg./cm.² | — — | — — | 2,900 (82)
203.9 |

After 2 Weeks at 302°F. (150°C.)

(Specially stabilized polymer)

Tensile strength, psi kg./cm.²	— —	3,470 (54) 243.9
Ultimate elongation, %	—	500 (67)
100% modulus, psi kg./cm.²	— —	est. 2,100 (100) 147.6
300% modulus, psi kg./cm.²	— —	est. 2,700 (116) 189.8

After 6 Weeks at 302°F. (150°C.)

(Specially stabilized polymer)

Tensile strength, psi kg./cm²	— —	2,330 (36) 163.8
Ultimate elongation, %	—	135 (18)
100% modulus, psi kg./cm.²	— —	est. 2,100 (100) 147.6

*Percent retention in parentheses.

Table 4-21. Addition of antioxidants improve heat aging properties from 5 to 10%.[16]

Physical Properties[f]	Effect of Added Antioxidant on Dry Heat Aging		
	HYTREL 5556 no added antioxidant	HYTREL 5556 1% aromatic amine antioxidant[g]	HYTREL 5556 1% polymeric dihydroquinoline antioxidant[h]
• Original			
Tensile Strength, psi [MPa]	5 200 [35.8]	5 625 [38.8]	5 800 [50.1]
Elongation at Break, %	450	480	460
• Aged 12 weeks at 250°F [121°C]			
Tensile Strength, psi [MPa]	4 050 [27.9]	4 900 [37.8]	3 875 [26.7]
Elongation at Break, %	520	600	540
• Aged 4 weeks at 275° [135°C]			
Tensile Strength, psi [MPa]	Failed in	4 725 [32.6]	4 925 [34.0]
Elongation at Break, %	4 weeks	580	580
		Failed in 5+ weeks	Failed in 5+ weeks
• Aged 2 weeks at 302°F [150°C]			
Tensile Strength, psi [MPa]	Failed in	3 650 [25.2]	3 750 [25.9]
Elongation at Break, %	7 days	580	550
		Failed in 20 days	Failed in 23 days

Table 4-22. Hytrel 5556 can be improved for oil aging by adding selected antioxidants using two ASTM oils as test mediums.[16]

	Effect of Added Antioxidant on Aging in Hot Oil		
Physical Properties[f]	HYTREL 5556 no added antioxidant	HYTREL 5556 1% aromatic amine antioxidant[g]	HYTREL 5556 1% polymeric dihydroquinoline antioxidant[h]
• Original			
Tensile Strength, psi [MPa]	5 850 [40.3]	5 625 [38.8]	5 800 [40.0]
Elongation at Break, %	520	480	460
• Aged in ASTM Oil No. 1			
3 weeks at 302°F [150°C]			
Tensile Strength, psi [MPa]	2 100 [14.5]	3 000 [20.7]	3 575 [24.6]
Elongation at Break, %	20	240	440
4 weeks at 250°F [121°C]			
Tensile Strength, psi [MPa]	4 700 [32.4]	4 850 [33.4]	5 350 [36.9]
Elongation at Break, %	610	550	570
6 weeks at 250°F [121°C]			
Tensile Strength, psi [MPa]	Failed	Failed	3 825 [26.4]
Elongation at Break, %			580
• Aged in ASTM Oil No. 3			
1 week at 302°F [150°C]			
Tensile Strength, psi [MPa]	3 100 [21.4]	2 975 [20.5]	4 450 [30.7]
Elongation at Break, %	380	380	480
2 weeks at 302°F [150°C]			
Tensile Strength, psi [MPa]	1 125 [7.8]	1 075 [7.4]	2 250 [15.5]
Elongation at Break, %	10	20	60
4 weeks at 250°F [121°C]			
Tensile Strength, psi [MPa]	1 800 [12.4]	1 575 [10.8]	3 050 [21.0]
Elongation at Break, %	20	10	340

[f] Stress-strain properties were measured by ASTM D-638 on dumbbells died from injection-molded slabs. Test temperature was 72°F [22°C], strain rate was 2 in/min [51 mm/min].

[g] NAUGARD 445[(12)] was used.

[h] AGERITE Resin D[(4)] was used. FLECTOL H[(')'] is also suitable.

and supplied in pellet form. It is designed to be dry blended and mixed with standard Hytrel grades during molding and extrusion operations. Oxygen indices of 28 to 32 (ASTM D-2863) and reduced burning rates and times-to-extinguish (ASTM D-635-74) are obtained.

Tables 4-27 through 4-29 summarize the effects of blending HTG-4450 in the 40D, 55D, and 72D Hytrels on oxygen index and burning rates. Stress-strain data are also shown. A let-down ratio of 1:6.7 (i.e., 1 part HTG-4450 to 6.7 parts Hytrel) is required to attain an oxygen index of at least 28 in 40D Hytrel. The same let-down ratio in 55D and 72D Hytrel gives an oxygen index of 30. Higher levels of HTG-4450 do not provide significant improvement in oxygen index, in the times-to-extinguish, or in the extent of burning, as measured by

Table 4-23. Hydrolytic stability of Hytrel is generally good and can be improved with the addition of a poly carbodiimide, particularly at lower temperatures.[17]

	TENSILE STRENGTH (PSI) ELONGATION AT BREAK (%)							
	HYTREL 40D		HYTREL 55D		HYTREL 63D		HYTREL 72D	
POLYCARBODIIMIDE, PHR (added as Hytrel 10MS)	0	2	0	2	0	2	0	2
S/S, Original, 22°C (All slabs)	All tests on injection molded test specimens.							
Tensile strength, psi	5625	6650	5750	6150	5690	4985	5630	5420
Elongation at break, %	820	815	720	710	325	360	330	355
After 2 weeks/100°C H₂O								
Tensile strength, psi	–	–	–	–	2245	4580	2310	5120
Elongation at break, %	–	–	–	–	10	325	5	360
After 4 weeks/100°C H₂O								
Tensile strength, psi	1175	4030	2705	6440	Failed	3335	Failed	4010
Elongation at break, %	90	850	95	735	–	265	–	260
After 8 weeks/100°C H₂O								
Tensile strength, psi	–	–	–	–	–	Failed	–	Failed
Elongation at break, %	–	–	–	–	–	–	–	–
After 3 months/100°C H₂O								
Tensile strength, psi	Failed	3120	Failed	3905	–	–	–	–
Elongation at break, %	–	880	–	640	–	–	–	–
After 1 month/70°C H₂O								
Tensile strength, psi	4880	4760	5615	5420	3720	4760	–	–
Elongation at break, %	335	360	390	360	875	805	–	–
After 2 months/70°C H₂O								
Tensile strength, psi	4550	4835	5180	5180	–	–	–	–
Elongation at break, %	335	365	330	320	–	–	–	–
After 3 months/70°C H₂O								
Tensile strength, psi	4100	4925	3560	5270	3100	4625	–	–
Elongation at break, %	340	365	130	325	820	790	–	–
After 6 months/70°C H₂O								
Tensile strength, psi	870	4580	1000	5060	2475	4290	2940	5020
Elongation at break, %	5	375	5	325	320	860	510	680
After 9 months/70°C H₂O								
Tensile strength, psi	Failed	3865	Failed	4275	1225	4350	–	–
Elongation at break, %	–	325	–	305	335	820	–	–
After 12 months/70°C H₂O								
Tensile strength, psi	–	–	–	–	–	–	2500	4670
Elongation at break, %	–	–	–	–	–	–	550	580

ASTM D-635-74.   In fact, higher concentrations of HTG-4450 result in a significant deterioration of stress-strain properties.   This deterioration is evidenced by reduced elongations at break for 55D and 72D grades containing high concentrations of HTG-4450.

At a let-down ratio of 1:6.7, no "bloom" or exudation of the additives has been observed in any Hytrel type after 4 months at 72°F (22°C) or after 7 days at 250°F (121°C).   In addition, these latter heat-aged blends still retain their original flame-retardant characteristics.

Table 4-24. Test results of Motor Vehicle Standard FMVSS-302 are summarized for all hardness grades of Hytrel.[18]

		FMVSS-302* RESULTS[a]			
HYTREL TYPE[b]	HARDNESS (DUROMETER D)	THICKNESS (MIL)	BURN TIME (SEC)	DISTANCE BURNED (IN.)	BURN RATE (IN./MIN.)
4056	40	20	63.5	2.875	2.71
5556	55	20	59	2.15	2.19
6346	63	20	16.5	0.4	1.45
7246	72	20	11	0.15	0.82
5556[c]	55	20	48.5	2.02	2.50
5556[d]	55	20	0	0	0
5556[e]	55	10	28.5	1.425	3.0

[a]Numerical values measured by this test are not intended to reflect hazards presented by this or any other material under actual conditions.
[b]No flame retardant added.
[c]This sample tested cross-machine direction (CMD). All others tested machine direction (MD).
[d]This sample tested glossy side down; all others tested dull side down.
[e]This sample tested at 10 mil thickness; all others tested at 20 mil.

4.5.4.1 Toxicity

The manufacturer of the halogenated component in HTG-4450 states that the material has an $LD_{50} > 10$g/kg of body weight in rats in a single-dose oral ingestion. It is nonirritating to the eyes and skin. Reasonable precautions should be observed to avoid undue exposure when handling.

The antimony trioxide contained in HTG-4450 has an intraperitoneal LD_{50} of 4 g/kg. Chronic daily inhalation of antimony oxide dust by guinea pigs over 2 to 3 hr daily at a mean level of 45.4 mg/m^3 produced pneumonitis and fatty degeneration of the liver. Hytrel has an oral approximate lethal dose (ALD) > 25 g/kg of body weight in rats. Normal precautions should be taken to avoid undue exposure when handling HTG-4450.

4.5.5 Plasticizers for Hytrel

A number of plasticizer types have been studied in blends with Hytrel polyester elastomer of 40 durometer D hardness (see Table 4-30). Those types that are compatible with Hytrel at a concentration of 50 parts plasticizer per hundred parts polymer all impart similar physical properties. Nevertheless, judicious choice of plasticizers can be made based on considerations of cost, volatility, color, flame retardancy, and oil and water extractability.

Physical properties of 40D Hytrel containing 50 parts of various plasticizers are summarized in Table 4-31. The curves in Figure 4-25 illustrate how plasticizer content affects the modulus of 40D Hytrel at low strains. Because the harder grades of Hytrel—i.e., the 55D, 63D, and 72D grades—have much greater

Table 4-25. The products of burning 40D and 63D in good and poor combustion conditions are high in carbon dioxide, with five other gases also present.[19]

PRODUCTS OF COMBUSTION OF HYTREL COPOLYESTER ELASTOMER.[a]

AMOUNT OF PRODUCT GENERATED

PRODUCT	SENSITIVITY LIMIT	40D		63D	
		ADEQUATE AIR	INSUFFICIENT AIR	ADEQUATE AIR	INSUFFICIENT AIR
Carbon dioxide	2.7[b]	2670	1602	2670	1282
Carbon monoxide	8	Nil	272	Nil	29.4
Methane	1.5	Nil	31.9	Nil	25
Ethylene	1.3	Nil	22.8	Nil	31.9
Benzene	4	Nil	26.6	Nil	39.1
Acetylene	0.5	Nil	9.7	Nil	7.1

[b]Units are in mg off-gas per gram of burned specimen.

[a]For procedure, see Section 4.5.2. Sensitivity limit indicates lowest amount of material that would be detected if it were present. (Water was generated in all cases, but was not quantitatively determined.) Hytrel 55D and 72D were not tested; they would be expected to give types and amounts of combustion gases very similar to those listed above for 40D and 63D.

Table 4-26. Aging of Hytrel 5555 HS in ASTM oils.[21]

	HYTREL 5556	HYTREL 5556 WITH POST-ADDED AMINE ANTIOXIDANT[a]	HYTREL 5555 HS
Original Properties[b] at 72°F (22°C)			
Tensile Strength, psi (MPa)	5500 (37.9)	5400 (37.2)	5050 (34.8)
Elongation at break, %	450	430	425
After aging in:			
ASTM Oil No. 1			
3 weeks at 302° [150°C]			
Tensile Strength, psi (MPa)	Failed	Failed	4000 (27.6)
Elongation at break, %	in	in	630
Volume Increase, %	10 days	10 days	< 1
ASTM Oil No. 3			
3 weeks at 302°F [150°]			
Tensile Strength, psi (MPa)	Failed	Failed	3525 (24.3)
Elongation at break, %	in	in	320
Volume Increase, %	10 days	10 days	18

[a]For example, 1% NAUGARD 445 (Uniroyal, Inc.). For further information, see bulletin HYT-111, "HYTREL 5556."
[b]Injection-molded samples. Strain rate was 2 in./min. (51 mm/min.).

fluid resistance than the 40D grade, plasticizers are generally less compatible with the harder polymers.

4.5.6 Blends of Hytrel with Flexible PVC Compounds

Incorporating Hytrel into plasticized vinyl, in such a way that the ratio of plasticizer to total resin (PVC plus Hytrel) is kept constant, provides some very significant effects. Work was carried out with a basic flexible vinyl compound, containing no additives for particular property enhancement, at two levels of plasticizer content (57 and 30 phr). The results are summarized in Tables 4-32 through 4-34. Tables 4-32 and 4-33 show that the incorporation of Hytrel into this particular compound significantly improves low temperature properties. Addition of Hytrel increases flexibility both at and below room temperature. The brittle points of the compounds are lowered with increasing amounts of Hytrel.

In addition, incorporating Hytrel into the compound reduces heat distortion at elevated temperature and improves abrasion resistance. Tear strength of the compound is sacrificed. Data showing retention of stress-strain properties of 40D material after aging 7 days at 100°C are presented on Table 4-33.

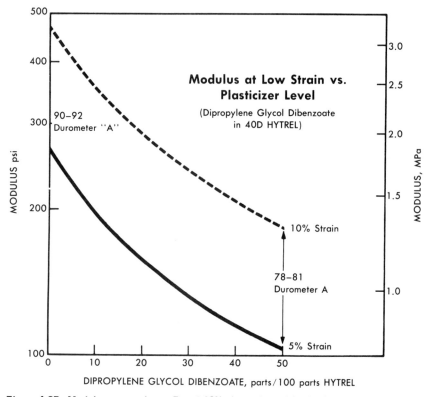

Figure 4-25. Modulus properties at 5 and 10% elongation with plasticizer levels of 0 to 50 parts per 100 of Hytrel 40D.

When Hytrel is added to a PVC system such that the plasticizer-to-vinyl ratio is kept constant, additional property improvements are observed (Table 4-34). In addition to improving low temperature flexibility, brittle point, heat distortion, and abrasion resistance, the addition of Hytrel in this manner increases tensile strength, modulus at 100% strain, elongation, hardness, and tear strength.

Addition of Hytrel further improves low temperature properties of specialty low temperature compounds (Table 4-35). Although these compounds are stiffer at room temperature, flexibility at -18, -29, and $-40°C$ is improved. The Ross flex test best demonstrates the ability of Hytrel to improve low temperature characteristics of a commercially supplied PVC compound. At $-18°C$, all PVC compounds listed failed before 4500 flexes, while the Hytrel containing compounds went on to 50,000 flexes with little growth.

Table 4-27. Physical properties of 40D with various ratios of flame-retardant concentrate.[22]

PROPERTIES OF BLENDS OF 40D HYTREL AND HTG-4450
(COMPRESSION-MOLDED TEST PIECES)

COMPOSITION	CONTROL	LET-DOWN RATIO (PARTS HTG-4450/HYTREL)					
		1:13.3	1:10	1:6.7	1:5	1:4	1:3
HYTREL 4056	100	100	100	100	100	100	100
HTG-4450	0	7.5	10	15	20	25	33.3
Properties							
ASTM D-2863, 3.2 mm (0.125 in.)							
Oxygen index, %	22	23	25	28	30	30	30
ASTM D-635-74, 3.2-mm (0.125 in.) bar							
Burning rate, cm/min.	1.9	1.6	1.3	–	–	–	–
Average burning time, sec	–	–	–	85	80	90	80
Average extent of burning, mm	–	–	–	45	40	30	20
Comments	Drips	Drips	Drips	Drips	Drips	Drips	Drips
UL subject 94 rating, 3.2 mm (0.125 in.) S/S, 72°F (22°C)	94HB	94HB	94HB	94V-II	94V-II	94V-II	94V-II
Hardness, durometer D	41	40	40	40	41	40	40
Tensile strength, psi	4720	3185	3125	3575	3785	3740	3240
Elongation at break, %	840	865	865	885	855	865	850

Table 4-28. Physical properties of 55D with various ratios of flame-retardant concentrate.[22]

	PROPERTIES OF BLENDS OF 55D HYTREL AND HTG-4450 (COMPRESSION-MOLDED TEST PIECES) LET-DOWN RATIO (PARTS HTG-4450/HYTREL)				
COMPOSITION	CONTROL	1:6.7	1:5	1:4	1:3
HYTREL 5556	100	100	100	100	100
HTG-4450	0	15	20	25	33.3
Properties					
ASTM D-2863, 3.2 mm (0.125 in.)					
Oxygen index, %	22	30	30	30	31
ASTM D-635-74, 3.2-mm (0.125 in.) bar					
Burning rate, cm/min.	2.1	–	–	–	–
Average burning time, sec	–	75	70	60	60
Average extent of burning, mm	–	30	20	20	20
Comments	Drips	Drips	Drips	Drips	Drips
UL subject 94 rating, 3.2 mm (0.125 in.)	94HB	94V-II	94V-II	94V-II	94V-II
S/S, 72°F (22°C)					
Hardness, durometer D	56	55	55	54	54
Tensile strength, psi	6845	4010	3965	3620	2360
Elongation at break, %	685	615	560	565	40

4.6 RHEOLOGY PROCESSING OF HYTREL

The Hytrel polyesters can be processed on standard thermoplastic processing equipment using conventional techniques. Processing conditions are generally based on the melting points of the polymers, which follow:

HARDNESS GRADE	MELT POINT	
	°F	°C
40D	334	168
55D	412	211
63D	403	206
72D	415	213

4.6.1 Melt Rheology

The effects of shear rate upon viscosity for the 55D extrusion and molding grades are shown in Figure 4-26. These curves are indicative of the entire family and show that these polymers have a relatively flat viscosity vs. shear rate curve, especially at low shear rate, such as in extrusion, melt casting, and rotational molding. The higher shear rates experienced in injection molding, with fast

Table 4-29. Physical properties of 72D with various ratios of flame-retardant concentrate.[22]

PROPERTIES OF BLENDS OF 72D HYTREL AND HTG-4450
(COMPRESSION-MOLDED TEST PIECES)
LET-DOWN RATIO (PARTS HTG-4450/HYTREL)

COMPOSITION	CONTROL	1:13.3	1:10	1:6.7	1:5	1:4	1:3
HYTREL 7246	100	100	100	100	100	100	100
HTG-4450	0	7.5	10	15	20	25	33.3
Properties							
ASTM D-2863, 3.2 mm (0.125 in.)							
Oxygen index, %	20	28	29	30	30	30	30
ASTM D-635-74, 3.2-mm (0.125 in.) bar							
Burning rate, cm/min	1.6	1.7	1.6	–	–	–	–
Average burning time, sec	–	–	–	90	80	85	60
Average extent of burning, mm	–	–	–	35	30	20	20
Comments	Drips	Drips	Drips	Drips	Drips	Drips	Drips
UL subject 94 rating, 3.2 mm (0.125 in.)	94HB	94HB	94V-II	94V-II	94V-II	94V-II	94V-II
S/S, 72°F (22°C)							
Hardness, durometer D	73	74	72	73	71	73	73
Tensile strength, psi	6215	6020	4820	4430	4655	4040	4190
Elongation at break, %	375	415	395	400	400	20	20

Table 4-30. Several plasticizers have been evaluated with Hytrel with the limits of compatibility indicated.[23]

Plasticizers for HYTREL

Chemical Type	Product Name	Manufacturer	Compatibility, Upper Limit Parts/100 HYTREL (40D)
Chlorinated paraffin, 40% Cl	several	several	>50
Methyl pentachlorostearate	MPS-500	Hooker	>50
Methyl abietate	ABALYN*	Hercules	>50
Methyl dihydro-abietate	HERCOLYN* D	Hercules	>50
Butyl phthalyl butyl glycolate	SANTICIZER* B-16	Monsanto	>50
N-ethyl-o and p-toluene sulfonamide	SANTICIZER 8	Monsanto	>50
Polypropylene glycol sebacate MW 8 000	PARAPLEX* G-25	Rohm & Haas	<10
Dipropylene glycol dibenzoate	BENZOFLEX* 9-88	Velsicol	>50
Di(2-ethyl-hexyl) phthalate	several	several	>30, <50
2-Ethyl-hexyl-diphenyl phosphate	SANTICIZER 141	Monsanto	>50
Tri(2-ethyl-hexyl) phosphate	several	several	>10, <20
Di(2-ethyl-hexyl) sebacate	several	several	>20, <30
Polyester	SANTICIZER 409	Monsanto	<50
Tetra-ethylene glycol-di (2-ethyl hexoate)	FLEXOL* 4G0	Union Carbide	<50
Polyester MW 1 850	FLEXOL R2H	Union Carbide	<50

Table 4-31. Physical properties, using several plasticizers, are shown for the 40D grade of resin.[23]

Physical Properties of 40D HYTREL Containing 50 Parts of Plasticizer

Plasticizer	40D HYTREL without plasticizer	Chlorinated Paraffin 40% Cl	Methylpenta-chloro-stearate	Methyl dihydro-abietate	Butyl phthalyl-butyl glycolate	N-ethyl-o, p-toluene sulfonamide	Dipropylene glycol diben-zoate	2-Ethyl-hexyl-diphenyl phos-phate
Hardness, durometer A	92	81	80	81	79	78	78	79
Tensile Strength, psi	4 650	2 175	2 450	2 475	2 300	3 000	2 375	2 225
Elongation at Break, %	850	1 000	1 100	1 100	1 100	1 060	1 080	1 080
5% Modulus, psi	275	115	100	110	100	120	100	100
10% Modulus, psi	475	205	190	200	180	175	180	190
100% Modulus, psi	1 050	550	550	575	550	525	500	550
Principal Advantages		Sl. Flame Retardancy Low Volatility	Sl. Flame Retardancy	Low Cost Low Sp. Gravity	Low Toxicity	Low Extractibility in Fuel & Oils	Low Volatility, Low Extractibility in Fuel & Oils	Sl. Flame Retardancy Good Low Temp., Broad FDA Approval
Principal Disadvantages		Needs Stabilizer, Extracted by Gasoline & Oil	Needs Stabilizer, Extracted by Gasoline & Oil	Color	Cost	Crystallized At Low Temp.		
Hardness, Durometer A	92	81	80	81	79	78	78	79
Tensile strength, MPa	32.1	15.0	16.9	17.1	15.9	20.7	16.4	15.3
Elongation at break, %	850	1 000	1 100	1 100	1 100	1 060	1 080	1 080
5% Modulus, MPa	1.9	0.8	0.7	0.8	0.7	0.8	0.7	0.7
10% Modulus, MPa	3.3	1.4	1.3	1.4	1.2	1.2	1.2	1.3
100% Modulus, MPa	7.2	3.8	3.8	4.0	3.8	3.6	3.4	3.8

Table 4-32. Physical properties of 40D and various loadings of Geon 103 EP vinyl, which has 57 parts per 100 parts of dioctyl phthalate plasticizer.[24]

Composition					
Geon[a] 103EP	100	95	90	80	70
DOP	57	57	57	57	57
Drapex 6.8	3	3	3	3	3
Mark LL	2	2	2	2	2
Stearic acid	.2	.2	.2	.2	.2
HYTREL® 40D	–	5	10	20	30
Properties					
Stress-strain					
Tensile strength, psi	2300	2160	2000	2000	1700
Elongation @ break, %	300	370	400	450	480
100% modulus, psi	1400	1100	1100	850	800
Hardness, Shore A	78	76	74	72	72
Graves tear, lb/in.	350	300	300	260	230
Torsional modulus, M psi					
23°C	1.2	1.1	.9	.7	.4
−18°C	16.0	11.0	9.0	6.0	3.5
−40°C	80.0	69.0	57.0	39.0	26.0
Taber abrasion					
CS-17 wheel, mg/10^3 rev	26	19	16	13	10
Brittle point					
°F	−47	−54	−62	<−76	<−76
°C	−44	−48	−52	<−60	<−60
Heat distortion, %					
(ASTM D-1047)					
121°C, 2000 gram	40	27	25	22	20

[a]B. F. Goodrich Co. trademark for its PVC homopolymer.

mold-fill rates, do not have profound effects on the finished part due to the high packing pressures used in the process.

In Figure 4-27, the effect of temperature on the melt viscosity of the 55D polymers is shown at a shear rate of 139 sec. Using a spiral flow mold with a $\frac{3}{16}$-by-$\frac{1}{8}$-in. channel, the distance of melt flow as a function of injection pressures is shown in Figure 4-28. As with other thermoplastics, it can be seen that at the same hardness, the melt flow properties can vary widely such as in the lines of the molding extrusion grades. Also shown, in Figure 4-29, is a comparison of melt viscosity vs. temperature with other thermoplastics such as nylon, acrylic, polyethylene, and acetal.

4.6.2 Handling and Drying

Hytrel taken from sealed bags does not need drying before use. The material is resistant to hydrolysis and does not react with moisture in the air; however, it

Table 4-33. Physical properties of 40D and various loadings of Geon 103 EP vinyl, which has 30 parts per 100 parts of dioctyl phthalate plasticizer.[24]

Composition			
Geon 103EP	100	85	75
DOP	30	30	30
Drapex 6.8	3	3	3
Mark LL	2	2	2
Stearic acid	.2	.2	.2
HYTREL® 40D	–	15	25
Properties			
Stress-strain			
Tensile strength, psi	3500	2900	2400
Elongation @ break, %	240	275	290
100% modulus, psi	2280	1450	1150
Hardness, Shore A	94	85	80
Stress-strain after			
7 days @ 100°C			
Tensile strength, psi	3550	3950	3560
Elongation @ break, %	140	280	260
100% modulus, psi	2200	2450	2160
Graves tear, lb/in.	760	560	500
Torsional modulus, M psi			
23°C	7.7	1.5	1.1
–18°C	104	52	33
–40°C	160	124	83
Taber abrasion			
CS-17 wheel, mg/10^3 rev	32	21	20
Brittle point			
°F	–8	–29	<–76
°C	–22	–34	<–60
Heat distortion, %			
(ASTM D-1047)			
121°C, 2000 gram	55	45	40

will absorb moisture from the air if left exposed. Moisture absorption rates on $\frac{1}{8}$-in. pellets are shown in Figure 4-30.

Generally, no degradation of the polymer or imperfections in the molding or extrusion occur if the moisture content is kept below 0.10%. From Figure 4-30, it can be seen that at 50% relative humidity, it takes a relatively short time to reach the 0.10% moisture-level content. Unused portions of the bags of resin and regrind should be dried prior to use.

4.6.3 Use of Regrind

The unusually good melt stability and completely thermoplastic nature of Hytrel allow use of scrap moldings, sprues, and runners. Hytrel can be reground and either blended with virgin polymer or used undiluted. Blending with virgin resin is

Table 4-34. Physical properties of 40D and various loadings of Geon 103
EP vinyl, which has 57 parts per 100 parts of dioctyl phthalate plasticizer.[24]

Composition			
Geon 103EP	100	100	–
DOP	57	57	–
Drapex 6.8	3	3	–
Mark LL	2	2	–
Stearic acid	.2	.2	–
HYTREL® 4056	–	10	20
Properties			
Stress-strain			
Tensile strength, psi	2300	2600	2850
Elongation at break, %	300	300	360
100% modulus, psi	1400	1450	1750
Hardness, Shore A	78	80	83
Graves tear, lb/in.	350	400	460
Torsional modulus, M psi			
23°C	1.2	1.2	1.5
–18°C	16.0	12.5	10.5
–40°C	80.0	70.0	57.0
Brittle point			
°F	–47	–65	–69
°C	–44	–54	–56
Heat distortion, %			
(ASTM D-1047)			
121°C, 2000 gram	40	18	16
Taber abrasion			
CS-17 wheel, mg/10^3 rev	26	23	15

preferred. The heat history of the regrind should be kept as low as practical to maintain the high quality of the polymer.

Scrap pieces should be chopped into chips approximately the same size as the original pellets. The scrap grinder should have well-adjusted, sharp knifes shaped for polyethylene cutting to produce clean sharp regrind. Size reduction is accomplished by cutting, not by fracture or impact.

4.6.4 Use of Colors

For color identification, the lowest levels of color possible should be used. Du Pont can furnish information on suppliers of recommended color systems to be used with these polymers.

Olefinic-based color concentrates, in high loadings, can give a scaling appearance and can detract from low temperature impact properties and brittle point. Certain PVC-based concentrates are somewhat better, but master batches with a Hytrel base are available from certain suppliers and are preferred. Some liquid

Table 4-35. Low temperature properties of Hytrel–PVC blends.[24]

COMPOSITION	LOW TEMPERATURE PVC COMPOUND	ULTRA-LOW TEMPERATURE PVC COMPOUND	LOW TEMPERATURE	COMPOUND	HYTREL
PVC compound	100	100	80	70	60
HYTREL 40D, %	0	0	20	30	40
Properties					
Stress-strain					
100% modulus, psi	1500	1200	1100	1000	1000
Tensile strength, psi	2500	2200	2600	2500	2800
Elongation @ break, %	300	300	450	470	560
Hardness, Shore A	86	83	83	86	86
Torsional modulus, M psi					
23°C	1.	1.	1.4	1.4	1.7
−18°C	14.	8.	10.6	7.7	6.6
−29°C	30.	16.5	20.	17.3	13.7
−40°C	56.	28.	35.6	31.3	23.
Ross flex (pierced) } 23°C −18°C		10^6 Flexes: No growth			
Flexes	1500	4500	50M	50M	50M
Cut-growth	Fail	Fail	5×	2×	0

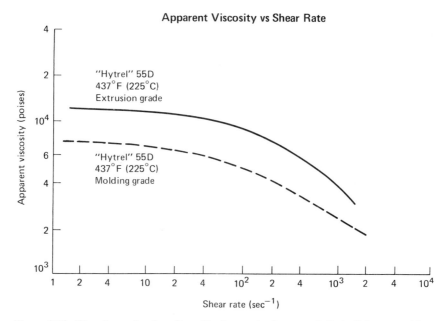

Figure 4-26. The change in viscosity with shear rate shows a relatively flat curve, at low shear, which is characteristic of most polymer processing.

color systems are also satisfactory, in many cases, if the processing machine is equipped to use these colors. In small and short-barrel equipment, it may be necessary to use a dispersion device for optimum color uniformity.

4.6.5 Safety Precautions

The polymer is not hazardous at ambient conditions and is slow to degrade at processing temperatures. Degradation can occur at high temperature or from long exposure times at processing temperatures. Degradation will produce gaseous products and can be dangerous to machines and/or personnel if confined until high pressures are attained.

To alleviate such conditions, shut off heaters and purge the machine. Polymer temperatures should be kept as low as practical within the processing range to minimize polymer degradation. Heat should be shut off if processing delays greater than 10 min. are anticipated.

Hytrel elastomers can decompose in the presence of acidic materials at elevated temperatures. Therefore, Hytrel should not be blended or compounded with acidic clays (pH 4.5 to 5.5), pigments, lubricants, and other acidic additives. Neutral or alkaline minerals do not catalyze decomposition.

Vapor from the decomposition of Hytrel is largely tetrahydrofuran, which is

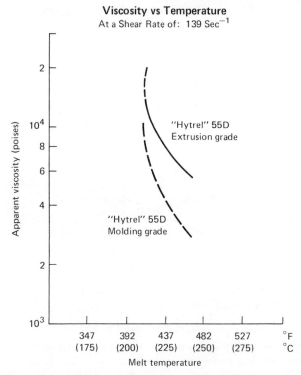

Figure 4-27. The change in viscosity with temperatures at the low end of shear, such as in extrusion. The rate of change for 5525 is quite high, which makes it difficult to process because of having to hold a narrow temperature range of melt strength.

toxic and highly flammable. The rate of tetrahydrofuran (THF) formation is less than 1% by weight when collected from Hytrel held 3 hr at 150°F (83°C) above the polymer melt point. Precautions against the inhalation of vapor are necessary.

The possibility of being exposed unknowingly to high vapor concentrations is remote because most people readily detect the odor of THF at concentrations of 27 to 50 ppm, well below the concentration mentioned previously. Thus, you can readily protect against exposure to high concentrations by adopting this practice: whenever the odor of THF is detected, increase your exhaust ventilation until the odor disappears.

4.6.6 The Recommended Use of Hytrel Scrap

Normal extrusion or injection molding following recommended procedures will not appreciably degrade Hytrel polymer. Thus, scrap from such processing

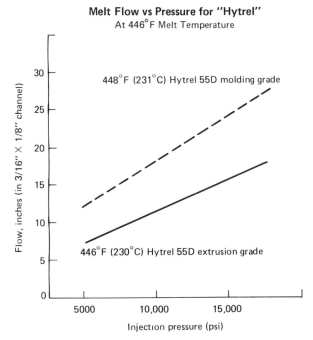

Figure 4-28. The distance of flow in a spiral mold, which indicates melt flow. Such data are valuable in filling thin, long sections during molding.

could conceivably be reused as 100% of the feedstock. However, since operators may overheat or may hold the polymer at normal temperatures too long, or their equipment may malfunction, more stringent control must be exercised. The only practical way for processors to monitor scrap quality is by running melt index on representative samples. With that in mind, the following recommendations are made for Hytrel scrap usage:

HYTREL TYPE	MELT INDEX SPECIFICATION RANGE (gram/10 min.)	MAXIMUM SCRAP USAGE (%)	MAXIMUM ALLOWABLE MELT INDEX OF SCRAP (gram/10 min.)
4056 4055	4.1–6.5 @ 190°C	25	10
5525	14–21 @ 220°C	25	31
5556	5–9 @ 220°C	25	15
6345	6–9 @ 220°C	25	13
5555HS	7–10 @ 220°C	25	14
7246	11–15 @ 240°C	25	21

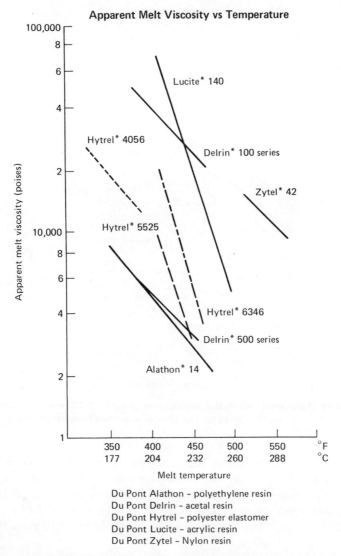

Figure 4-29. The slope of Hytrel's viscosity with temperature is shown in comparison to other engineering plastics. All grades of Hytrel mold well, and all but the 5525 polymer will extrude with sufficient melt strength.

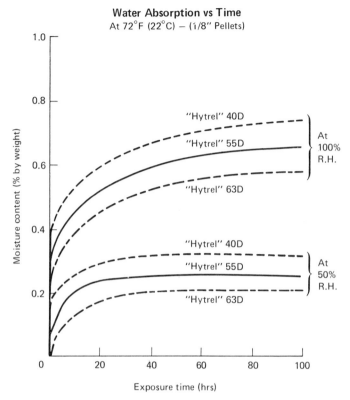

Figure 4-30. As shipped, the Hytrel polymers are below the 0.1% level of moisture. Above 0.3%, the material should be dried for accurate extrusion and consistent molding.

Melt index in effect measures restricted flow of molten polymer and thus inversely relates to viscosity. The higher the index, the lower the viscosity and therefore the molecular weight—thus an indication of polymer degradation. As an example, from the preceding, up to 25% of Hytrel 4056 feedstock can be scrap (regrind) provided that the scrap has a melt index of 10 gram/10 min. or less.

4.7 PROCESSING OF HYTREL

4.7.1 Injection Molding

4.7.1.1 Molding Equipment

Hytrel elastomers have been injection molded in machines ranging from 3-oz. to over 16-lb total shot size. A variety of shapes, complex configurations, and wall thicknesses are possible because of the wide processing range of these polymers. No special machines are required, and standard thermoplastic injection-molding practices are followed. Standard, general purpose screws of the type used for polyethylene with gradual transition are recommended.

4.7.1.2 Molding Parameters

Molding conditions can be varied over a broad range of temperatures since polymers of Hytrel have excellent melt stability and low melt viscosity. Higher melt temperatures can be used for thin-walled parts to aid filling the mold, while thicker parts can be molded with melt temperatures very close to the polymer melt points.

Thin parts need not have as long a cycle time and might require higher mold temperatures. When a dehumidifying hopper drier is used, where the polymer can enter the feed section of the screw at 180 to 220°F, the screw rpm could be slower, and screw rotation times could be less to match shorter injection and booster times on small parts.

Large and/or thick sectioned parts can encompass a greater spread of parameters. If possible, lower mold temperatures should be used for low shrinkage but can affect heat sinking and optimum low temperature properties. The right conditions must be determined by part use and dimensional integrity. If large gates are possible for thick sections, they will help heat sinking of the part as will mold temperatures in the 70 to 140°F (21 to 60°C) range. If the molding machine is equipped to provide a higher boost pressure than the fill pressure, this procedure might be employed. If the gate is large enough so that freeze-off is not a problem, it might be helpful in eliminating sinks to allow just enough time for surface freeze-off at the mold parting line at low to medium injection pressure, followed by higher boost pressures.

In general, mold coolant temperatures from 40 to 150°F (4 to 66°C) have been used. The lower temperature range will reduce cycle time and prevent dimples near ejecter pins with cooler surfaces, particularly on medium to thick sections. The higher mold temperatures improve flow in thin sections and give the best surface finishes. Parts have been molded with thick areas within the part that contain material still hot enough to flow. Slow cooling in air after ejection, rather than a forced quench, is preferred for part uniformity. If the gate and runner or direct sprue gate (depending on mold design) are left on the part for several minutes after ejection, there is no possibility of losing material from these thick areas. This is particularly evident with the 55D to 72D polymers, where the nature of this material gives good surface stiffness allowing ejection without having the whole mass at temperatures below or approaching the first-order glass-transition temperature.

Injection pressures are usually in the range of 6000 to 14,000 psi (421 to 982 kg/cm^2). The lower the hardness of Hytrel being molded, the greater effect a higher molding pressure has on controlling mold shrinkage. Overpacking will only lead to sticking in the mold.

Mold filling rates vary with part thickness and geometry. Thin wall moldings ($<\frac{1}{8}$ in.) should be filled rapidly before the polymer viscosity becomes too high. However, less-than-maximum fill rate may be required to prevent flow lines. Slow filling rates are needed for part thickness greater than $\frac{1}{4}$ in. and to prevent jetting into the mold cavity. Such jetting can cause turbulence and produce rough surfaces. In general, for most parts, a medium to medium-fast injection rate can be used. Air entrapment within the mold can reduce filling rate and/or require abnormally high injection pressure. Molds should be vented at the parting line to minimize air entrapment; generally, however, vents should be broad and not deeper than 0.0015 in. (0.038 mm).

Molding cycle time is dependent on part size and on polymer melt and mold cavity temperatures. Cycle time ranges from 0.5 to 3 min. For a simple part of $\frac{1}{4}$-in. thickness, a cycle time of 1 to 1.5 min. would be a good starting point.

These settings are not critical and are normally dictated by the hold time required to cool the part. For straight Hytrel polyester elastomers, a medium to fast speed of 60 rpm and a low back pressure of 500 to 800 psi are usually adequate. If color concentrates are used or other additives are being mixed in, higher screw speed and/or back pressure (up to the maximum available) may be required to obtain sufficient shear for adequate mixing.

It is suggested that the first few shots be adjusted intentionally short to preclude overpacking and sticking in the mold. Shot size should be increased gradually and injection pressure adjusted until a full part is obtained without flash or sink. Injection time (ram forward time) should be varied until the minimum injection time is defined that will produce the maximum part weight without flash. This injection time plus a few seconds as a safety factor should be used at the specified polymer melt temperature and mold temperature.

Deep-sectioned parts may jam in the mold, especially with 40D Hytrel, which can be "compressed" in the mold. Molds should be designed with 1 to 2 percent draft or side taper to aid ejection. A dry fluorocarbon-type release such as Vydax* spray or Korox 1711 can be used to aid part ejection. They should be lightly applied and wiped almost clean. Nonsilicone-type release agents are recommended if parts are to be painted. Other techniques to aid ejection include larger ejecter pins and/or a greater number of pins, vapor-honed mold surfaces wherever possible, and slow mold opening so that the ejector pins do not "slam" into the part rapidly.

High density polyethylene or acrylic molding resins can be used for purging Hytrel. Due to their good melt stability, purging may not be necessary when the machine is shut down. Simply turn off the heats on the injection-molding ma-

---

*Trademark of E. I. du Pont de Nemours & Company, Wilmington, Delaware.

chine. Since some degree of degradation does take place with time, the material in the barrel should be expelled and not used. The venting of gases that may be generated should be considered.

At fast inject rates, runners and gates should be streamlined as much as possible to preclude turbulence and excessive heat buildup. Full round runners are recommended for low resistance and ease of removal. Most gate types can be used. Round, rectangular, ring flash, and fan-type gates have been used successfully. In general, for parts more than $\frac{1}{16}$ in. thick, the thickness of rectangular and fan-type gates should be at least one-half the part thickness. Gates should be equal in thickness to parts with a thickness of $\frac{1}{16}$ in. or less. If gates are too thin or too small, premature freeze-off and unfilled parts will result. Submarine gating can be used with the 55D to 72D polymer very successfully. Subgating with the softer grade is a delicate balance, with medium to thick parts between a large gate, which will stretch rather than shear, and a small gate, which will break easily but which can cause heat sinks and surface defects. Depending on the part, subgating can be quite successful.

When cooler mold temperatures are used, generous cold slug wells should be used in the runner system. Hot runner molding can be used with Hytrel. Sufficient heat capacity and control must be provided to insure that freezing does not occur to block the runners. Conversely, temperature control must be adequate to positively prevent overheating and possible degradation of polymer in the runners. Such degradation can generate high gas pressure, which can be extremely dangerous.

4.7.1.3 Shrinkage
Part shrinkage varies significantly with configuration and molding conditions. Variations from the standard molding conditions may be utilized to modify shrinkage to accommodate existing molds. Standard molding conditions are given in Table 4-36. These conditions provide a common base for comparing

Table 4-36. These conditions of molding are the basis for further data (Table 4-40 and Figure 4-32) for indicating part shrinkage.[26]

PARAMETER	DU PONT HYTREL POLYESTER ELASTOMERS POLYMERS		
	40D	55D AND 63D	72D
Melt temperature, °F (°C)	350 (177)	420 (216)	440 (227)
Screw speed, rpm	60	60	60
Mold temperature, °F (°C)	70 (21)	70 (21)	70
Injection pressure	Maximum possible without producing flash		
Post-molding conditions	Ambient (75°F [24°C], 50% RH)		

Table 4-37. This table can be used as a reference of shrinkage as well as the basic data for using Figures 4-31 and 4-32, where other conditions are used. Molding conditions of pressures, gate size, and fill time can affect values of part shrinkage as well.

Mold cavity Shape (L × W), in. (cm)	DISC 4 DIAMETER (10.2)			BAR 5 × 0.5 (12.7 × 1.3)		SLAB 5 × 3 (12.7 × 7)
Thickness, in.	0.063	0.125	0.25–0.50	0.125	0.5	0.125
(mm)	(1.59)	(3.18)	(6.4–12.7)	(3.2)	(12.7)	(3.2)
Volume, in.^{3}	0.8	1.6	3.2–6.3	0.3	1.3	1.9
(cc)	(13.4)	(25.7)	(52.0–103.7)	(5.4)	(21.5)	(30.5)
Gate size						
Depth, in.	0.05	0.095	0.130–0.187	0.065	0.250	0.060
(mm)						
Width/depth ratio	(1.3)	(2.4)	(3.3–4.8)	(1.7)	(6.4)	(1.5)
Opening, % cavity volume	1.9	1.9	1.3–1.1	2.5	7.2	6.1
Shrinkage (in./in.)[a]						
Hytrel 40D						
Length	0.001	0.008	0.010	0.003	0.008	0.001
Width	0.009	0.008	0.010	0.004	0.015	0.006
Thickness	0.000	0.020	0.050	0.040	0.050	0.000
Hytrels 55D, 63D, 72D						
Length of width	0.012	0.015	0.017	0.011	0.018	0.011
Thickness	0.010	0.040	0.050	0.030	0.055	0.010

[a]Typical reproducibility of these shrinkage values was ±0.2% in length and width and ±1.5% for values in the thickness direction.

mold shrinkage of the types of Hytrel shown in Table 4-37. Mold shrinkages as a function of part geometry and gate designs are also shown utilizing the same standard conditions.

The effects of specified variations in melt and mold temperature on shrinkages are shown in Figures 4-31 and 4-32. These figures provide adjustments to the shrinkages in Table 4-37 resulting from changes from the standard melt temperatures and mold temperatures.

These data were obtained using relatively simple cavity configurations in thicknesses from $\frac{1}{16}$ in. (1.59 mm) up to $\frac{1}{2}$ in. (12.7 mm). For more complex parts involving multiple shapes and thicknesses, an appropriate combination of several values from Table 4-37 may be required to derive part shrinkage. Shrinkage for parts outside the size range covered may follow the same trends indicated, but should be evaluated where sizing is critical.

The following generalizations are made based on the data shown in Table 4-37 and Figure 4-32:

1. Minimum shrinkage is normally obtained utilizing the standard conditions: (a) melt temperature about 10° to 30°F (6° to 17°C) above the polymer melting points; (b) low mold temperature less than 100°F (<38°C); and (c) maximum injection pressure without flash.

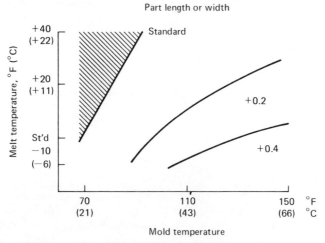

Figure 4-31. As with all thermoplastic, accurate molding involves knowing the shrinkage of the resin. The relative change in shrinkage, in %. Above, the standard conditions of Table 4-36 are shown for both part width, length, and thickness.

2. Greater shrinkage is observed as part thickness increases within the thickness range tested. Differences in shrinkage between machine length and cross-machine width dimensions can occur in thin parts and where configuration causes orientation. Data for Hytrel 40D indicate this.
3. The effect of gate size on shrinkage is kept to a minimum by utilizing a gate depth between 40 and 80% of cavity thickness to 0.5 in. (12.7 mm).

4.7.2 Extrusion[27]

Hytrel thermoplastic polyester elastomers are used in a variety of applications including: coatings and jackets for wire and cable tubing, hose, film, and sheet.

All Hytrel grades, except Hytrel 5526, can be processed by extrusion techniques. The viscosity characteristics of Hytrel 5526 are too low to permit acceptable dimensional control of profile extrusions. For those grades that are extrudable, hardnesses range from 40D to 72D, flexural moduli from 7000 psi (48.3 MPa) to 75,000 psi (517.1 MPa), and melting points from 168° to 218°C.

Several characteristics of Hytrel should be considered in all extrusion processes:

1. All grades have a sharp crystalline melting point, which increases (and becomes sharper) with increasing hardness and crystallinity.
2. Melt viscosity is strongly dependent upon melt temperature.
3. Crystallization rates increase with increasing hardness, and the ability to supercool the melt without the onset of crystallization decreases with increasing hardness.

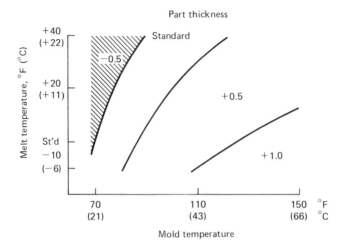

Figure 4-32. As with all thermoplastic, accurate molding involves knowing the shrinkage, in %. Above, the standard conditions of Table 4-36 are shown for both part width, length, and thickness.

4.7.2.1 Extrusion Equipment

Hytrel in the molten state is noncorrosive to metals since it is based solely on carbon, hydrogen, and oxygen. Screws should have hardened (nitrided) surfaces but need not be made of corrosion-resistant alloys. Xaloy 306* or Xaloy 800* are suitable alloys for barrel liners.

4.7.2.2 Caution

Hytrel compounds containing PVC or halogen-containing flame retardants require the use of corrosion resistant metals for screws, adapters, breaker plates, screens, crossheads, and dies. Hastelloy C† or Monel 400‡ are suitable materials for this purpose. In such cases, corrosion is accelerated by high processing temperatures, long residence times, or by a lack of streamlining ("dead" spots) in the die.

Extruders suitable for use with common thermoplastics such as nylon or polyolefins are also suitable for the extrusion of Hytrel. Length-to-diameter ratios of at least 20:1 and preferably 24:1 provide the best melt quality for precision extrusions; the longer the barrel, the higher the output rate of a uniform melt for a given extruder size.

*Xaloy Inc., New Brunswick, NJ.
†Cabot Corp., Kokomo, IN.
‡International Nickel Co., New York, NY.

The barrel should have at least three, and preferably more, independently con-trolled heating zones. The temperature of each zone should be regulated by a separate thermocouple and control instrument, both of which should be recali-brated at regular intervals.

Barrel cooling, either by air or water, may also be required to prevent tempera-tures in certain zones from overriding the controller set-point. This is particu-larly true at high extrusion rates. Screw cooling is not necessary.

Overhead or tangential-type feed throats have been used successfully with Hytrel. Water-cooling of the throat is suggested to prevent excessive heating of the resin entering the screw and to protect the drive bearings. A breaker plate of streamlined design (e.g., counter-bored on both sides) is usually placed between the end of the screw and the adapter and is used to support the screen pack. Two 80-mesh screens, supported by coarser screens to prevent rupture, are to protect the die from foreign matter and to provide increased back pressure. In-creased back-pressure is often needed when mixing fillers or pigments.

Both the adapter and the neck must be of streamlined design. Adequate heat capacity must be provided for the adapter since it is generally a heavy piece of metal. It is especially important to control the temperature of the adapter and neck *separately* since they usually differ greatly in size and energy requirements.

4.7.2.3 Screw Design

A schematic design and dimensional recommendations for various screw sizes are contained in Table 4-38. A wide variety of screws normally used for the extru-sion of polyethylene have been successfully used for processing Hytrel.

The three areas of the screw are:

1. *Feed zone.* This should comprise 20 to $33\frac{1}{3}$% of the total screw length. If this zone is too short, nonuniform output or bridging may occur.
2. *Transition zone.* A gradual transition zone is preferred for the extrusion of Hytrel. Rapid transition screws have been used successfully, but they tend to give unacceptably high barrel pressures in that zone, as well as higher-than-desired melt temperatures, particularly at high screw speeds.
3. *Metering zone.* For optimum control of temperatures and output unifor-mity, a balance must be maintained between the length and the depth of the metering zone. A screw with a very long or shallow metering zone will tend to produce excessive melt temperatures. On the other hand, nonuni-form output may result from the use of short or deep metering zones.

The *compression ratio* is defined as *the ratio of the feed zone flight depth to the metering zone flight depth* (h_1/h_2 in Table 4-38).

The screw should also have a rounded head to prevent the occurrence of a "dead spot" in front of the screw where the molten polymer can degrade.

Table 4-38. General screw configurations for extruders from 1½ to 6 in. are shown, although the screw design can vary somewhat from the above.[27]

DIAMETER (D) INCHES	PITCH (P) INCHES	CHANNEL DEPTH OF FEED SECTION (h_1) INCHES	CHANNEL DEPTH METERING SECTION (h_2) INCHES	LAND WIDTH (W) INCHES
1½	1½	0.240	0.075	0.150
2	2	0.320	0.085	0.200
2½	2½	0.380	0.095	0.250
3¼	3¼	0.440	0.110	0.325
3½	3½	0.440	0.110	0.350
4½	4½	0.500	0.125	0.450
6	6	0.580	0.145	0.600

4.7.2.4 Instrumentation

The function of an extruder is to pump molten thermoplastics at a constant rate and temperature. Sohpisticated instrumentation is a prerequisite for quality production. To gauge the extruder performance, it is important to determine the pressure and temperature of the melt as well as to provide adequate methods of control.

4.7.2.5 Pressure Gauges

Melt pressure should be monitored during an extrusion process, particularly at the start-up. Recording and monitoring of melt pressure during start-up will indicate proper flow of the material or whether a bridging or freeze-off situation exists. During production, pressure changes will also indicate output and viscosity changes of the molten plastic.

Bourdon gauges are the most common pressure indicator in use in extrusion. However, they supply only average pressure readings and are unsuitable if quick response and high sensitivity are required. In addition, to transmit melt pressure, they use silicone grease, which can leak into the melt stream and cause contamination.

For accurate measurement and rapid response, a diaphragm-type transducer is available, which can measure pressure fluctuations as small as 1 psi within less than 0.1 sec. Such minute long-term or short-term fluctuations may influence the quality and uniformity of the product.

4.7.2.6 Temperature Controllers

The device used for heating the barrel, particularly the front end and die, greatly influences extrudate quality. Generally, the lower the extrusion rate (longer residence), the greater the influence. An on-off temperature controller is not recommended with Hytrel. With this type of controller, a ±5°F (±3°C) cycle of temperature is not uncommon. With the strong dependency of viscosity upon temperature usually observed with Hytrel, this variation is unacceptable.

For optimum temperature control, controllers should be of the proportioning or variable voltage type, rather than the on-off type, in order to obtain a thermally homogenous melt.

4.7.2.7 Melt Temperature
Thermocouples are used to indicate the actual melt temperature of the extrudate. Such thermocouples are an absolute necessity when extruding Hytrel. For rapid response, they should be of the unshielded variety and located either in the adapter plate or, preferably, in the die or as close to it as possible.

4.7.2.8 Start-up Procedures
The start-up technique is important as it involves the safety of both operating personnel and the equipment. Start-up techniques vary depending on whether the machine is clean.

4.7.2.9 Clean Machine
To start up a clean empty extruder, the temperature controllers at the die, neck, adapter, and barrel extension are set at the operating temperature in Table 4-41 for the particular resin being used. At this time, the operation of the controllers should also be checked. When these zones reach their operating temperatures, the remaining barrel zones are also brought up to the desired temperature and are held at the point for 20 to 30 min. before resin is fed to the screw. Feed throat cooling water is turned on. Cooling of the entire screw is not recommended, but cooling of the feed zone of the screw may be used and is sometimes effective in solving specific feed problems such as erratic and nonuniform feeding.

When all zones have been at their set temperatures for 20 to 30 min., the screw should be turned on at a slow speed (5 to 10 rpm), and the resin may be fed through the hopper. When the melt appears at the die, it should become clear after a few minutes, and both the melt temperature and head pressure should have leveled out. It is desirable to use an ammeter and a pressure gauge to monitor performance at start-up. For maximum safety of the equipment and the operator, the gauge should be located between the end of the screw and the breaker plate.

4.7.2.10 Full Machine
Sometimes, the extruder may have been shut down when filled with Hytrel resin. The melting point of the particular grade should be considered during start-up. Care should be taken in starting a full machine to prevent bridging in

Table 4-39. Processing parameters for extrusion on smaller screws are shown below for general parameters. Variations will exist depending on screw length and die configuration.[27]

	HYTREL		
	40D	55 AND 63D	72D
Barrel temperature, °C			
Zone 1	155–165	195–210	205–210
Zone 2	170–180	210–225	210–215
Zone 3	170–180	210–225	215–225
Adapter and neck, °C	170–180	210–225	215–225
Die, °C	170–180	210–230	215–230
Melt, °C	170–190	210–230	225–235

the feed zone, localized overheating resulting in degradation, and cold spots (plugs of unmelted resin occurring primarily in the adapter or barrel extension).

Set all controllers at the temperatures in Table 4-39 for the particular Hytrel resin in use. When the controllers have reached the desired temperatures and have been held at those temperatures for 20 to 30 min., the screw should be slowly increased in speed up to 10 rpm until molten polymer flows smoothly from the die. It is important at this time to check for any excessive die pressure or amperage requirements that may indicate a plug of unmelted resin. When smooth flow of clear molten polymer has been obtained, the screw speed may be increased as desired.

4.7.2.11 Shutdown Procedures

For brief shutdowns of 30 min. or less, no changes are required. If the extruder is to be shut down for lunch or overnight, simply turn off the heat controllers. If the extruder is so equipped, barrel cooling should be used to cool the melt rapidly and prevent degradation. During the next start-up, the material contained in the screw should be expelled and not used. Venting of gases that may be generated should be considered (see Safety Precautions, pp. 172-173).

4.7.2.12 Purging

Purging of the extruder may be done with either medium- or high-density polyethylene. A low melt index grade is preferred. Cycling of the screw speed during purging will assist in purging. It is important that all temperature controllers be set at 200°C (minimum) during this operation. The extruder may then be shut down as recommended previously.

Alternatively, cast-acrylic resins may be used to purge the extruder. Since these cross-lined materials do not melt but only soften, the die, extension, screens, and breaker plate should be removed prior to its use. If this is not done, unsafe amperages and pressures may result, which may damage the machine or injure the operators.

4.7.2.13 Wire-Coating Techniques with Tubing Dies

The *draw-down ratio* is defined as *the ratio of the cross-sectional area of the tube, as extruded, to the cross-sectional area of the finished insulation.* Thus,

$$DDR = \frac{D_D{}^2 - D_T{}^2}{D_{CW}{}^2 - D_W{}^2}$$

where DDR = drawdown ratio
   D_D = diameter of the die orifice
   D_T = diameter of the guider tip
   D_{CW} = diameter of the coated wire
   D_W = diameter of the bare wire.

Satisfactory wire coatings of Hytrel have been made at drawdown ratios as high as 100 for 40D Hytrel. However, lower ratios are preferred. For 40D Hytrel, ratios of 10 to 20 are preferred, whereas, for the harder types, ratios of 4 to 15 are preferred.

For a given insulated wire construction, there are unlimited die and tip combinations that yield the same drawdown ratio. To determine the appropriate combination of die and tip, the following guidelines should be considered:

1. The ratio of tip diameter D_T to bare wire size D_W should be equal to the ratio of the die diameter D_D to the coated wire diameter D_{CW} or,

$$D_T/D_W = D_D/D_{CW}$$
$$D_T/D_D = D_W/D_{CW}$$

2. Each of the preceding ratios should be equal to the square root of the drawdown ratio. For example, if one wished to coat 24-gauge wire (D_W = 20.1 mil) with 5 mil of Hytrel (D_{CW} = 30.1 mil) using a drawdown ratio of 9, then the die diameter is:

$$D_D/D_{CW} = (DDR)^{1/2} = 3$$
$$D_D = 90.3 \text{ mil}$$

and

$$D_T/D_W = 3$$
$$D_T = 60.3 \text{ mil}$$

It is not necessary to have these relationships hold precisely, but it is generally a good practice. Many problems in maintaining insulation tolerance may be traced to deviations from these guidelines. The ratio of D_D/D_{CW} to D_T/D_W is called the *draw ratio balance* and equals 1 for a balanced draw, as in the preceding case. The ratio should be maintained between 0.9 and 1.1. Ratios below 0.9 may result in loss of roundness or loose insulation (possibly desirable). Ratios above 1.1 can result in pinholes or actual tears in the resin cone as it exits from the die.

The cone length is the distance from the die face to the point where the tube of resin is drawn down into contact with the wire. For a given setup at a fixed line speed, cone length may be controlled by the vacuum applied to the core tube of the crosshead, as well as by the position of the guider tip relative to the die face. If the cone is too long, the melt may sag, or it may freeze before drawing is completed. These factors will result in variations in wall thickness, loose insulation (some looseness may be desirable to facilitate stripping of very thin stranded wire), out-of-roundness, poor concentricity, and possibly a high degree of orientation. If the cone is too short, the excessive draw rate may result in pinholes, tears, cone breakage, or possibly melt fracture (this last problem has only been observed with 40D Hytrel). Typical cone lengths range from $\frac{1}{2}$ to 2 in.

An air-cooling gap usually precedes entry of the coated wire into a water-cooling trough. By adjusting this air gap, the amount of shrinkage of the coating can be varied, thus giving some control over insulation tightness. Normally, the longer the air gap, the more the shrinkage and the tighter the insulation. The proper balance of cone length and air gap is largely a matter of experiment. Generally, the air gap is less than 6 in. unless a very heavy insulation is being applied.

The water-cooling trough is usually maintained at ambient temperatures. In some cases, however, a warm quench (120 to 150°F, 49 to 66°C) is used, particularly with the harder grades of Hytrel. These higher quench temperatures increase the growth rate of the crystallites and give a higher modulus coating. This prevents excessive postcrystallization of the coating, which can cause curling of the wire. Warmer quench temperatures, however, will reduce the transparency of the coating.

4.7.2.14 Extrusion of Tubing—Free Extrusion

Small-size tubing can be prepared from Hytrel by free extrusion using the same types of dies and temperature ranges used for wire coating by the tubing die method (described previously). The method is most generally used for tubing up to $\frac{1}{4}$-in. OD.

Larger sizes, up to perhaps $\frac{3}{8}$-in. OD, can be made by the differential pressure-sizing method (also called vacuum-sizing). The process consists of extruding a tube of resin and pulling it through one or more precisely sized metal rings immersed in a trough of cold water. The process is inexpensive since a variety of sizes can be made from one die-mandrel combination by simply varying the dimensions of the sizing plate(s), the screw speed, the takeoff rate, and the internal air pressure (if used).

The extrusion is normally carried out in a horizontal mode, but the slow-to-crystallize 40D Hytrel has also been extruded vertically into a cooling tank. This method is often used with slow-to-crystallize polymers or those that are very rubbery, such as urethanes and heavily plasticized PVC.

When using the free-extrusion method, satisfactory results are obtained when the drawdown ratio is in the range of 4 to 10. The following empirical method has been used successfully for designing tubing for the free extrusion of $\frac{1}{4}$-in. OD tubing of Hytrel:

- Use a mandrel (pin) approximately 50 percent larger than the desired OD of the tube.
- Calculate the die diameter using the assumed mandrel size and the drawdown equation.

As an example, suppose one wished to extrude 0.250-in. tubing using a 4:1 drawdown:

$$D_M = 1.5 \times D_{OD} = 1.5 \times .250 = .375 \text{ in.}$$

$$DDR = \frac{D_D^2 - D_M^2}{D_{OD}^2 - D_{ID}^2} = 4 \qquad \text{(Eq. 1)}$$

Upon substitution, this equation reduces to:

$$D_D = (6.25\, D_{OD}^2 - 4D_{ID}^2)^{1/2} \qquad \text{(Eq. 2)}$$

where

$$D_D = \text{die diameter}$$
$$D_{ID} = \text{desired } ID \text{ of the tube.}$$

When extruding tubing by the free extrusion method, it is often necessary to supply air or (preferably) nitrogen under regulated pressure through the mandrel to act as an internal support to prevent collapse of the tube. If this method is used, one must employ a very sensitive control valve or manostat to minimize small pressure variations, which can result in diametral variations in the tubing.

4.7.2.15 Differential Pressure (Vacuum-Sizing) Method

The free extrusion method is not used for Hytrel tubing of $\frac{3}{8}$-in. OD or greater because roundness is difficult to control. The most popular procedure for sizing this larger tubing is the differential pressure or vacuum-sizing technique. This method usually requires no internal gas pressure to support the tube, permitting the tubing to be cut to any length without disrupting the process. Roundness is maintained by using sufficient vacuum in the air space of the quench tank to compensate for the weight of the water over the molten tube.

One sizing method has been to use plate dies consisting of a stack of aluminum or brass plates each containing a precisely drilled hole. Some tubing manufacturers use the so-called Flotaire type or its equivalent with success. This latter design is a tubular former generally fabricated of brass or phosphor bronze with peripheral holes bored into the tube. The inside is sandblasted and often has one or more shallow grooves or "rifling" to decrease the surface drag of the extruded tube.

Both designs require suitable lubrication between the extruded polymer and the metal surface of the calibrator. Often this can be accomplished by a fine waterflow through capillary holes at the front of the Flotaire die or through a water ring mounted on the front of the plate die. Occasionally, more efficient lubrication is required, and a very dilute water solution of a liquid dish detergent can be fed through a "drip feed" oil dispenser. Also found promising is a 50:50 solution of a water-soluble oil, UCON-50-HB260 (Union Carbide Corp.).

The plate die and the Flotaire tube are normally made 3 to 4% oversize to compensate for shrinkage of the extrusion.

Hytrel 40D has not been successfully run in either the plate die or the Flotaire die. Its very rubbery nature and its slower crystallization rate causes the polymer to "bind" or "grab" in the sizing die. Thus far, Hytrel 40D has been extruded into tubing only through the free extrusion method.

An approximate drawdown ratio of 2:5 is a good starting point for vacuum sizing. This drawdown ratio is not fixed and can be varied widely. As in the case of wire coating via a tubing die, a balanced draw ratio should be used, namely,

$$D_D/D_{OD} = D_M/D_{ID}$$

where

$$D_D = \text{die diameter}$$
$$D_{OD} = \text{tube } OD$$
$$D_M = \text{mandrel (pin) diameter}$$
$$D_{ID} = \text{tube } ID.$$

Film and sheet can be extruded on conventional equipment with either fishtail or coat-hanger dies, the latter either with or without a restrictor bar. Long lip land lengths can result in slight surface roughness, but most film dies are suitable.

The film stack can be either high polish or matte finish. The material produces a good gloss when conditions are right. Speed ratios of the top and middle rolls should be between 1:1 and 1:1.25. High shear is not necessary. A slightly higher speed on the bottom roll is desirable to help strip off the stock of the middle roll, but a high ratio here will wrinkle the film as it is an elastomer.

Clear film can be produced in thin gauges. The faster the heat removal on the first nip, the clearer the film and the heavier the gauge that can be made clear.

The lower the durometer of Hytrel, the heavier the gauge of clear film that can be made at a given roll temperature. Film run at borderline clarity should not be stored in a very warm area, as the crystalline segments, which were kept smaller than the wavelengths of the light that pass through the film by using a rapid quench, can grow to a size to opacify the film. The 4056 grade, in thin gauge, is somewhat tacky when rolled up, but all other grades release well as film or sheet. Edge trim can be removed easily by using a razor knife cut, even in heavy gauges. Score and shear cutting of trip can also be used in thin to moderate gauge, but, since the material is resilient, high forces are needed for score cutting heavy gauge sheet.

Tubing can be run by either a vacuum-sizing box or free extrusion. The harder durometers are easier to process in a vacuum sizer as the surface friction drag is less than the 4056, but all grades can be processed under the proper conditions of vacuum, temperature of melt, and quench.

Thin, medium, and even heavy walls of tubing can be made by free extrusion. Very heavy walled Hytrel 4056 tubing may be difficult to keep entirely round because the surface does not attain full hardness quickly; however, if the tubing is closed off at the start of the length, internal air introduced helps keep the tubing round during quench.

Profiles can be extruded in all grades. Gradual lead-ups give the best results, with final die land lengths from $\frac{3}{8}$ to 3 in. depending on size and shape. Profiles with sharp corners should have die lands as short as possible.

Blown film can be produced on standard dies. The tack on the internal surface of the bubble, when extruding the 4056, makes it difficult to separate after the nips unless a release agent can be atomized into the cooling airstream. This, of course, is dictated by end use.

Extruding cellular Hytrel has been accomplished with the use of chemical blowing agents selected to decompose within the processing temperature range of the specific polymer used. Successful blowing is dependent on a relatively narrow range of conditions, which include proper concentration and dispersion of the blowing agent, temperature and pressure profiles consistent with screw and die design, and throughput.

Few, if any, equipment design changes may be necessary to process cellular Hytrel. The following points should be considered:

1. Screw design is not critical provided sufficient mixing is obtained where the blowing agent has been "dusted" on the Hytrel pellets and adequate back pressure can be maintained. This normally necessitates a screw L/D of at least 16:1 and a relatively high compression ratio.
2. Die design if important. Allowance should be made for the expansion when sizing the die. Streamlined dies with no dead spots and uniform pressure and flow rates to all points are important. Variations in residence time can cause unequal expansion. Short or no die land is recommended.

Table 4-40. Starting-point conditions for extrusion of cellular Hytrel with blowing agent. Machine size and line speeds will create deviations from the above, and die design is important to a uniform product.[28]

PROCESS CONDITIONS	40D	HYTREL HARDNESS 55D	63D
Polymer melting point, °F	334	412	403
Specific gravity			
Blowing agent, phr			
Azodicarbonamide[a]	.375	.25	.25
P, P 1 OXY-BIS			
(benzene sulfonyl			
hydrazide)[b]	.125	–	–
1.5-in. extruder conditions			
Barrel temperature, °F			
Rear zone	300	380	390
Center zone	325	385	425
Front zone	360	430	440
Head	365	425	445
Die	330	400	–
Melt temperature, °F	350	410	460
Head pressure, psi	1050– 1250	700– 900	1000– 1300
Screw speed, rpm	40	40	80
Screen pack, mesh	20-40– 60	40-20– 40	20-40– 60-80– 100
Die-orifice diameter, in.	.161	.125	.125
Extrudate			
Specific gravity	0.8	0.6	0.7
Durometer hardness	80–A	90–A	95–A

[a]Celogen AZ, Uniroyal Inc., dry blended with pellets.
[b]Celogen OT, Uniroyal Inc., dry blended with pellets.

Table 4-40 summarizes some conditions under which cellular Hytrel was extruded in the Du Pont laboratories.

Expansion must not occur early in the extruder barrel, or the gases created will escape back through the feed throat. The extrudate will collapse if it is quenched rapidly or if there is insufficient melt viscosity.

4.7.3 Melt Casting

A melt casting process combines elements of both extrusion and injection molding and can even be approximated to full flow molding (Figure 4-33). The mold should be vented, and another small hole far from the fill hole is used to show the operator when the mold is filled. When the mold is completely filled, extruder pressure will rise rapidly. The machine should be shut off to prevent high

Use of Extruder for Melt Casting

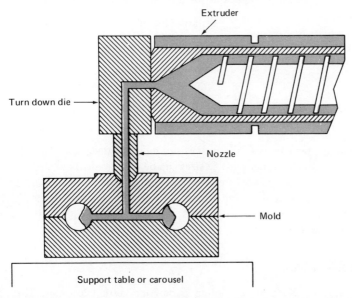

Figure 4-33. A typical schematic of making a part of slab stock by melt casting from an extruder.

pressure in the mold. To prevent shrink marks on the part, the mold should be maintained in contact with the extruder until sufficient time has elapsed for the fill part to freeze off. Molds do not have to be heated in most cases and can be made of easily machinable metals because low pressure is involved. This can provide reasonably good prototypes, with inexpensive tooling, in many cases. Slab stock can also be prepared in this manner.

4.7.4 Rotational Molding

Hollow parts such as balls, boxes, and small pneumatic tubeless tires having void-free surfaces and good thickness uniformity, are rotationally molded using 35-mesh powders of these polymers. They are made on commercial rotomolding machines equipped with independent speed controls for the major and minor axis and which incorporate high heat capacity ovens and water-quench boxes.

The quality of parts produced by rotational molding is determined by rotation speeds, time-temperature cycles, particle size, type of mold release, and complexity of mold design. Pneumatic tires, 12 by 4 in., which weigh 1 lb are routinely produced using 35-mesh powder in an aluminum mold having a wall thickness of $8\frac{1}{2}$ in. Molding conditions for these tires are:

Rotation Speeds

Major axis	6 rpm
Minor axis	2 rpm

Molding Conditions

Oven temperature	700°F
Oven time	5.5

The oven temperature of 700°F does not cause degradation of the polymer in this 5.5 min. cycle. Finer particle sizes can be rotomolded, but the 35-mesh size is sufficient to produce void-free, smooth outer surfaces with no orange peel on the inside surfaces of the molded part. A release agent may be used to provide lubrication for the polymer as it melts, permitting it to displace air pockets as it flows across mold surfaces.

4.7.5 Blow Molding

Hytrel HTG-4275 is a blow-molding grade copolyester elastomer. This polymer has high melt viscosity and melt strength with correspondingly low melt index. These characteristics are all consistent with those of the other commercial blow molding resins; based on these characteristics, one would expect HTG-4275 to

Table 4-41. Starting-point conditions of processing HTG-4275 by extrusion blow molding from data evaluated in the Du Pont laboratories.[30]

TYPICAL CONDITIONS	
Barrel temperatures, °C	
Rear	230
Front	220
Head	210
Die bushing temperature, °C	215
Melt temperature, °C	215
Mold temperature, °C	45
Screw	
rpm	100
Back pressure	Medium-high
Injection (melt) pressure, MPa	44.8–51.7
Blow air pressure, MPa	0.55
Cycle, sec	
Injection	1–3
Blow	10
Exhaust	2–5

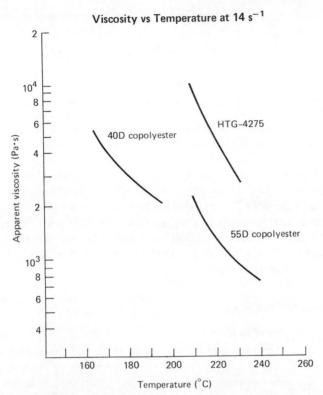

Viscosity vs Temperature at 14 s^{-1}

Figure 4-34. A rheological diagram of viscosity vs. temperature at low shear rate (simulating blow molding) shows how much higher the viscosity is for the HTG-4275, which makes it suitable for the blow-molding process.

exhibit good blow molding performance. This was confirmed in blow molding trials in extrusion blow molding equipment. Conditions are shown in Table 4-41.

Satisfactory products have been made only by extrusion blow-molding techniques. Surface finish and other mold detail have been very good on all parts. Good release from the blow mold has been possible without the need for release agents. Wall uniformity has been good and parisons up to 18 in. in length have been processed without excessive sag. Melt viscosity and melt strength have been found to be sensitive to the melt processing temperature. This was not unexpected because of the relatively steep melt viscosity vs. temperature curve for HTG-4275 consistent with those of standard-grade copolyesters (Figure 4-34). This characteristic has the advantage of enabling selection of processing temperatures to obtain the melt viscosity desired for the parison-forming step.

The viscosity temperature characteristic is such that melt temperature control is quite sensitive. This has not been proven to be a problem in the evaluations to date, and satisfactory parts have been made consistently once machine conditions have equilibrated.

4.7.6 Welding

Hytrel film stock can be heat welded; the softer grades are easier to seal. With moderate pressure, the 4056 grade will form strong bonds. The hard grades will give the best bonds if the surface is first wiped with a mixture of one-third methylene chloride and two-thirds dimethyl formamide. Without an aid to "bite" through the high crystalline formation of the 63D and 72D, bond strengths will not equal the properties of the material itself.

Ultrasonic welding is relatively poor on all but the 40D grade due to the polarity of the material. Solvent welding can be accomplished with the aforementioned mixture of MeCl and DMF. The working time, however, is short, and moderate pressure should be used.

4.7.7 Bonding and Adhesion

4.7.7.1 Bonding Hytrel to Metal[31]

Hytrel polyester elastomers can be bonded to various metals during injection molding, compression molding, or melt casting operations by using the specific procedures and adhesion primers described. The peel strength of bonds to properly prepared metal surfaces ranges from about 50 lb/in. (8.8 kN/m) in injection molding to over 500 lb/in. (87.5 kN/m) in compression molding or melt casting by a 90° peel test at room temperature under static conditions.

4.7.7.2 Preparation for Molding

A stepwise procedure for bonding Hytrel to metal inserts and substrates during injection molding is given in Table 4-42. For best results, this procedure should be followed carefully.

4.7.7.2.1 Preparation of metal surface.

Proper preparation of the metal surface is very important, because any trace of oil, grease, moisture, or oxide film will reduce adhesion. Proper preparation consists of grit-blasting and degreasing, followed by priming. Degreasing must be done *after* grit-blasting, because the grit may be contaminated with oil. Avoid using fast-evaporating solvents (e.g., acetone or methylene chloride) to degrease; they can cause moisture to condense on the metal surface when they evaporate.

No adhesion will be obtained unless the clean surface is primed. Grit-blasting and degreasing alone are not sufficient preparation.

Table 4-42. Using these guidelines will insure optimum adhesion to metal substrates during injection molding.[31]

PROCEDURE FOR BONDING HYTREL TO METAL
DURING INJECTION MOLDING

1. Grit-blast the metal surface using clean, sharp 90 mesh aluminum oxide grit.
2. Degrease the grit-blasted surface with toluene or methyl ethyl ketone. Use a clean, lint-free cloth.
3. Brush-apply a thin coat of CHEMLOK AP-134 adhesion promoter as soon as possible after grit-blasting and degreasing. Allow the coat to dry 40 minutes at room temperature. The dry film should be no more than one mil [25 μm] thick; heavier coats will reduce bond strength.
4. Brush-apply a coat of mixed CHEMLOK primer (100 parts CHEMLOK 7000 adhesive with 5 parts CHEMLOK 7203 curing agent—pot life, 12 hours). Allow the primer coating to dry 30 minutes at room temperature. The dry primer film should be approximately 2 mils [50 μm] thick. Total adhesion promoter + primer film thickness = 3 mils [75 μm].
5. Protect cleaned and primed surfaces from contamination by dirt, oil or grease during storage.
6. Injection-mold HYTREL onto the primed surface using a normal molding cycle. (See Bulletin HYT-402, "Injection Molding," for standard injection molding conditions)
   (a) For optimum bond strength, molding must be done within 2.5 hours after priming.
   (b) Preheating of the metal insert is not necessary if the substrate is steel. However, some increase in bond strength to aluminum can be achieved by preheating the insert to 375°F [190°C].

4.7.7.2.2 Primer system. One primer system that produces acceptable bond strength is a coat of Chemlok* AP-134 primer, followed by a coat of Chemlok 7000/Chemlok 7203 adhesive. Use of Chemlok AP-134 as an adhesive promoter yields a substantial increase in bond strength compared to that obtained with the Chemlok 7000/Chemlok 7203 system alone (see Table 4-43). Thixon† AB-1244 bonding agent can also be used as a primer system, but good bond strength is achieved only if the metal insert is preheated within a rather specific temperature range (Table 4-43).

4.7.7.2.3 Substrate type and temperature. Workable levels of adhesion can be obtained in bonding Hytrel to tool steel, stainless steel, aluminum, and brass, using the specified primer system (see Tables 4-43 and 4-44). With a steel insert, no increase in bond strength is achieved by heating the substrate; with an aluminum insert, however, some benefit is gained by preheating to 375°F (190°C).

---

*Chemlok is a trademark of Lord Corporation, Erie, PA.
†Thixon is a trademark of Dayton Chemical Products Co., West Alexandria, OH.

Table 4-43. Effect of polymer and metal type on bond strength.

EFFECT OF PRIMER AND SUBSTRATE TEMPERATURE ON BOND STRENGTH

Bonding procedure as in Table 4-42 (except primer system)
Open Time—less than 1.5 hours
Polymer—HYTREL 5525; thickness—0.125 in [3.2 mm]
Standard injection molding conditions for HYTREL 5525
Bonds aged 5 days at 75°F[24°C] before testing

SUBSTRATE	PRIMER SYSTEM	SUBSTRATE TEMPERATURE, °F[°C]	BOND STRENGTH (90° peel) lb/in [kN/m]
Steel	CHEMLOK 7000/7203	75 [24]	47[8.2]
	with CHEMLOK AP-134	250[121]	44[7.7]
	primer	375[190]	48[8.4]
Steel	CHEMLOK 7000/7203	75 [24]	20[3.5]
	alone	250[121]	15[2.6]
		375[190]	19[3.3]
Steel	THIXON AB 1244	75 [24]	1[0.2]
		250[121]	45[7.9]
		375[190]	0 [0]
Aluminum	CHEMLOK 7000/7203	75 [24]	34[6.0]
	with CHEMLOK AP-134	250[121]	35[6.1]
	primer	375[190]	44[7.7]
Aluminum	CHEMLOK 7000/7203	75 [24]	17[3.0]
	alone	250[121]	17[3.0]
		375[190]	44[7.7]

4.7.7.2.4 Open time. Open time is the time period between application of the primer and use of the primed insert in the injection molding operation. For optimum bond strength, open time should be no more than 2.5 hr. Bond strength is reduced considerably at longer open times (see Table 4-45). If open time exceeds 4 hr, there will be essentially no adhesion between Hytrel and the metal insert.

4.7.7.2.5 Type of Hytrel. All types of Hytrel polyester elastomer can be bonded to a variety of substrates using the procedure and primer system shown in Table 4-46. Bond strength tends to be greater for the lower hardness polymers, and decreases slightly as polymer hardness increases.

4.7.7.2.6 Bonding During Compression Molding or Melt Casting. Considerably stronger bonds between Hytrel and metal can be achieved during compression molding or melt casting than during injection molding, because of the substantially longer contact time under heat and pressure that is inherent in these operations. A stepwise procedure for bonding during compression molding or melt

Table 4-44. Effect of polymer and metal type on bond strength.[31]

EFFECT OF POLYMER AND METAL TYPE ON BOND STRENGTH

Bonding Procedure as in Table 4-42
Primer System—CHEMLOK AP-134 plus CHEMLOK 7000/7203
Open Time—less than 1.5 hours
Substrate Temperature: 75°F[24°C]
Standard injection molding conditions for the various types of HYTREL
(See HYT-402)
Bonds aged 5 days at 75°F[24°C] before testing

POLYMER	SUBSTRATE	BOND STRENGTH (90° peel) lb/in [kN/m]
HYTREL 4056	Steel	73[12.8]
	Aluminum	46 [8.1]
	Brass	84[14.7]
	Stainless Steel	85[14.9]
HYTREL 5525	Steel	55 [9.6]
	Aluminum	40 [7.0]
	Brass	70[12.3]
	Stainless Steel	65[11.4]
HYTREL 6345	Steel	29 [5.1]
	Aluminum	30 [5.2]
	Brass	50 [8.8]
	Stainless Steel	54 [9.5]
HYTREL 7246	Steel	30 [5.2]
	Aluminum	13 [2.3]
	Brass	45 [7.9]
	Stainless Steel	45 [7.9]

casting is given in Table 4-46. Additional information about specific elements of this procedure is given in the following paragraphs.

4.7.7.2.7 Preparation of metal surface. The same precautions cited in the discussion of preparation of metal surfaces for bonding during injection molding apply to the compression molding and melt casting operations as well. The metal surface must first be grit blasted and degreased to remove all traces of oil, grease, or oxide film, and then must be primed with a commercial adhesive bonding agent. Data are shown in Table 4-47.

4.7.7.2.8 Primer system. Thixon AB-1244 bonding agent gives excellent adhesion between Hytrel 5556 and heated or unheated brass or steel, producing bond strength in excess of 500 lb/in. (87.5 kN/m) (see Table 4-48). It should also be satisfactory for use with other types of Hytrel polyester elastomer.

Thixon XAB-894 is an effective primer with Hytrel 4056 at substrate temperatures up to 350°F (177°C), as shown in Table 4-47. However, poor bonds are

Table 4-45. Procedure for bonding Hytrel to metal during compression molding or open casting.[31]

EFFECT OF OPEN TIME ON BOND STRENGTH

Bonding Procedure—as in Table 4-42
Primer System—CHEMLOK AP-134 plus CHEMLOK 7000/7203
Substrate Temperature: 75°F [24°C]
Polymer—HYTREL 5525
Standard injection molding conditions for HYTREL 5525 (See HYT-402)
Bonds aged 5 days at 75°F [24°C] before testing

OPEN TIME* HOURS	BOND STRENGTH (90° peel) lb/in [kN/m]
1.0	30 [5.2]
1.5	50 [8.8]
2.0	45 [7.9]
2.5	48 [8.4]
3.0	30 [5.2]
3.5	28 [4.9]
4.0	10 [1.8]
16.0	0 [0]

*Open time is the time period between application of the primer and use of the primed insert in the injection molding operation.

Table 4-46. Procedure for bonding HYTREL to metal during compression molding or open casting.[31]

PROCEDURE FOR BONDING HYTREL TO METAL
DURING COMPRESSION MOLDING OR OPEN CASTING

1. Grit-blast the metal surface using clean, sharp 90 mesh aluminum oxide grit.
2. Degrease the grit-blasted surface with toluene or methyl ethyl ketone. Use a clean, lint-free cloth.
3. Brush-apply a prime coat of THIXON AB-1244 or THIXON XAB-894 bonding agent as soon as possible after grit-blasting and degreasing. Allow the coat to dry for 30 minutes at room temperature. The dry coating should be approximately one mil [25 μm] thick; heavier coats will reduce bond strength.
4. If desired, brush-apply a second coat of THIXON bonding agent and allow it to dry for 30 minutes at room temperature.
5. Protect cleaned and primed surface from contamination by oil, grease and mold lubricants during storage.
6. Preheat metal to molding temperature if desired (see text).
7. Melt cast or compression mold HYTREL onto the primed metal, using standard techniques for these operations.

Table 4-47. Effect of variables in bonding procedure.[31]

EFFECT OF VARIABLES IN BONDING PROCEDURE

Bonding Procedure as indicated
Compression molding or Open casting
Substrate–Steel
Primer–THIXON XAB-894
HYTREL 4056 polyester elastomer

GRIT-BLASTED	DEGREASED	NO. OF PRIME COATS	SUBSTRATE TEMPERATURE °F[°C]	PRESSURE APPLIED TO MELT	BOND STRENGTH (90° peel) lb/in [kN/m]
No	Yes	0	75 [24]	Yes	10 [1.8]
Yes	Yes	0	75 [24]	Yes	10 [1.8]
No	No	1	75 [24]	Yes	4 [0.7]
Yes	Yes	1	75 [24]	Yes	370[64.8]
Yes	Yes	2	75 [24]	Yes	460[80.5]
Yes	Yes	2	75 [24]	No	370[64.8]
Yes	Yes	2	350[177]	Yes	480[84.0]

Table 4-48. Bonding Hytrel 5556 to brass and steel.[31]

BONDING HYTREL 5556 TO BRASS AND STEEL			
	Bonding Procedure as in Table V Primer–THIXON AB-1244		
SUBSTRATE TYPE	NO. OF PRIME COATS	SUBSTRATE TEMPERATURE °F [°C]	BOND STRENGTH (90° peel) lb/in [kN/m]
Steel	1	75 [24]	500 [87.5]
Steel	2	75 [24]	500 [87.5]
Steel	1	400[204]	530 [92.8]
Steel	2	400[204]	520 [91.0]
Brass	1	75 [24]	590[103.2]
Brass	2	75 [24]	580[101.5]
Brass	1	400[204]	500 [87.5]
Brass	1	400[204]	580[101.5]

obtained if the substrate is preheated to 400°F (204°C). Thixon XAB-894 is useful with Hytrel 5556 if the metal substrate is preheated. Another Thixon bonding agent, XAB-936, can also be used, but it produces lower bond strength than do the preferred primers.

4.7.7.2.9 Substrate type and temperature. Excellent adhesion between Hytrel and brass or steel is obtained with the bonding agents cited (Table 4-48). Although no data are shown, adhesion to other metals should also be satisfactory if the preferred primers are used.

The type of primer used is the principal factor in determining whether the metal substrate must be preheated or not. Slightly better adhesion is obtained if pressure is applied to the polymer melt, as in compression molding, than in open casting. Applied pressure probably produces more intimate contact between the melt and the primed surface.

4.7.7.3 Adhesion to Fabrics[32]
Preparation of structures using Hytrel polyester elastomers with fabric and braid of nylon or Dacron polyester fiber have shown a low order of adhesion. Substantial bond improvement can be achieved by applying an isocyanate composition to either the formed surface of Hytrel or the fabric. Heating the composite structure enhances the bond.[32]

Since there are a large number of ways these structures can be fabricated, the methods of applying the isocyanate can be varied considerably. In general, conventional methods of brushing, spraying, or roll coating can be employed. With low-viscosity isocyanates, the base material can be immersed, with the excess removed by squeeze rolls, doctor knives, or simple draining. Dispersions of solid isocyanate compositions have a low viscosity and can be applied by immersion methods. When bonding a hose tube or cover to braid, more viscuous isocyanates can be employed. Isocyanate prepolymers have adequate viscosity, but if necessary, thickening agents can be used to raise the viscosity.

Bond formation is accomplished by contacting the Hytrel and the fabric under the action of pressure, with or without heating. For a bond at ambient temperatures, sufficient pressure must be maintained for 12 to 120 hr. The time to form satisfactory bonds can be reduced by increasing the temperature. By operating at temperatures near the melting point of Hytrel, i.e., 330°F (166°C) for Hytrel 4056 to 410°F (210°C) for Hytrel 5556, bonding can be accomplished in minutes.

A convenient method of bonding involves applying the isocyanate treatment to the fiber substrate, such as woven cloth or braid on hose tubes, and immediately applying molten Hytrel. Bond formation can be acheived provided sufficient heat is attained by the isocyanate. Examples of the bonds that have been achieved follow:

1. A thin coat of Adiprene urethane rubber L-315 liquid urethane prepolymer was applied to fabric of Dacron (7.5 oz/yd^2), and a 75-mil tensile sample of Hytrel 5556 was placed on the coated side of the fabric. The assembly was placed between steel platens at a temperature of 450°F (232°C) for 5 min. with a pressure of less than 1 psi to insure intimate contact. It was removed from the platens and allowed to cool to room temperature. The sample, after standing 1 day, had a 180° peel strength of 55 pli at room temperature when pulled at 2 in./min. When prepared in the same way, but without Adiprene L-315, the 180° peel strength is 13 pli.

2. If Adiprene L-167 urethane rubber is used in place of Adiprene L-315 with fabric of Dacron polyester fiber with the procedure in (1), peel strength is 37.5 pli.

3. Using nylon woven fabric (6 oz/yd^2) instead of fabric of Dacron, the peel strength, using the same procedure as in (1), is 32 pli. In the absence of Adiprene L-315, the peel strength is 6 pli.

4. With Hytrel 4056 polyester elastomers instead of Hytrel 5556 on fabric of Dacron and the same procedure as in (1)—except the press temperature is lowered to 400°F (204°C)—the assembly has a peel strength of 25 pli. Omitting Adiprene L-315, the peel strength was 15 pli.

5. Hytrel 5556 with a thin coating of Adiprene L-315 applied to fabric of Dacron was assembled for 1 week with a pressure of less than 1 psi. The peel strength is 17 pli. Without Adiprene L-315, no adhesion was achieved.

6. Using Adiprene L-167 instead of L-315 as in (5), the peel strength is 15 pli.

The use of prepolymers permits a wide latitude in handling and processing procedures. The use of these materials allows heat to be used to effect an immediate cure, or at room temperature allows structures to be made that are more flexible than with conventional adhesives using epoxies. The use of these materials is adaptable to braided hose construction, flat belting, V-belts, and coated fabrics. Since low temperature flexibility is a consideration, the rubberlike characteristics of isocyanate-terminated prepolymer systems have a decided advantage over other adhesive systems.

4.8 PRODUCT APPLICATIONS

The Hytrel polyesters have a unique combination of physical properties, which make these materials well suited for use in industrial, recreational, and chemical environments. These materials, because of their service life and functionality, have been able to replace urethanes and nylons as well as some rubbers, PVC, and other plastics in applications ranging from hydraulic hose, seals, and latches to military tracted vehicles, light-duty tires, and fuel tanks.

As mentioned earlier, the high modulus, low and high service temperature, and chemical resistance—combined with the ease of processing haul—enabled Hytrel to become a premium elastomer for many uses. The following discussions will illustrate the wide variety of existing applications that are being successfully designed and fabricated using these elastomers.

4.8.1 Hydraulic Hose

A hose constuction utilizing a Hytrel tube and cover is shown in Figure 4-35. This hose contributes great strength in a relatively thin cross-section and stays flexible at subzero temperatures that stiffen many rubber hoses. Typically,

Figure 4-35. Typical cross section of braid-reinforced Hytrel hydraulic hose.

Figure 4-36. Telephone retractile cord using Hytrel polyester.

100 R7 hydraulic hose is rated for service from −65 to 250°F (and 275°F for intermittent use).

The hose contains no plasticizer, as with nylon compounds, and therefore remains flexible over long periods of time. There is no carbon black, as with rubber, so the hose constructions are nonconductive. Since these polymeric materials require no postcuring and can be extruded in continuous lengths, faster production rates can be achieved.

The combination of the polyester inner and outer layer with a double ply of polyester fiber in the carcass gives the physical strength and pressure resistance, along with oil compatibility, for use in aerial lifts, construction equipment, farm machinery, machine tools, trucks, and processing equipment such as hydraulic tubing on injection molding machines.

Similarly related applications using a Hytrel-coated tinsel wire overjacketed with PVC for telephone retractile cord (Figure 4-36) and coiled air hose take advantage of the flex fatigue resistance and low creep of Hytrel, providing a lively coil that does not droop with age.

4.8.2 Tires

Pneumatic tires, as shown in Figure 4-37a and b, combine strength, light weight, and flex fatigue resistance. These tires do not need reinforcement and have high load-bearing capacity. The unit construction design allows the single-step fabrication technique of rotational casting.

4.8.3 Poppets

An injection molded compressor poppet is shown in Figure 4-38b. Originally, this design consisted of metal sandwiched between two fabric reinforced rubber

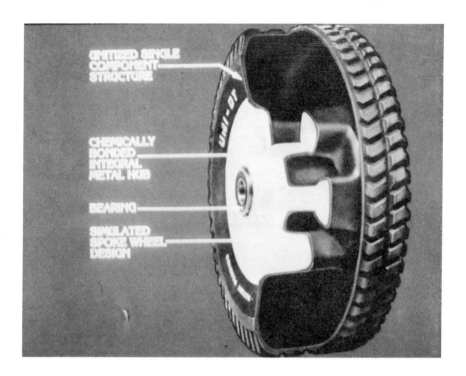

Figure 4-37. Typical cross section of pneumatic tire of Hytrel.

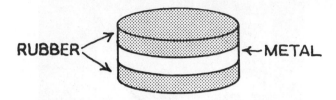

Figure 4-38. Injection-molded compressor poppet showing new Hytrel design and schematic of what it replaced.

disks (Figure 4-38a). Bond failure, with this construction, resulted in compressor failure. The high compressive strength of the copolyester, coupled with resilience, permitted the designer to eliminate the bond by converting to a unit construction. This one-piece poppet cost less to produce than the original rubber design.

4.8.4 Flexible Couplings

Used in mechanical drive applications, properly designed couplings in Hytrel (Figure 4-39) can replace similar urethane, metal, and plastic devices. The application manifests itself in high starting torque, heavy-duty usage, flexibility, low heat buildup, and high load-bearing capabilities, while close tolerance and ease of fabrication make this part more than competitive with earlier designs. A certain amount of misalignment can also be tolerated.

Figure 4-39. Flexible coupling (above) and other drive parts are natural articles for Hytrel elastomers.

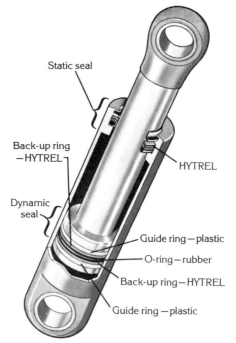

Figure 4-40. Hytrel backup rings are shown mounted in a hydraulic piston device.

4.8.5 Backup Rings

A major European fabricator of elastomer goods has successfully designed a backup ring or support seal for a hydraulic piston device used in mining industry (Figure 4-40). Tests indicate that the seal offers a service life up to several times longer than that of the conventional fabric reinforced rubber seal. Although material costs are higher than the fabric-rubber seals, the design offers economics attendant with short cycles, no scrap, and reduced downtime of the machinery on which it is used.

4.8.6 Drive Belting

Due to the high modulus and low creep characteristics of these polyesters, they can replace the fabric-rubber laminated drive belts for many applications (Figure 4-41). Since the extruded lengths can be spliced at the machine, sizing by length is easily done. In addition, the belts on machines with pulleys (which are difficult to get at because of frames, bearings, and journals) can be fabricated on the spot, without costly downtime to install a preformed endless belt. Lower stack inventories of belting material can also realize a substantial savings.

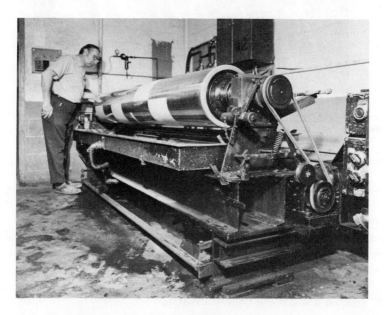

Figure 4-41. Numerous drive belt applications give the flexibility of on-the-spot installation from reeled stock and tough long-lasting drive systems.

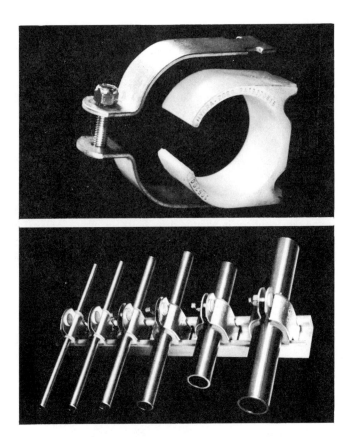

Figure 4-42. Pipe clamp liner dampers eliminate metal-to-metal contact and vibration problems.

4.8.7 Pipe Clamps

A cushion-clamp assembly, using Hytrel for supporting piping and tubing, has been developed because of its strength-to-weight ratio, impact resistance, chemical stability, broad thermal range, and resilience. The injection molded liners (Figure 4-42) eliminate metal-to-metal contact and damper vibration. Easily installed, they are normally mounted on a special steel or aluminum channel, accommodating piping from 0.25 to 4 in. diameter.

4.8.8 Tracked Vehicles and Conveyor Belting

Various recreational, farm, and military vehicles have employed Hytrel tracks from injection molded segments, joined by rod stock. Figure 4-43 shows a mod-

Figure 4-43. Tracked vehicles, particularly for snow and rough terrain, can be designed from molded Hytrel.

ified four wheel drive vehicle, which can travel in deep snow, demonstrating Hytrel's low temperature flexibility, high modulus, load-bearing, and excellent cut growth properties.

Similar types of designs can be used for some conveyor applications to handle hot materials or to handle chemicals that will attack rubber or metals. Belt length can be adjusted by adding or removing segments, thus eliminating the costly replacement of vulcanized belts.

Another use, combining chemical resistance with good flex and impact properties from −20 to 250°F, involves a liner for one manufacturer's butterfly values. Hytrel provides the additional features of resilience for tight seals, strength at full vacuum, and no brittleness since there is no plasticizer. Figure 4-44 shows the light-colored liner in a typical value. Molding of this material gives good dimensional tolerance and stability.

4.8.9 Other Uses

Automotive applications involving noise suppression and wearability have been developed. One is a cover over a chrome-manganese steel door latch on the Audi 80 sedan. No measurable wear was found after 50,000 lock-unlock cycles. The Hytrel elastomer quiets the latch very well because of its resilience, and it keeps this property with age and weathering.

Figure 4-44. Liners for butterfly valves combine chemical and flex resistance.

Another application involves millions of 1974 and 1975 model cars that rely on the strength of a small plunger, injection molded from Hytrel for instant locking of seat/shoulder belts in response to an impact. The $\frac{1}{8}$-in.-diameter plunger is forced against a locking plate by a 1-in.-diameter solid metal ball moving inside a circular housing, which is also molded in Hytrel (see Figure 4-45).

Three critical parts of a leading manufacturer of air guns are molded with Hytrel. Using Figure 4-46, the sliding plunger heat takes advantage of the low coefficient of friction, resilience, and impact strength of the material. The front and rear seals of the transfer assembly capitalize on the abrasion and flex fatigue resistance of this elastomer.

Electrical applications include pressure switches, cable junction covers, and panel insulators and covers, the latter being illustrated by Figure 4-47. Bare terminals and electrical equipment are an obvious hazard and should be protected from accidental contact. Safety-minded operators have covered these bare connections with tape, which is time-consuming, or rubber boots, which can fall off if bumped. Hytrel is used for this irregularly shaped cover because of its ease of fabrication, its electrical integrity, and its physical durability.

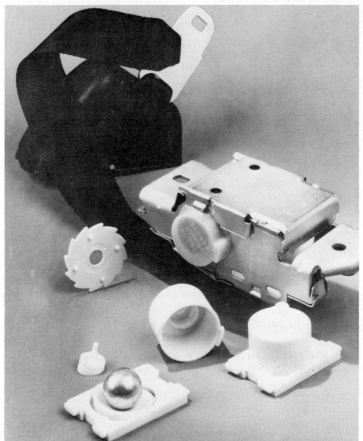

Figure 4-45. Molded parts of hard yet resilient Hytrel in belt reel are both strong and silent.

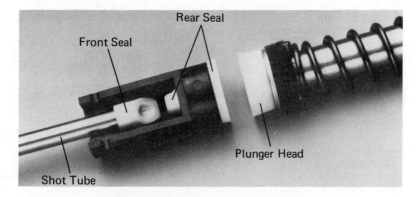

Figure 4-46. Critical air gun components in Hytrel.

Figure 4-47. Electrical panel covers are only one of several applications involving Hytrel.

ACKNOWLEDGMENTS

In Chapter 4, all figures and tables and some content of the text are courtesy of the Elastomer Chemicals Department of E. I. du Pont de Nemours & Company.

REFERENCES

1. (Morton Brown), (Contribution No. 321), E. I. du Pont de Nemours & Company, Elastomer Chemicals Dept.
2. Hytrel Bulletin E-09898, *Hytrel Polyester Elastomer—Type, Properties, Uses;* E. I. du Pont de Nemours & Company, Elastomer Chemicals Dept., 1974.
3. Hytrel Bulletin I-27, E. I. du Pont de Nemours & Company, 1976.
4. Hytrel Bulletin HYT-501, *General and Thermo Mechanical Properties*, E. I. du Pont de Nemours & Company, 1975.
5. Hytrel Bulletin HYT-501A, *Mechanical Properties of Hytrel*, E. I. du Pont de Nemours & Company, 1976.
6. Hytrel Bulletin HYT-601, *Hytrel for Dynamic Applications*, Figure 6, E. I. du Pont de Nemours & Company, 1974.
7. Hytrel Bulletin HTY-503, *Compression Set*, E. I. du Pont de Nemours & Company, 1974.
8. Hytrel Bulletin HYT-502, *Tensile Creep Characteristics*, E. I. du Pont de Nemours & Company, 1974.
9. Hytrel Bulletin A-99054, *Hytrel Polyester Elastomers*, p. 7, E. I. du Pont de Nemours & Company, 1974.
10. Hytrel Bulletin HYT-508A, *Electrical Properties*, E. I. du Pont de Nemours & Company, 1976.

11. Hytrel Bulletin HYT-507, *Resistance to Mildew & Fungus*, E. I. du Pont de Nemours & Company, 1974.
12. Hytrel Bulletin HYT-409, *Radiation Resistance*, E. I. du Pont de Nemours & Company, 1974.
13. Hytrel Bulletin HYT-504A, *Fluid and Chemical Resistance of Hytrel*, E. I. du Pont de Nemours & Company, 1976.
14. Hytrel Bulletin HYT-505A, *Fuel Permeability*, E. I. du Pont de Nemours & Company, 1976.
15. Hytrel Bulletin HYT-506A, *Gas Permeability*, E. I. du Pont de Nemours & Company, 1976.
16. Hytrel Bulletin, I-18, *Upgrading the Hot Air/Oil Resistance of Hytrel 5556*, E. I. du Pont de Nemours & Company, 1976.
17. Hytrel Bulletin I-10, *Hydrolytic Stability of 63 and 72D Hytrel Polymers*, E. I. du Pont de Nemours & Company, 1976.
18. Hytrel Bulletin I-16, *Hytrel Passes FMVSS-302*, E. I. du Pont de Nemours & Company, 1976.
19. Hytrel Bulletin I-26, *Products of Combustion of Hytrel Copolyester Elastomer*, E. I. du Pont de Nemours & Company, 1976.
20. Hytrel Bulletin, *Hytrel 5556, Addition of Antioxidants to Improve Heat Aging*, E. I. du Pont de Nemours & Company, 1976.
21. Hytrel Bulletin E-00937, *Hytrel 5555 HS*, E. I. du Pont de Nemours & Company, 1974.
22. Hytrel Bulletin I-17, *HTG-4450*, E. I. du Pont de Nemours & Company, 1974.
23. Hytrel Bulletin HYT-302, *Plasticizers for Hytrel*, E. I. du Pont de Nemours & Company, 1976.
24. Hytrel Bulletin I-25, *Blends of Hytrel Polyester Elastomer with P.V.C.*, E. I. du Pont de Nemours & Company, 1976.
25. Hytrel Bulletin A-87313, *Rheology and Handling*, E. I. du Pont de Nemours & Company, 1974.
26. Hytrel Bulletin HYT-406, *Mold Shrinkage*, E. I. du Pont de Nemours & Company, 1976.
27. Hytrel Preliminary Draft, "Extrusion of Hytrel Polyester Elastomer," M. Brown, E. I du Pont de Nemours & Company, 1976.
28. Hytrel Bulletin, *Extruding Cellular Hytrel*, Morton Brown, E. I. du Pont de Nemours & Company, 1973.
29. Du Pont Paper presented at 1972 ACS meeting, "Melt Properties and Processing of a Series of Polyester Elastomers," Domonic Bianca, 1972.
30. Du Pont paper presented at the ACS meeting, April, 1976, "Blow Moldable Copolyester Elastomer," A. L. Goodman et al., 1976.
31. Hytrel Bulletin HYT-408R, *Bonding Hytrel to Metal*, E. I. du Pont de Nemours & Company, 1976.
32. Hytrel Bulletin HTY-407, *Adhesion to Fabrics of Nylon & Dacron Polyester Fiber*, E. I. du Pont de Nemours & Company, 1974.

5

Thermoplastic Polyurethane Elastomers

Steven Wolkenbreit
Uniroyal Chemical Company
Naugatuck, Connecticut

5.1 INTRODUCTION

Thermoplastic urethanes are an outgrowth of the solid urethane elastomers technology that was developed in Europe in the early 1940s. Design engineers first recognized urethanes for their inherent toughness, excellent abrasion resistance, and the wide range of hardnesses and flexibilities from soft, flexible elastomers to rigid plastic. Thermoplastic polyurethanes, which could be processed on standard thermoplastic equipment, were commercially introduced in the 1960s and offered many processing advantages over the two-component liquid cast and millable-gum types of polyurethanes, which required lengthy vulcanization or curing.

Thermoplastic polyurethanes (TPUs) are fully reacted polymers, available in pellet or granular form. These pellets can be formed by conventional thermoplastic processing techniques into injection-molded parts, extruded forms, and calendered sheet. The processing temperatures will range from 300 to 420°F depending on the polymer hardness and the processing method. TPUs have been found to have many applications such as exterior automotive body parts, cable jacketing, industrial hose, tubing, gears, seals, belting, ski boots, and wheels.

The outstanding characteristics of thermoplastic urethane are excellent abrasion resistance, high tensile strength and elongation with relatively low permanent set, high tear strength, low compression set, environmental and chemical resistance, flexibility at low temperatures, and high load-bearing capacity.

TPUs are available in two basic polymer types, polyester and polyether, in a wide range of hardnesses, from Shore A 65 to Shore D 80. It should be noted that physical and mechanical properties vary greatly over this range. Design engineers must, therefore, define the characteristics that are most important to their particular application before attempting to select a urethane to do the job. The following discussion will attempt to describe in more detail the characteristics of thermoplastic polyurethanes and their application.

5.2. CHEMISTRY

Thermoplastic polyurethanes are typically formed as the reaction product of a diisocyanate with a hydroxyl terminated polyether or polyester polyol and a low molecular weight glycol chain extender. The diisocyanate that is most commonly used in the preparation of thermoplastic urethanes is known as MDI (diphenyl methane-4,4' diisocyanate). The polyol is the amorphous soft segment of the polymer and is usually an aliphatic polyester or polyether. The glycol, which is a short chain hydroxyl terminated diol, provides the strongly hydrogen bonded hard segment of the polymer.

5.2.1 Property Variations

The main characteristics of the polymer can be varied in three basic ways:

1. Hardness is controlled by the ratio of hard (glycol) to soft (polyol) segments in the polymer (i.e., the higher the hard-to-soft segment ratio, the harder the polymer).
2. The degree of cross-linking (which must be minimal to maintain thermoplasticity) is controlled mainly by the ratio of diisocyanate to total hydroxyl groups (polyol and glycol). It may also be affected by the addition of a cross-linking agent to the reaction. Slight degrees of cross-linking will improve set properties and oil and heat resistance while most often interfering with easy thermoplastic processability.
3. Variation of the polyol type, polyester vs. polyether, will affect physical, mechanical, and aging properties of the polymer. At similar hardnesses, polyether-based TPU generally will exhibit better low temperature flexibility, higher resilience, and better hydrolytic stability and fungus resistance, while polyesters will exhibit better abrasion, toughness, and oil resistance.

The tremendous flexibility in the chemistry of thermoplastic polyurethanes accounts for the numerous products on the market. Each product has been formulated by the manufacturer to obtain an optimum balance of characteristics for an application.

The hardness and the amount of cross-linking in the polymer are the factors that most greatly affect the temperature at which a particular compound will be processed. The processing temperatures will generally increase with increasing hardness and amount of cross-linking. In general, the interchain forces and covalent cross-links in a TPU begin to break down at approximately 320 to 350°F through a thermally reversible mechanism that allows them to be processed as thermoplastics. Thermal degradation will generally occur when material is processed above 430°F or when material is held at lower temperatures (350 to 430°F) for long periods of time (greater than 0.5 hr). This will be evidenced by a bubbly, very low viscosity polymer melt.

5.2.2 Effect of Moisture

Thermoplastic polyurethanes are hygroscopic by nature; when left exposed to the atmosphere, they will absorb sufficient moisture to negatively affect their processing. The TPU will expose reactive sites, as it is melted during processing (>350°F) that can react with moisture. The reaction of moisture with the molten urethane will generate carbon dioxide, which causes a blistering effect as well as a reduction in the melt viscosity. It is therefore essential that mositure be controlled to a minimal level during processing.

5.2.3 Toxicity

Thermoplastic urethanes are stable at room temperature and present no known health hazard. As with most thermoplastic materials, at elevated melt-processing temperatures small amounts of fumes are normally generated, which could be potentially irritating over long periods of exposure. Therefore, melt-processing equipment should be used in ventilated areas. As already mentioned, overheating of TPU can cause degradation. The decomposition products are normally aromatic and aliphatic compounds, carbon monoxide, carbon dioxide, and water.

5.3 CHARACTERISTICS OF TPU

5.3.1 Hardness

Thermoplastic polyurethanes vary in shore hardness, as shown in Figure 5-1, from 65A (elastomeric region) to 80D (plastic region), thus spanning a vast design region without the use of plasticizers or reinforcing agents.

Generally, with pure urethanes, as hardness increases, the

1. tensile strength and tear strength increase
2. elongation decreases

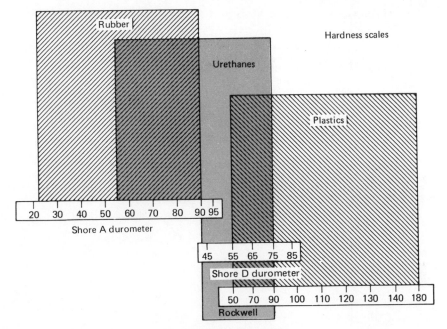

Figure 5-1. Hardness scales.

3. specific gravity increases
4. stiffness increases
5. environmental resistance increases
6. compressive stress (load-bearing capacity) increases
7. dynamic heat buildup increases.

5.3.2 Flexibility

Hardness is not always directly related to the apparent flexibility of a TPU and may therefore not always be the best design parameter. The flexibility or urethane is perhaps best described by the flexural modulus or torsional modulus (Gehman) measurements, which describe relative flexing or twisting forces, respectively.

5.3.4 Tensile Stress-Strain

The tensile stress-strain relationship describes the amount of force needed to stretch a sample to varying elongations. It can also be used as a relative measurement of stiffness. The greater the stress required to stretch a sample to a

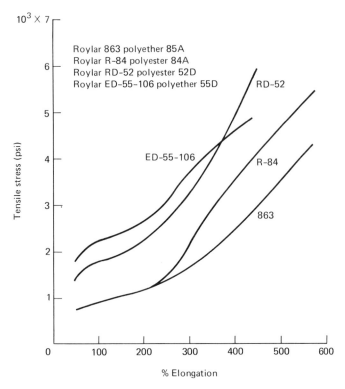

Figure 5-2. Stress-strain curves of 0.080-in. thickness samples stressed at 20 in./min.

particular elongation, the stiffer the material appears to be. The ultimate tensile strength is measured at the elongation at which the sample ruptures. The area under the stress-strain curve is a measurement of toughness. Figures 5-2 to 5-4 describe the stress-strain relationships of polyether- and polyester-based TPUs at two hardnesses (85A and 55D).

Stress-strain information for thermoplastic urethanes is typically developed according to ASTM Test D-412. Unless otherwise noted, the standard conditions for this test call for a rubberlike material, approximately 0.080-in. thick, with a 0.25-in. sample width to be stressed at 20 in./min. The test allows for samples of 0.060 to 0.120 in. thicknesses and of various widths to be stressed at other rates as long as those conditions are stated. It has been determined that variations in these test parameters affect the stress-strain relationships of urethanes. This is most likely caused by variations in the degree of orientation of the polymer as it is stressed under different conditions. Figure 5-2 illustrates four materials (two ethers and two esters, at 85A and 55D hardness), which have been tested at "standard" conditions. Figure 5-3 illustrates that the effects of a slower

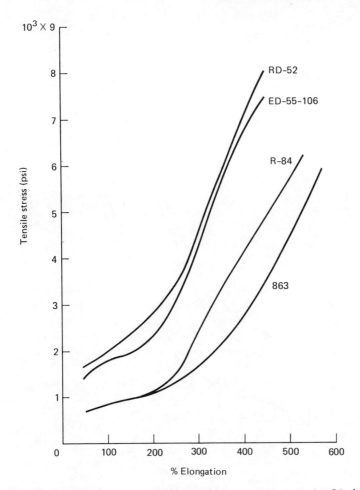

Figure 5-3. Stress-strain curves of 0.080-in. thickness samples stressed at 2 in./min.

stress rate (2 in./min. instead of 20 in./min.) on the same four materials are also associated with higher ultimate tensile strengths and greater stress at equal elongation. Samples tested with two different die shapes (Die C = 0.25-in. width, and Die D = 0.125-in. width) have also shown that the thinner cross section (Die D) resulted in higher ultimate tensile values (Figure 5-5).

5.3.5 Postcuring

Since thermoplastic urethane develops a substantial degree of its toughness after processing simply by being held at room temperature for several days, most pro-

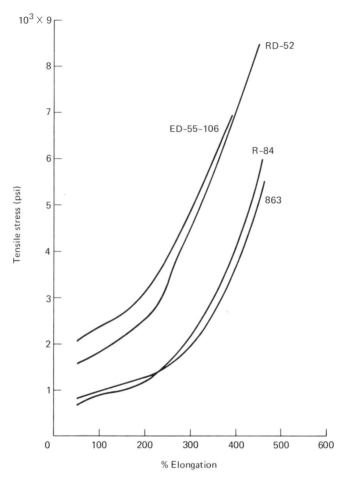

Figure 5-4. Stress-strain curves of 0.030-in. thickness samples stressed at 20 in./min.

duction parts are not subjected to a postcuring heat cycle. It has been shown that TPU develops higher ultimate tensile strength through postcuring cycles, as shown in Figure 5-6. Several explanations of this mechanism have been offered including stress relaxation, cross-linking, and rearrangement of crystalline structure.[1-3] Optimum postcuring cycles will vary with each material. Since postcuring is time-consuming and means additional work, it is most often recommended only as an improvement for compression set properties and not for improved toughness.

The design engineer should define the test parameter, such as stress conditions, which most directly relate to the particular application in mind before studying

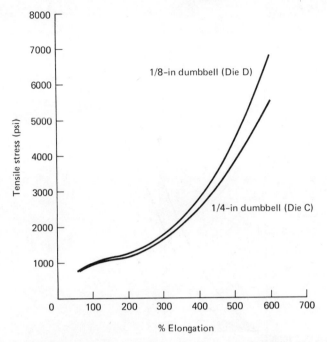

Figure 5-5. Test sample cross-section width vs. tensile strength (0.080-in. thickness samples stressed at 20 in./min.), Roylar R84.

stress-strain relationships of urethanes. This will allow one to define the material properties according to test conditions that most closely represent the actual use conditions. It should also be noted that many TPU material suppliers describe material properties according to different test conditions. Comparisons of competitive materials should be made according to the same test procedures wherever possible.

5.3.6 Specific Gravity

The specific gravity is the relationship of the material's weight versus the weight of an equal volume of water at room temperature. The gravities normally range from approximately 1.10 to 1.25 for pure urethanes. Ether-based urethanes have lower specific gravities than esters of equal hardness. This means that at equal volumes, the ether-based TPU will weigh less than the ester-based TPU. This should be accounted for in the design economics.

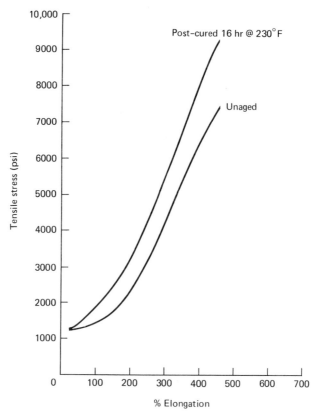

Figure 5-6. Effect of postcuring on stress-strain properties of 0.080-in. thickness samples stressed at 2 in./min., Roylar RD52.

5.3.7 Tear Resistance

Thermoplastic urethanes generally have high tear resistance. Tear strength appears to be related to tensile strength (although not proportionally), and tear resistance generally increases with increasing polymer hardness. There are several different standard tear tests, which measure various types of tearing (i.e., split, Graves, Die C). The measurements from these different tests cannot be directly compared to each other as they are results of different tearing mechanisms.

5.3.8 Compression Set

Compression set properties are related to polymer type, degree of cross-linking, and sample conditioning. TPUs that are slightly cross-linked tend to have lower set values especially at higher temperature. As stated earlier, post curing of samples has been shown to drastically reduce compression-set properties, especially set properties at high temperature. Conditioning of samples has been shown to improve high temperature set properties by as much as 40%.[1] Compression-set properties of TPUs are usually determined by ASTM method D-395 using method B, which includes 22-hr loading at a constant 25% deflection. Values at room temperature typically range from 10 to 50% depending on the polymer and the conditioning cycles.

5.3.9 Abrasion and Wear Resistance

The excellent abrasion resistance of urethane is best documented by its selection for use by design engineers in highly abrasive environments over almost all other materials. There are several different mechanisms of abrasion (i.e., impact and rubbing), and laboratory tests do not generally relate directly to field experience. The most common tests for abrasion resistance are Taber and NBS. Abrasion resistance can be even further improved in some cases by the addition of lubricants (i.e., silicone, MDS, etc.). An abrasion weight loss comparison of urethane to other materials is shown in Table 5-1. In severe continuous use, such as applications where heat buildup may occur, urethanes may soften with time, resulting in increasing abrasion.

Table 5-1. Comparative Taber Abrasion Resistance, run with CS17 wheel, 1000 gram/wheels for 5000 rev at 73°F. (Partially from *Comparison of Hi-Tuff Solid Polyurethane with Rubber and Plastics,* **courtesy of J. P. Stevens & Co., Inc.)**

MATERIAL	LOSS (mg)
Urethane	0.5–3.5
Nylon 6/10	16
Polyester film	18
Nylon 11	24
High-density polyethylene	29
Polytetrafluoroethylene	42
Nitrile rubber	44
Nylon 6/6	49
Low-density polyethylene	70
High-impact PVC	122
Natural rubber	146
Normal-impact PVC	160
Styrene butadiene rubber	177
Plasticized PVC	187
Butyl rubber	205
ABS	275
Polychloroprene	280
Polystyrene	324
Nylon 6	366

5.3.10 Suppliers

Thermoplastic polyurethanes are produced for use in thermoplastic processing and solution applications. The major applications for thermoplastic processing compounds are extrusion, injection molding, and other melt processing (i.e., calendering). Soluble polymers are used in coated fabrics, adhesives, and other solvent coating applications. The commercially available thermoplastic processing compounds are listed in Table 5-2. The major suppliers are Uniroyal Inc. (Roylar), B. F. Goodrich Co. (Estane), Mobay Chemical Corp. (Texin), Upjohn Co. (Pellethane), American Cyanamid Company (Cyanaprene), and Hooker Chemicals & Plastics Corp. (Rucothane). Thermoplastic polyurethanes that are soluble in solvents are available from Goodrich, Hooker, K. J. Quinn & Co., and Uniroyal.

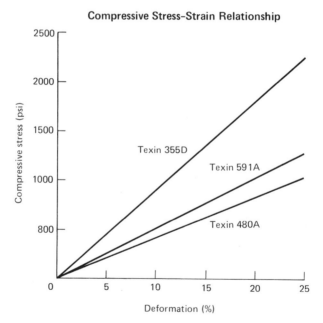

Figure 5-7. Compressive stress-strain relationship. (From *An Engineering Handbook for Texin Urethane Elastoplastic Materials*, courtesy of Mobay Chemical Corp.)

Table 5-2. Thermoplastic Polyurethane Compounds.

PRODUCT	TYPE	HARDNESS	SPECIFIC GRAVITY	TENSILE STRENGTH (psi)[a]	TENSILE MODULUS 100% (psi)	300% (psi)	ELONGATION (%)	NOTES	PRIMARY PROCESSING[b]
Roylar (Uniroyal Inc., Chemical Division)									
E-80	Ether	80A	1.10	3500	650	1100	600	Excellent low temperature	I, II
E-82	Ether	82A	1.11	4000	650	1350	550		I
R-84	Ester	84A	1.18	5000	1000	1500	550		I, II
863	Ether	85A	1.12	4000	1000	2100	550	Excellent extrusion	I
E-85S	Ether	85A	1.12	4000	1000	1800	550	High clarity	I, II
863FR	Ether	87A	1.17	3500	1100	1800	550	Flame retardant added	I
E-9	Ether	90A	1.13	4500	1300	3200	450		IV
E90-106	Ether	90A	1.27	2500	1100	1800	450	UL94 flame rated V-0	I
E2A	Ether	47D	1.11	3000	1800	2500	350		II
RD-52	Ester	52D	1.20	5000	1800	4200	450		II
ED-65	Ether	65D	1.17	5000	3400	5200	350	Excellent extrusion	I, II
Estane (B. F. Goodrich Co., Chemical Division)									
58121	Ester	75A	1.21	3000	600	1400	450		II
58300	Ether	80A	1.13	3000	800	1000	730		I, II
58630	Ester	82A	1.14	(6500)c	650	1500	570		III
58370	Ether	86A	1.18	4300		950	630	Flame retardant added	I
58013	Ester	86A	1.21	7800		1200	360		I, II
58271	Ester	86A	1.21	7800		1200	360	FDA approval	I
58610	Ester	87A	1.22	(8400)c	8000	2100	520		III
58109	Ester	88A	1.20	4100	1700	3750	330		II
58600	Ester	93A	1.22	(8500)c	1650	4900	410		III
58277	Ester	95A	1.25	8550		4900	410	FDA approved	I
58360	Ester	97A	1.28	4800	1200	2100	500	Flame retardant added	I
58092	Ester	48D	1.25	5000		3100	450		IV
58130	Ester	50D	1.21	5000	1350	3100	450	Replaces 58111	II
58133	Ester	55D	1.22	5000	1900	3700	500		II
58091	Ester	70D	1.15	4000	-	-	200		IV

Table 5-2. Thermoplastic Polyurethane Compounds.

PRODUCT	TYPE	HARDNESS	SPECIFIC GRAVITY	TENSILE[a] STRENGTH (psi)	TENSILE MODULUS 100% (psi)	300% (psi)	ELONGATION (%)	NOTES	PRIMARY PROCESSING[b]
Texin (Mobay Chemical Corp.)									
480A	Ester	86A	1.20	4500	700	1600	600		I, II
985A	Ether	86A	1.12	6000	950	1800	500		I
986A	Ether	87A	1.11	4500	850	1400	600		I
192A	Ester	91A	1.23	5500	1300	2500	500		I
591A	Ester	91A	1.22	6500	1250	3000	540		II
345D	Ester	47D	1.22	5000	1650	3000	490		II
845D	Ether	48D	1.15	5000	2000	4000	430	Hydrolytic stability	II
3202	Ester	51D	1.21	3000	2350	–	300		II
355D	Ester	55D	1.23	5000	2100	3600	450	"DXH" =	II
3203	Ester	57D	1.22	4500	3400	–	250	Hydrolytic stability	II
Pellethane (Upjohn Co., CPR Division)									
2102-80A	Ester	83A	1.18	5000	800	1800	550		I, II
2103-80A	Ether	83A	1.13	4500	800	1675	600		I, II
2103-90A	Ether	90A	1.14	5000	1530	3430	475		I, II
2102-90A	Ester	93A	1.20	5500	1550	3600	500		I, II
2103-55D	Ester	55D	1.22	6000	2750	5000	450		II
2103-55D	Ether	55D	1.15	5500	2600	5000	425		II
Cyanaprene (American Cyanamid Company)									
5138	Ester	75A	(1.24)	4-6000	500	1500	700		IV
1880	Ester	80A	1.25	5500	700	1400	750		IV
9341	Ester	82A	(1.24)	4-6000	920	2140	600	Development	I
5140	Ester	85A	(1.24)	4-6000	810	2030	780		IV
1890	Ester	90A	1.25	5000	1100	2200	700		IV
9346	Ester	92A	(1.24)	4-6000	1350	2650	600	Development	I
5145	Ester	92A	(1.24)	4-6000	1370	2760	660	Development	IV
1850	Ester	50D	1.27	4500	1800	3000	650		IV
5150	Ester	52D	(1.24)	4-6000	2300	3400	600	Development	IV
1857	Ester	57D	1.27	6500	2250	3850	530		II
9380	Ester	73D	(1.24)	4-6000	3900	7600	320	Development	II

Table 5-2. (*continued*)

Rucothane (Hooker Chemicals & Plastics Corp., Ruco Division)

P 465	Ester	65A	1.20	4000	450	—	675		I
P 341L	Ester	70A	1.17	5000	650	—	525	UV stabilized	I
P 53	Ester	70A	1.17	5000	550	—	525		I
P 49	Ester	72A	1.15	5000	550	—	500		I
P 455	Ester	78A	1.17	5000	600	—	650		IV
P 342L	Ester	80A	1.20	5000	900	—	415	UV stabilized	I
P 450	Ester	82A	1.20	4500	950	—	575		IV
P 602	Ether	84A	1.10	5000	875	—	530		IV
P 440	Ester	90A	1.21	5000	1700	—	550		IV
P 650	Ether	90A	1.13	5000	2000	—	360		I, II
P 360	Ester	55D	1.23	5000	1300	—	400		IV
P 371	Ester	76D	1.20	4000	3300	—	315		II

[a]ASTM D-412 approximate typical values of 0.080-in. samples stressed at 20-in./min. (samples not postcured).
[b]I = extrusion, II = injection molding, III = melt process, IV = general purpose.
[c]ASTM D-882 typical value of 0.005-in. film stressed at 20-in./min.

deformation for polyester TPUs of 86A, 91A, and 55D hardnesses (Texin 480, 591, and 355D, respectively). The higher hardness urethanes typically have greater load-bearing capacity.

5.3.12 Effect of Low Temperature

The flexibility of TPUs are fairly constant over a range from −20°F to approximately 160°F. Ether-based urethanes in general exhibit less stiffening with decreasing temperatures than do esters (down to −40°F). They are therefore sometimes specified for low temperature applications. Impact brittle points for most urethanes (ethers and esters) are below −80°F.

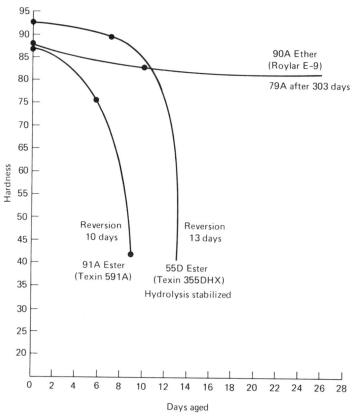

Figure 5-8. Hydrolysis comparison of ether- vs. ester-based TPU hardness vs. days aged at 95% RH, 200°F.

5.3.13 Stability Under Various Use Conditions

The *hydrolytic stability* of ether-based TPUs has been shown to be far superior to esters in humid environments.[4-6] Ester-based TPUs can be somewhat stabilized by the addition of poly (carbodiimide) stabilizer (see Figure 5-8).

The polyether-based urethanes generally exhibit higher resilience (at equal hardnesses), lower hysteresis, and therefore less heat buildup in dynamic applications.[7]

Both ether- and ester-based TPUs have been shown to exhibit excellent resistance to *ozone*. Roylar E-9 was exposed to 2000 hr of 200 pphm ozone at 100°F with essentially no effect on physical properties (see Figure 5-9).

The polyether-based TPUs have been shown to be resistant to *fungus growth* according to Military Specification MIL-E-5272C. Ester-based TPUs have supported fungus growth in this test. Fungicides have been shown to have some inhibiting effect when incorporated in ester-based urethanes.

The polyester-based urethanes generally exhibit better *oxidative resistance* than polyethers at high temperatures. When materials are oxygen aged for 28 days at 158°F, ester-based urethanes lose approximately 5% of tensile strength, while ethers lose about 20% of their tensile strength.[7]

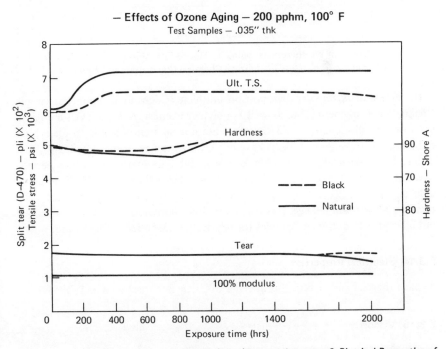

Figure 5-9. Effects of ozone aging, Roylar E-9. (From *Advantages & Physical Properties of Roylar E-9*, courtesy of Uniroyal Chemical Co., division of Uniroyal Inc.)

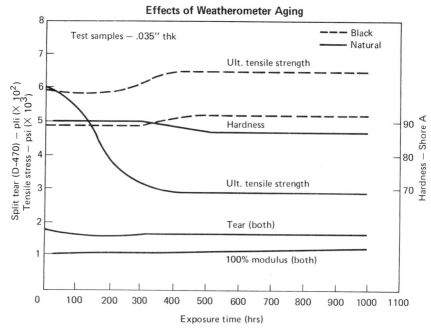

Figure 5-10. Effects of Weatherometer aging on Roylar E-9. (From *Advantages & Physical Properties of Roylar E-9*, courtesy of Uniroyal Chemical Co., division of Uniroyal Inc.)

The effect of *ultraviolet exposure* on urethane is dependent upon the sample thickness and pigmentation, as well as polymer chemistry. Most TPUs are based on aromatic diisocyanate and therefore are not inherently stable to ultraviolet radiation. Ultraviolet stabilizers have been shown to have some stabilizing effect on urethane, especially carbon black, which stabilizes urethane for long periods of exposure (see Figure 5-10). Unpigmented TPU will generally begin to show color aging after 20 to 50 hr of Fade-Ometer exposure to ultraviolet light. The tensile strength will change drastically for thin samples, but most materials will not alter greatly in thicker samples for relatively long periods of exposure.

5.3.14 Electrical Properties

Typical thermal and electrical properties of urethanes are shown in Table 5-3.

5.3.15 Viscosity

The melt viscosity of thermoplastic urethane is dependent on temperature and shear rate. Viscosity typically decreases with increasing temperature and shear.

Table 5-3. Typical electrical and thermal values for polyurethanes.

Thermal conductivity	10^{-4} cal/sec/cm^2/$^\circ$C/cm	2–7
Specific heat	cal/$^\circ$C/g	0.40–0.45
Thermal expansion	10^{-5} in./in./$^\circ$C	10–20
Volume resistivity	10^{12} ohm-cm	2–50
Dielectric constant	@ 60 cycle	5–7
	@ 10^3 cycle	5–7
	@ 10^6 cycle	4–5
Dissipation factor	@ 60 cycle	0.015–0.050
	@ 10^3 cycle	0.020–0.050
	@ 10^6 cycle	0.050–0.100
Arc resistance	sec	0.122
Dielectric strength	V/mil	300–500

Higher hardness compounds generally exhibit somewhat higher viscosity at a particular temperature. They are therefore normally processed at a higher temperature. The shear sensitivity of urethanes decreases with increasing temperature because of the low viscosity (see Figure 5-11).

The degree of retention of tensile strength at elevated temperatures is most related to the hardness of a thermoplastic urethane. High hardness TPUs will maintain a larger percentage of their toughness at elevated temperatures (see Figure 5-12).

5.3.16 Chemical and Solvent Resistance

Thermoplastic urethanes have been shown to exhibit good resistance, for example, to oil, weak acid and base solutions, aliphatic type solvents, and salt solutions. (See Table 5-4 and Figure 5-13.)

5.4 PROCESSING

5.4.1 Injection Molding

Thermoplastic urethanes have been injection molded on both plunger and reciprocating-screw types of machine. The screw-type machine is preferred as it is better suited for plasticizing the urethane and providing a more uniform melt. The plunger-type machine requires that the material be kept at high temperatures (420 to 450°F) for relatively long periods (>1 min.) to provide a constant melt flow. It is therefore not well suited for large parts or fast molding cycles.

Reciprocating-screw machines with L/D ratios of 18:1 to 24:1 have been used to mold urethanes. The higher L/D ratio is often preferred for more uniform melt. Both general purpose and gradual transition metering screws with compression ratios between 2.5:1 and 3.5:1 can be used. A nonreturn valve is rec-

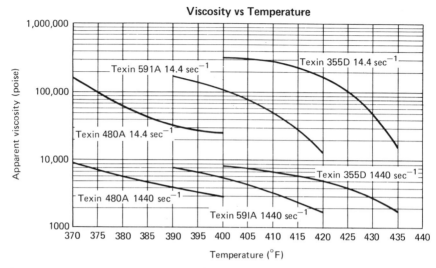

Figure 5-11. Viscosity vs. temperature. (From *An Engineering Handbook for Texin Urethane Elastoplastic Materials,* courtesy of Mobay Chemical Corp.)

ommended to insure that maximum pressure is developed. A free-flowing nozzle with a reverse taper is most often recommended. It is important that the temperature of the nozzle can be controlled, as a cold nozzle may cause "cold slugs," while an overly hot nozzle may overheat the material.

Since drooling can most often be controlled by adjusting nozzle temperature, a shutoff valve is not recommended because it increases the shear and provides dead spots.

5.4.2 Importance of Drying

The most critical factor in processing TPU is that it be *dry*. As discussed previously, TPU is hygroscopic and thus will pick up atmospheric moisture readily upon exposure. The molding of improperly dried TPU can result in parts with bubbles, flow lines, poor surface finish, sticking, and loss of physical properties. These effects have been evidenced at moisture levels greater than 0.08%. Exposure of TPU pellets to atmospheric relative humidity above 50% for less than 1 hr can result in excessive moisture pickup. Even when material is received in a predried condition, proper drying prior to processing is recommended once containers have been opened. Drying of pellets may be accomplished in shallow trays in a hot air circulating oven or in hopper dryers. Desiccant dryers are the most efficient and should be preferred where possible. Drying temperatures will vary from approximately 200 to 230°F with residence times of 1 to 2 hr. Low

Stress/Strain Properties
High Temperature

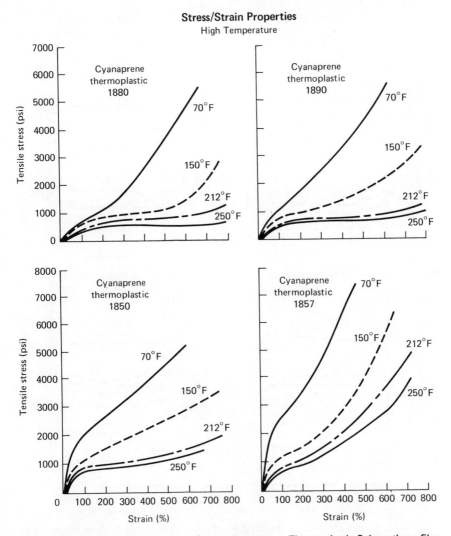

Figure 5-12. Stress-strain properties. (From *Cyanaprene Thermoplastic Polyurethane Elastomers*. Data courtesy of American Cyanamid Company, Polymer & Chemicals Dept., Bound Brook, NJ.)

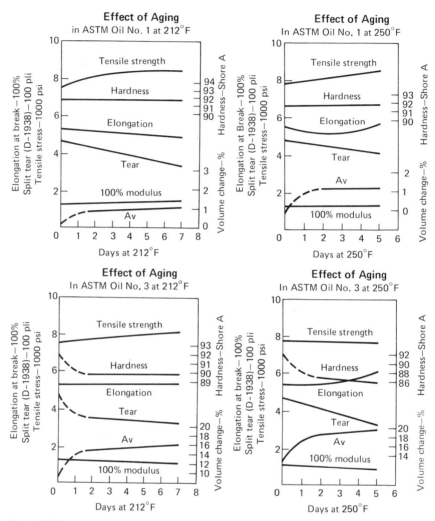

Figure 5-13. Effects of aging on Roylar E-9. (From *Advantages & Physical Properties of Roylar E-9*, courtesy of Uniroyal Chemical Co., division of Uniroyal Inc.)

temperatures and long times should be used with softer materials to prevent heat agglomeration and to insure dryness, respectively. Temperatures below 200°F will not effectively dry pellets unless a desiccant dryer system is used. Prolonged exposure to drying temperatures should be avoided (greater than 12 hr) as pellets may begin to exhibit a slight yellowing effect.

When material is tray-dried, excessive hopper loading should be avoided unless

Table 5-4. General environmental resistance by type. (From *The Environmental Resistance of Estane Thermoplastic Compounds*, courtesy of B. F. Goodrich Chemical Co.)

CHEMICAL RESISTANCE	POLYESTER TYPES	POLYETHER TYPES
Acids		
Formic, 20%	Poor	Poor
Sulfuric 20%	Fair-Good	Fair
Sulfuric, 30%	–	Fair
Alcohols		
Isopropyl	Poor	Fair-Poor
Methyl	Fair	–
BASE		
Sodium hydroxide, 20%	Fair-Poor	Fair
Detergent		
Mr. Clean	Good	–
Fuels		
ASTM Fuel A	Good	Good
ASTM Fuel B	Fair-Good	Fair
ASTM Fuel C	Fair	Fair-Poor
Gasoline, 100 Octane	Good	Fair
Kerosene	Good	–
Glycols		
Ethylene	Good	Good
Ethylene/water 50/50	Good	Good
Propylene	Good	Good
Propylene/water 50/50	Good	Good
Oils		
ASTM #1	Excellent	Good
ASTM #2	Excellent	Good
ASTM #3	Excellent-Good	Good-Fair
Brake Fluid Type A	Fair-Poor	Poor
Detergent 20W	–	Good
Non-Detergent 20W	–	Good
Skydrol Type B	–	Dissolves
Transmission Type A	Excellent	Good
Plasticizer		
Didecyl adipate	Good	–
Dioctyl adipate	Good	–
Dioctyl phthalate	Good	Fair
Tricresyl phosphate	–	Poor
Salt solutions		
Calcium chloride, Saturated	Good	–
Sodium chloride, Saturated	Good	Good
Synthetic perspiration	Good	Good
Solvents		
Benzene	Fair-Poor	Poor
Carbon tetrachloride	Fair	Poor
Cyclohexanone	Dissolves	Dissolves
Dimethyl formamide	Dissolves	Dissolves
Dimethyl sulfoxide	Dissolves	Dissolves
1,4 Dioxane	Dissolves	Dissolves
Ethylene dichloride	Poor	–

Table 5-4. (*continued*)

CHEMICAL RESISTANCE	POLYESTER TYPES		POLYETHER TYPES	
Methyl ethyl ketone	Fair-Poor		Poor	
N-Methyl-2 Pyrrolidone	Dissolves		Dissolves	
Perchloroethylene	Fair		Poor	
Pyridine	Dissolves		Dissolves	
Tetrahydrofuran	Dissolves		Dissolves	
Toluene	Fair		–	
Trichloroethylene	Poor		Poor	
HYDROLYSIS RESISTANCE				
Water immersion				
23°C	Poor-Fair		Good	
70°C	Poor		Fair-Good	
DRY HEAT RESISTANCE				
Properties:				
At elevated temperature	Fair-Good to 130°C		Fair-Good to 80°C	
After aging at elevated temp.	Fair-Good to 100°C		Fair-Good to 100°C	
WEATHERING	UNPIGMENTED	PIGMENTED	UNPIGMENTED	PIGMENTED
Outdoor				
Arizona	Poor	Fair-Good	Poor	Good
Florida	Poor	Fair-Good	Poor	Good
Ohio	Poor	Fair-Good	Poor	Good
Accelerated				
Fade-Ometer	Poor	Fair-Good	Poor	Good
Weatherometer	Poor	Fair-Poor	Poor	Good

the hopper is heated to maintain a dry atmosphere. Regrind or colorants should also be predried before blending with virgin dried material.

5.4.3 Design Considerations

Some general design considerations for molding TPU are:

1. Sprues should be as short as possible with a taper. A cold sink at the base of the sprue will accept the initial cool plug of material.
2. Full round runners with large diameters greater than $\frac{1}{4}$ in. are preferred; trapezoidal and half-round runners have been successfully used but they provide more area for cooling to take place.
3. Gates should be relatively large and have short land lengths. Pingates, which cause excessive shear heating of material, should be avoided.
4. Sharp changes in flow direction should be avoided.
5. In multiple-cavity molds, cavities should be laid out symmetrically.
6. Adequate venting should be allowed to avoid burning and prevent surface voids. Vents and parting lines should be located at noncritical areas.
7. Vapor-honed matte-finished cavities will provide easier release.

8. Ejectors should have as large as possible surface areas to prevent distortion and penetration of parts (especially soft material).

5.4.4 Shrinkage

The shrinkage of a molded part is dependent on the part thickness, processing condition, and characteristics of the particular urethane. In general, shrinkage increases with increasing part thickness and will range from 0.005 to 0.020 in./in. depending on the material type and the molding condition.

5.4.5 Molding Considerations

The parameters that most affect the processing characteristics of thermoplastic urethane are:

1. *Barrel temperature.* Most TPUs will be molded in the range of 360 to 430°F. A temperature must be achieved that provides the proper melt viscosity for filling out the part. Increasing temperatures decrease the melt viscosity and cause easier flow.
2. *Screw speed.* Screw speeds from 20 to 80 rpm have been used. The speed should be set so that the screw finishes retracting within the cooling cycle. Faster speeds generally cause faster screw retraction, but excessive speed should be avoided as it may cause overheating.
3. *Back pressure.* Screw back pressures from 50 to 200 psi are used to assist in plasticizing the polymer to provide a uniform melt. High back pressure will add shear heat and may cause overriding temperatures.
4. *Injection pressure.* Injection pressure should be sufficient to completely pack out parts (typically from 5000 to 10,000 psi). Excess pressure may cause flashing and will cause difficult part release from the mold. A lower secondary pressure is generally used for holding pressure after initial injection at the higher primary pressure.
5. *Injection speed.* Moderate speeds are generally used. Excessively fast speeds may cause shear heating and air entrapment, while slow speeds may result in premature freezing before the part is filled.
6. *Mold temperature.* Mold temperatures from 50 to 120°F have been used. Temperature is generally set low enough to quickly cool the part, but not so low that it causes flow lines from premature freezing.
7. *Cycle time.* Cycle times are dependent on the time it takes for injection, screw retraction, and cooling, as well as material hardness and part thickness. They may take from 15 sec (i.e., small, thin parts of hard materials) to several minutes (i.e., large, thick parts or very soft materials).

5.4.6 Injection Molding: Problems and Solutions

PROBLEM	CAUSE	SOLUTION
Short shot	Insufficient material	Increase feed setting
	Poor flow	Increase injection pressure
		Increase barrel temperature
		Increase injection speed
		Increase gate size
	Premature freezing	Increase mold temperature
Sink marks	Insufficient material	Increase pressure
		Increase holding time
		Increase feed
		Increase gate
	Overheating	Reduce barrel temperature
		Reduce back pressure
		Decrease injection speed
	Insufficient clamp pressure	Increase clamp pressure
Bubbles and voids	Overheating	Decrease temperature
		Decrease speed
	Wet material	Dry thoroughly
	Not plasticized	Increase back pressure
	Inadequate venting	Increase venting
Splay marks	Overheating	Decrease temperature
	Wet material	Dry thoroughly
Burn marks	Overheating	Decrease temperature
	Filling mold too fast	Decrease injection speed
	Inadequate venting	Increase venting
Part sticking in mold	Overheating	Decrease temperature
	Overpacking	Decrease injection pressure
	Hot mold	Increase cooling
Flow lines	Overheating	Decrease temperature
	Cold mold–premature freezing	Increase mold temperature
Flashing	Insufficient clamp pressure	Increase clamp
	Overheating	Decrease temperature
	Overpacking	Decrease temperature
		Decrease injection pressure

5.4.7 Cleanout

Since TPU should not be left at high temperatures for excessively long periods (as discussed previously), it is recommended that machines be purged when they are to be left idle for more than 1 hr. Polystyrene, acrylic, and ABS have been used as purging compounds.

5.4.8 Use of Regrind

An economically important fact concerning TPU is that rejected parts and runner systems can be ground up and remolded, thereby eliminating scrap. Although

100% regrind has been used at times and will maintain good physical properties when properly dried, it is not a recommended standard procedure. Reground TPU typically will have a slightly decreased melt viscosity and may mold at somewhat different conditions when used at the 100% level. A level of approximately 25% regrind has been shown to maintain excellent properties with little or no effect on molding conditions. (See Table 5-5.)

5.4.9 Extrusion

Thermoplastic polyurethanes have been extruded on machines having screw length-to-diameter (L/D) ratios as low as 20:1, while preferred L/D ratios are in the range of 24:1 to 30:1. The higher ratios are preferred because they allow longer residence time at temperature at high throughput rates and insure a homogeneous melt flow.

As previously stated in the injection-molding discussion, the most important factor in processing TPU is that it be dry. The comments concerning drying procedures apply to extrusion processing as well. Extrusion of a material that has not been properly dried will result in a bubbly, low viscosity extrudate, which will have poor strength properties.

5.4.10 Screw Design

The most efficient screw design for TPU extrusion appears to be a single-stage screw with a 3:1 compression ratio and approximately equal sections of feed, transition, and metering. The high compression ratio provides mechanical shear and results in good mixing and a homogeneous melt. Shallow flight depths in the metering zone about 5% of the screw diameter are often recommended.

5.4.11 Processing Temperature Range

Thermoplastic urethanes are extruded at temperatures ranging from about 350 to 430°F depending upon type, machine design, and line speeds. Generally, higher hardness TPUs are processed at slightly higher temperatures. Temperature profiles are generally graduated from the feed zone to the metering section by as much as 50°F to provide uniform feed and shearing of the pellets. A reverse temperature profile is often used with an extruder of low L/D ratio or with a low compression screw. The reverse profile in conjunction with low screw speed provides enough residence time to plasticize the pellets. While a coarse screen pack is often employed to screen out any contaminants, a fine screen pack may be used (100 mesh) to provide some back pressure for better mixing.

A water-cooled throat section is normally recommended to prevent heat from

Table 5.5. The effects of regrind content and number of molding cycles on the physical properties of Pellethane 2102-90A. (From: *Pellethane Processing Information for Urethane Elastoplastic Compounds*, reprinted by permission of Upjohn Co.—CPR Division.)

MOLD CYCLE	100% REGRIND			50% REGRIND			25% REGRIND		
	#1	#5	% CHANGE	#1	#5	% CHANGE	#1	#5	% CHANGE
Hardness, Shore A	90	91	+1.1	91	90	1.1	89	91	+2.2
Tensile str., psi	6600	6020	-9.1	6200	6610	+6.5	6800	6210	-8.8
Elongation %	465	550	+20.4	490	520	+6.1	485	500	+3.1
Tensile set %	40.0	75	+87.5	50	45	-10.0	41	50	+21.9
Modulus, psi-100%	1400	1450	+3.6	1460	1410	-3.4	1505	1470	-6.9
300%	3125	2820	-9.8	3135	3020	-3.7	3280	3055	-6.9
Compression set, Method B, %	37.5	39	+9.2	23.5	32.2	+37.0	37.9	30.9	-18.5
Tear strength, Die C, pli	1010	960	-4.9	965	980	+1.6	935	965	+3.2
Gardner color test	4⁻	6⁻	–	4⁻	5	–	4⁻	4⁻	–

the feed section causing agglomeration of pellets and subsequent bridging in the hopper feeder. Excessive heat in the feed section can also cause premature softening of the pellets in the barrel, which might result in erratic or pulsating feed.

5.4.12 Die Design

The extruder head should be designed to be free from dead spots and to insure smooth parallel flow from the die. The recommended die land length is generally one to two times the diameter of the extrudate.

In order to maintain its extruded shape, TPU must be rapidly cooled upon exit from the die. This is more often accomplished by passing the extrudate through a water-cooling trough. The necessary immersion time to prevent distortion will depend upon water temperature, melt temperature, polymer type, and thickness.

5.4.13 Extrusion: Problems and Solutions

PROBLEM	CAUSE	SOLUTION
Bubbles	Wet material	Dry thoroughly
	Overheating	Decrease temperature; check thermocouples
	Shallow metering section	Use proper compression ratio screw
Surging	Rear barrel temperature too low or too high	Increase or decrease rear temperature
	Low back pressure	Increase screen pack
	Improper metering length	Use proper screw design
Rough	Melt temperature too low	Increase temperature
Surface	Die temperature too low	Increase die temperature
	Wet material	Dry thoroughly
	Rough die surface	Smooth die
	Die land too long	Reduce land length
Overheating	Improper screw design	Use lower compression screw
	Restriction to flow	Check die for restrictions
	Barrel temperature too low	Increase temperature
Die Lines	Scratched die	Refinish die surface
	Contamination	Clean head and die
	Cold polymer	Check for dead spots in head; adjust barrel and head temperature to prevent freezing
Flow lines	Overheated material	Decrease temperature
	Poor mixing	Use correct screw design
	Contamination	Clean system
	Improper temperature profile	Adjust profile

5.4.14 Purging

As with injection molding, TPU should not be left idle at high temperatures in the extruder barrel. The molten polymer should be purged from the extruder before shutdown with polystyrene or acrylic compounds.

5.4.15 Other Melt Processing Techniques

Specially lubricated versions of TPU can be calendered into sheet and film using a standard Banbury-mill-calender, or extruder-calender setup. Processing temperatures are generally in the range of 280 to 330°F. If temperatures become excessive, the urethane may stick tenaciously to the calender rolls. Lowering temperatures generally cause the material to release, but a clean-out compound such as vinyl may have to be used if the material does not release.

5.4.16 Lubricants

Most TPU compounds are specially formulated, but improved processing may be desired in specific applications, and lubricants such as bisamide and fatty acid ester waxes are compatible at low levels.

5.4.17 Colorants

TPUs are generally colored by the addition of dried inorganic pigment powders or color concentrates. Color concentrates are available in low-density polyethylene and in urethane. When LDPE concentrates are used, they should not be used in levels above 3% as they may affect polymer properties or processing. Any type of reactive additives as well as stearates should be avoided with TPU as they may cause degradation or other changes in the polymer, as discussed previously.

5.4.18 Time for Property Reassociation

TPUs undergo some bond dissociation during their thermal processing. Upon cooling, these bonds begin to reassociate, and the polymer regains the majority of its strength within the first 24 hr after processing. Depending on the degree of stress and orientation developed during processing, it often takes several days for the newly shaped polymer to attain its optimum properties.

Table 5-6. Comparison of properties.

PROPERTY	THERMOPLASTIC URETHANE	THERMOPLASTIC RUBBER	HYTREL POLYESTER ELASTOMER	FLEXIBLE VINYL	NEOPRENE CHLOROPRENE	NYLON
Tensile, psi	3000–7000	650–3000	3000–7000	1000–3000	1000–3000	7000–12,000
Hardness	75A–75D	65–90A	90A–70D	40–90A	20–90A	80R–115R
Specific gravity	1.05–1.25	0.83–1.20	1.17–1.22	1.2–1.4	1.23	1.0–1.15
Elongation, %	300–700	150–1000	500–800	200–400	100–700	40–300
Abrasion resistance	Excellent	Fair	Good to excellent	Good	Good	Good to excellent
Compression set	Good	Good	Poor	Poor	Good	–
Tear resistance	Excellent	Fair	Excellent	Good	Excellent	Excellent
Low temperature flexibility	Excellent	Good	Good	Poor	Good	–
Resistance to Aliphatic hydrocarbon	Excellent	Fair to good	Excellent	Good	Good	Excellent
Aromatic hydrocarbon	Good	Poor	Excellent	Fair	Fair	Excellent

5.5 APPLICATIONS OF THERMOPLASTIC POLYURETHANE

The following illustrates how the distinctive properties of TPU are utilized:

Exterior automotive parts: light weight, flexible, abrasion-resistant.

Wire and cable jacketing: flexible, abrasion-resistant, good environmental weathering (ethers, low temperature flexibility).

Industrial hose: Flexible, abrasion-resistant, tough, oil-resistant.

Animal identification tags: tough, flexible, abrasion-resistant, good weathering, oil-resistant.

Gears: tough, abrasion-resistant, low temperature impact.

Shoe soles and heels: abrasion-resistant, flexible.

Caster wheels: abrasion-resistant, nonmarking, load-bearing capacity.

Sheet: abrasion-resistant, oil-resistant, tough, heat-sealable.

Drive belts: tough, flexible.

Bumpers: vibration damping, tough, abrasion-resistant.

Gaskets and Seals: cut-resistant, oil-resistant, flexible.

Film: tough, flexible.

Skateboard wheels: good clarity, abrasion-resistant, flexible.

Ski boots: abrasion-resistant, low temperature flexible.

Tire chains: abrasion resistant, flexible, tough.

Tubing: clarity, abrasion-resistant, fluid resistant, flexible.

5.6 COMPARATIVE PROPERTIES OF TPUs

A comparison of some properties of thermoplastic urethanes with other competitive materials is given in Table 5-6.

REFERENCES

1. Uniroyal Chemical Division, Uniroyal Inc., *Advantages & Physical Properties of ROYLAR E-9*, Naugatuck, CT.
2. Mobay Chemical Corp. *Processing Methods for Texin*, Pittsburgh, PA.
3. K. W. Rausch, Jr., and W. J. Farrissey, Jr., The Effect of Microcrystalline Structures upon the Physical Properties of Polyurethanes, *J. Elastoplastics* 2 (April 1970): 114–129.
4. F. H. Gahimer and W. Nieske. Hydrolytic Stability of Urethane & Polyacrylic Elastomers in Humid Environments, *J. Elastoplastics* 1 (October 1969): 266–280.
5. W. J. Pentz and R. G. Krawiec. Hydrolytic Stability of Polyurethane Elastomers, *Rubber Age* (December 1975): 39–43.
6. C. S. Schollenberer and F. D. Stewart, Thermoplastic Polyurethane Hydrolysis Stability, *J. Elastoplastics* 3 (January 1971): 28–56.
7. R. J. Ferrari, Polyether & Polyester Urethane Elastomers—A Comparison, *Rubber Age* (February 1967).

The author wishes to thank Charles Shedd, Doris Johnson, Barbara Feeley, and Janis Wolkenbreit for their assistance in the preparation of this chapter.

6

Emerging Thermoplastic Elastomers

Robert D. Lundberg, Ph.D.
Exxon Research and Engineering Company
Linden, New Jersey

6.1 INTRODUCTION

The thermoplastic elastomers that are relevant to this discussion can be considered to be phase separated, or physically cross-linked. In other words, these materials generally derive their rubbery properties from a combination of a continuous elastomeric phase and a separate phase (usually a discontinuous phase), which softens at some elevated temperature. The elastomeric phase can be based on a number of different materials; however, they all share the common characteristic of an elastomer that has a glass transition well below room temperature.

The dispersed phase is often a plastic block such as polystyrene, which is glassy or crystalline. Alternatively, the hard block phase can be crystalline as is the case with Hytrel. In the case of materials whose physical cross-links are based on crystalline interactions, we can consider, as a special class, selected olefin copolymers. These materials, such as ethylene-vinyl acetate copolymers at sufficiently high vinyl acetate contents, are rubbery, yet they possess sufficient polyethylene crystallinity to provide a physical cross-link that melts at moderately elevated temperatures.

Plasticized polyvinyl chloride can be regarded similarly wherein the plasticized amorphous PVC chains comprise a continuous phase, and the semicrystalline chains represent the crystalline hard block.

In addition to the crystalline and glassy hard blocks based on conventional "plastic" polymer chains, there is a special class of physical cross-links based on ionic interactions. These ionic cross-links as represented by metal carboxylates incorporated into an elastomer backbone can effect a cross-link that is more labile than a covalent cross-link and can be disrupted by the influence of heat. While soft rubbery thermoplastic elastomers are not now commercially available based on such ionic cross-links, there is a substantial amount of activity in this area.[1-4]

Within the framework just described, combining various elastomers with suitable physical cross-links, a large number of different block and graft copolymers and related materials have been described in the literature. Ideally, it would be desirable to achieve the permanence of a covalent cross-link, combined with the processibility of thermoplastic.

One of the consequences of achieving a thermally reversible physical cross-link is that the properties normally associated with vulcanized rubber systems are compromised. Typically this means that properties such as resistance to deformation (creep or compression set), upper use temperature, and resilience are sacrificed for reasons of good fabrication. Other desirable improvements in the area of TPEs for newer commercialized products also include:

- improved environmental resistance
- lower cost
- better stress-strain behavior.

This chapter is concerned with a number of materials that can be classified as TPEs, which meet one or more of the preceding criteria. In some cases, these materials have not been commercialized but have been described at various scientific meetings or in selected journals.

6.2 ETHYLENE COPOLYMERS

Ethylene copolymers are thermoplastics containing from about 5 to about 35% of a comonomer, usually vinyl acetate or ethyl acrylate. These materials have been available commercially for many years and can be competitive with thermoplastic elastomers and plasticized polyvinyl chloride. Because their properties are similar in some respects to thermoplastic elastomers, they are included in this text as reference materials. The copolymerization of suitable comonomers in high-pressure ethylene polymerization results in ethylene copolymers of reduced crystallinity. Provided that sufficient comonomer is incorporated, the resulting products can have many of the properties of a thermoplastic elastomer. As compared to conventional low-density polyethylene, these copolymers have more elastomeric properties and greater resilience. Generally, the range of comonomer incorporated in these materials to achieve flexibility extends from about 10 up to 35 wt%. While a number of comonomers have been employed, those that are best known and most widely employed are vinyl acetate and ethyl acrylate.

6.2.1 Ethylene–Vinyl Acetate Copolymers (EVA)

The incorporation of vinyl acetate in the ethylene chain increases flexibility, toughness, and clarity, as compared to low-density polyethylene. These effects are primarily due to a reduction of the crystallinity of the polyethylene. In addition to vinyl acetate content, EVA properties are influenced by melt index.

6.2.1.1 Physical Properties

The physical properties of EVA polymers are shown in Table 6-1[5] and are compared with some typical plasticized vinyl compounds. It is evident that one of the outstanding characteristics of EVA is its toughness at low temperature with brittleness temperatures well below −100°F. The flexibility of these materials is also apparent when compared to typical low-density polyethylene. Except at very high levels of vinyl acetate, the tensile strength of the EVA material is also substantially above that of polyethylene. Similarly, the EVA materials exhibit excellent stress crack resistance.

The limitations of EVA are seen most clearly in their heat resistance. Their softening point depends on vinyl acetate content and varies from about 170°F at 10% vinyl acetate to about 120°F at 33% vinyl acetate. In this respect, EVA is more limited than low-density polyethylene and similar to some classes of plasticized vinyl.

6.2.1.2 Processing

EVA copolymers can be injection molded, extruded, or blow molded as with other thermoplastics or TPEs. They do not require curing to achieve the properties shown. (Another class of vinyl acetate–ethylene copolymers with even higher vinyl acetate levels—VAE polymers—are commercially available but are designed for vulcanization and therefore are not classified as TPEs.)

Some typical recommended conditions for injection molding EVA resins are provided in Table 6-2.[6]

The conditions for injection molding EVA copolymers are similar to those for polyethylene. However, the higher melt flow materials may require lower temperatures for optimum processing.

The extrusion requirements of EVA copolymers are similar to those required for low-density polyethylene with melt temperatures of from 350 to 420°F. Extrusion temperatures greater than 450°F should be avoided. In summary, owing to their melt flow rates, and similarity to polyethylene, little difficulty is experienced in conventional fabrication of EVA copolymers.

6.2.1.3 Applications

EVA copolymers have found applications where their combination of flexibility, impact strength, clarity, and good processing characteristics is required.[7] These

Table 6-1. Physical property test results. (*Source:* Data from Technical Information Brochure A95645, E. I. du Pont de Nemours & Company)

ASTM STD.	GENERAL PHYSICAL PROPERTIES	[1]LOW DENSITY POLY-ETHYLENE	EVA 4210 9½% VINYL ACETATE	EVA 3130 12% VINYL ACETATE	EVA 3170 18% VINYL ACETATE	EVA 3175 28% VINYL ACETATE	EVA 3185 33% VINYL ACETATE	TYPE I PLASTI-CIZED VINYL	TYPE II PLASTI-CIZED VINYL	TYPE III PLASTI-CIZED VINYL	TYPE IV PLASTI-CIZED VINYL	[1]STYRENE BUTADIENE RUBBER COMPOUNDS	[1]NEOPRENE W RUBBER COMPOUNDS
D 1238	Melt index (gram/10 min.)	1.9	0.8	2.5	2.5	6.0	43	NC	NC	NC	NC	NA	NA
D 792	Density (grams/CC)	.915	.928	.935	.94	.95	.95	1.34	1.32	1.27	1.24	1.14–1.64	1.2–1.8
D 638	Ult. tensile strength @73°F (psi)	1800	2700	2800	2760	2000	1440	2890	2400	1990	1490	760–3800	1600–3200
D 638	Ult. tensile strength @100°F (psi)	NC	1600	1800	>1380	ND	ND	2390	2130	ND	ND	NC	NC
D 638	Ult. elongation @73°F (%)	600	725	750	750	800	900	270	280	370	400	200–840	200–1000
D 638	Ult. elongation @100°F (%)	NC	750	750	>870	ND	ND	310	330	ND	ND	NC	NC
D 747	Stiffness @73°F (psi)	14,000	11,000	9500	4400	1770	1000	4040	1690	<400	<400	NC	NC
D 1822	Tensile impact @73°F (ft #/in.^{2})	128	NC	315	315	330	200	216	257	295	320	NC	NC
D 746	Low temp. brittleness °F	<–105	<–159	<–159	<–159	<–159	<–159	0	–10	–20	–30	>–73	–40 to –90
D 1894	Dynamic c.o.f. (to s. steel)	.7	.7	.7	1.2	2.2	Block	.75	2.2	2.5	1.7	NC	NC
D 542	Index of refraction	1.51	NC	NC	1.494	1.485	1.480	NC	NC	NC	NC	NC	NC
D 1693	Stress crack resistance (hrs)	40	NC	>1000	>1000	>1000	>1000	NC	NC	NC	NC	NC	NC
	Thermal conductivity Btu/hr sq ft·°F-in.	1.8	2.0	2.1	2.34	2.39	2.40	NC	NC	NC	NC	1.7	NC
D 1525	Vicat softening point °F	190	172	150	138	127	120	143	132	120	113	NA	NA

[1]Data collected from intra-company reports and other technical publications. NC—Data not run or collected. NA—Test does not apply. ND—Could not be determined.

Table 6-2. Approximate conditions for injection molding EVA copolymers.[6]

Rear cylinder temperature, °F	250
Center	300–350
Front	300–400
Nozzle	250–400
Maximum melt temperature	400–450
Injection pressure	5000–15,000
Mold temperature, °F	40–120

include sheeting, wire and cable coatings, flexible tubing, shoe soles, gaskets, automotive applications, grommets, etc. EVA copolymers have also received FDA approval for use in food packaging. EVA film can be heat sealed by common techniques. In addition to their intrinsically good processability, EVA copolymers can be readily pigmented to provide a range of colors and can be extended to a high level with suitable fillers.

6.2.2 Ethylene–Ethyl Acrylate Copolymers

Ethylene-ethyl acrylate (EEA) copolymers are similar in some respects to EVA copolymers. The incorporation of the ethyl acrylate comonomer increases flexibility and reduces the softening temperature. Similarly, the low temperature properties of EEA materials parallel the EVA copolymers.

The properties of several EEA copolymers of varying ethyl acrylate content are shown in Table 6-3. In general, the properties of EEA copolymers are similar to those of the EVA systems when compared at about the same comonomer content. EEA systems can be somewhat superior in stress cracking resistance. In resistance to organic solvents such as aliphatic and aromatic hydrocarbons, EEA copolymers are poorer than polyethylene homopolymer. When compared .to plasticized vinyl, EEA tends to be more resistant than plasticized vinyl to distilled water, methyl ethyl ketone, and tetrachlorethylene. In these cases, the lack of a plasticizer in the EEA copolymers gives these materials an advantage over plasticized vinyl.

6.2.2.1 Processibility

These materials can be injection molded, extruded, and blow molded. Processing temperatures similar to those employed for EVA copolymers (Table 6-2) are recommended. As with EVA copolymers, the processing conditions are determined by the particular grade of copolymer employed as well as the type of fabrication equipment.

Table 6-3. Properties of ethylene-vinyl acetate (EVA) and ethylene-ethyl acrylate (EEA) copolymers. (Source: Materials Engineering, August 1974, p. 40.)

Property	ASTM	Ethylene-vinyl acetate (EVA)[a]				Ethylene-ethyl acrylate (EEA)[b]				
		Injection and blow molding grades			Blow mldg grade	Injection molding grades			Extr and blow mldg grades	
		Vinyl acetate content, %				Ethyl acrylate content, %				
		12	18	33	9.5	5.5	6.5	18	15	20
Melt index, g/10 min	D 1238	2.5	2.5	25.0	0.8	8.0	8.0	6.0	1.5	2.2
Density, g/cm³ (kg/m³)	D 972	0.935 (935)	0.94 (940)	0.95 (950)	0.928 (928)	0.946 (946)	0.938 (938)	0.931 (931)	0.930 (930)	0.933 (933)
Ult ten str, ksi (mPa)	D 638									
Rt		2.8 (19)	2.76 (19)	1.44 (9.9)	2.7 (19)	2.4 (17)	1.7 (12)	1.6 (11)	2.1 (15)	2.0 (14)
100 F (311 K)		1.8 (12)	>1.38 (>9.5)	—	1.6 (11)	—	—	—	—	—
Ult elongation, %	D 638									
Rt		750	750	900	725	50	200	700	700	750
100 F (311 K)		750	>870	—	750	—	—	—	—	—
Stiffness, ksi (MPa)	D 747	9.5 (66)	4.4 (30)	1.0 (6.9)	11.0 (76)	70 (483)	40 (276)	5.0 (35)	7.5 (52)	4.1 (28)
Stiffness (secant mod), ksi (MPa)	D 638	315 (0.28)	315 (0.28)	200 (0.18)	—	—	—	—	—	—
Ten imp str, ft-lb/in.² (J/m²)	D 1822	—	—	—	—	—	—	—	—	—
Hardness, Shore D		—	—	—	—	56	50	32	32	29
Softening temp (Vicat), F (K)	D 1525	150 (339)	138 (332)	120 (322)	172 (351)	—	—	140 (333)	—	—
Brittle pt °F (K)	D 746	<-159 (<167)	<-159 (<167)	<-159 (<167)	<-159 (<167)	—	—	-157 (168)	—	—
Res to stress cracking[c], hr	D 1693	>1000	>1000	>1000	—	—	—	>1000	—	—

[a] Data source: Du Pont. [b] Data source: Union Carbide. [c] Point of 50% failure.

6.2.2.2 Applications

The applications for EEA copolymers are largely based on the outstanding toughness, good low temperature properties, and use of fabrication. Suggested applications include automotive sight shields, flexible hose, and household products such as trash cans, doormats, film packaging, electrical terminal covers, and appliance parts. Many of the applications served by EVA copolymers can also be considered for EEA systems.

6.3 IONIC THERMOPLASTIC ELASTOMERS

6.3.1 Carboxylate Ionomers

Substantial work has been done over the past 15 years or so on hydrocarbon materials containing a small amount of ionic groups that can act as cross-links under suitable conditions. In general, the strength of this ionic association decreases with increasing temperature, and can provide fluidity at elevated temperatures, coupled with good green strength at ambient temperatures. The bulk of the prior art in this area deals with materials based in hydrocarbon backbones, specifically the carboxylated elastomers.

The early work reviewed by H. P. Brown[8] in this area clearly demonstrated that copolymerization of dienes with acrylic acid or methacrylic acid led to products whose properties could be changed markedly by reaction with metal oxides. The incorporation of carboxyl groups at moderate levels (i.e., 2 to 10%) generally increased the hardness and tensile strength of the elastomer and provided improved resistance to hydrocarbon solvents. A substantial volume of such copolymers are currently prepared as latices and sold as such rather than in coagulated form.

The carboxylated elastomers will react readily with metal salts or oxides. The moderately high tensile strengths of the carboxylated rubbers are further enhanced by this "vulcanization" process. The type of base employed in this acid neutralization process can have a substantial influence on the properties of the final vulcanizate. For example, the reaction of a butadiene-methacrylic acid copolymer (0.12 equivalents of acid per 100 parts rubber) with sodium hydroxide, converted the raw rubber from a tensile strength of 0.7 MN/m^2 and 1600% elongation to a tensile of 11.7 MN/m^2 and elongation ot 900%.

In general, the use of monovalent salts to neutralize these carboxylated rubbers apparently gives rise to a modest ionic cross-link at ambient temperatures; but, if heated to 100°C, this structure is dissociated. On the other hand, the use of divalent metal salts gives a network that is considerably stronger. Nevertheless, these vulcanizates manifest substantial flow at elevated temperatures and yet reversibly regain their strength at ambient temperatures.

It has been pointed out in previous references[9] that these carboxylated ionomers can be employed in the design of thermoplastic elastomers. However, the disadvantages associated with these materials of poor compression set, high stress relaxation, and limited upper use temperature range have served to limit their use in those applications normally considered for conventional thermoplastic elastomers. Despite a substantial number of references in the patent literature, there is as yet no significant commercialization of the carboxylated rubbers in such applications, at least insofar as soft (Shore A 50-80) rubbery applications are concerned.

At the present time, a substantial volume of carboxylated rubbers is sold commercially, largely as carboxylated latex for use in textile and paper fields. It has been emphasized[9] that the similar morphologies of the carboxylate ionomer and segmented ABA elastomers suggest a use for this technology in the preparation of thermoplastic elastomers.

A recent patent[1] to E. I. du Pont de Nemours & Company describes a useful thermoplastic elastomer obtained by reacting an ethylene-propylene-diene terpolymer (EPDM) having carboxylic groups attached with a suitable rosin salt of a divalent metal. The resulting ionomers are reported to be thermoplastic at elevated temperatures, and yet possess good physical properties at use temperatures. The incorporation of the required carboxylic groups is effected by grafting maleic anhydride on the EPDM to a level of 0.5 to 5 wt%. The grafted adduct can then be reacted with the rosin salt to provide the thermoplastic elastomer. Alternatively, the grafted EPDM adduct can be compounded with carbon black and oil and then neutralized with the rosin salt to provide a thermoplastic elastomeric compound.

6.3.2 Thionic Polymers

A new class of polymers has been developed within Exxon Research and Engineering Company based on ionic associations.[3] The particular class of ionomers described by workers at Exxon are based on metal sulfonated ethylene propylene terpolymers (Sulfo EPDM). The incorporation of a low level of metal sulfonate groups provides a strong physical cross-link at ambient temperatures, but at elevated temperatures the presence of suitable plasticizing agents permits a reversible dissociation of the ionic groups. Materials based on metal sulfonated-EPDM have been described as thionic polymers,[10] and are not yet available commercially.

One of the initial polymer candidates based on this technology, Thionic Polymer 201, is a zinc sulfonated EPDM, which is recommended for compounding with a variety of polymers, fillers, and oils. The physical properties of Thionic Polymer 201 are:

Hardness, Shore A		70
Tensile strength, psi		2000
Elongation, at break, %		500–600
Softening point, approximate, °C		100°

Some specific compounds based on Thionic Polymer 201 are described in Table 6-4.[10] The hardness range (Shore A) from 55 to 90 can be achieved by adjusting the composition of the formulations. Combinations of fillers and oils, with or without plastics such as high-density polyethylene, are described. The tensile strengths of the resulting compounds range from 1000 to 2700 psi.

The suggested applications for the compounds described are those related to thermoplastic processing techniques. Among the areas suggested for thionic polymers were mechanical goods, footwear, electrical goods, hose, sheet, and film.

Thionic Polymer 352[11] is described as having a Shore A hardness of 92. The physical properties of this compound are seen in Table 6-5. Based on the data in Table 6-5, this compound appears to have good tensile properties and abrasion resistance. Further information relating to the temperature dependence of tensile strength and flex modulus of Thionic Polymer 352 is presented in Table 6-6.

6.3.2.1 Processing Characteristics

The processing of thionic compounds appears similar to that of other thermoplastic elastomers. The ionic associations present in thionic polymers provide a relatively high viscosity at low shear rates. This ionic association is temperature dependent, and therefore a combination of high temperature and high shear is required to effectively process thionic polymers. Some typical processing conditions for thionic compounds are presented in Table 6-7. It is emphasized that the nature of the compound will determine the amount of injection pressure required during injection molding, ranging from less than 500 up to 15,000 psi for the more viscous compounds.[10]

Table 6-4. Typical Thionic Polymer 201 compounds.[10]

Hardness, Shore A	90	65	55
Density, g/cm^3	1.05	1.23	1.08
Tensile strength, psi	2700	1000	1100
Elongation, %	550	600	625
Set at break, %	220	50	50
Melt flow 190°C, 43 psi	0.14	0.5	6
Compositions, phr	100 Thionic 201	100 Thionic 201	100 Thionic 201
	53 High-density polyethylene	65 Oil	85 Oil
	25 Filler	10 Process aids	10 Process aids
		120 Filler	65 Filler

Table 6-5. Typical properties of Thionic Polymer 352 (compression molded pads).[11]

Thionic Polymer 352

TYPICAL PROPERTIES
(Compression Molded Pads)

Hardness, Shore A (initial/after 10 sec.)	92/91
Tensile strength (psi)	2700
Taber abrasion (weight loss in mg/ 1000 cycles, CS-17 wheel)	13
Resilience (%)	64
Elongation at break (%)	550
Tensile set at break (%)	220
Stress at 300% strain (%)	1700
Tensile strength at 100°C (psi)	250
Elongation at 100°C (%)	400
Tear strength (lb./in.)	
Die C	380
Brittle point (°F)	< -100
Compression set (%) (22 hrs., 30 min. recovery)	
77°F	45-55
158°F	95
Melt Index at 190°C (g/10 min.)	
43 psi	.1
430 psi	5
Specific gravity	1.05
Flammability (burning rate, in./min.)	.7

The extrusion conditions for thionic polymers are also provided in Table 6-7. In general, polymer melt temperatures of 350 to 390°F are required. The persistence of some ionic association at elevated temperatures provides an extrudate of substantial melt strength; therefore, thionic polymer technology is particularly suited to this fabrication technique.

6.4 THERMOPLASTIC POLYOLEFINS: VISTAFLEX* THERMOELASTICS

Vistaflex thermoelastic materials are a new family of products available commercially from Exxon Chemical Company. They are thermoplastic olefin materials

*Registered trademark for Exxon Chemical's thermoplastic olefin materials.

Table 6-6. Tensile and flex modulus[a] data of Thionic Polymer 352 at various temperatures (test results on compression molded pads).[11]

Thionic Polymer 352

TENSILE DATA AT VARIOUS TEMPERATURES
(Test Results on Compression Molded Pads)

Temperature °C	Tensile Strength psi	Elongation % at B.	Stress at 300%
25	2700	550	1700
60	1050	620	790
100	260	150	—
125	140	210	—

FLEX MODULUS[a]
AT LOW TEMPERATURES

Temperature °C	Modulus psi
25	9,000
-20	16,000
-30	20,000
-40	31,000

*Torsional Pendulum Results

[a] Torsional pendulum results.

based on ethylene and propylene units. A number of grades of Vistaflex TPEs are available ranging in hardness from 50 (Shore A) to 45 (Shore D).[12] In general, the Vistaflex TPEs are suitable for most thermoplastic fabrication processes such as injection molding and extrusion.

6.4.1 Physical Properties

Some representative products of the current series of Vistaflex TPEs are described in Table 6-8.[13] The softest grades currently available have a hardness (Shore A) of about 45. The physical properties of some of these materials are also presented in Table 6-8. In general, the Vistaflex materials provide a combination of good tensile properties at room temperature and elevated temperature (70°C) along with good flow behavior.

Table 6-7. Some typical processing conditions of thionic compounds.[10]

Thionic Polymer 352

TYPICAL PROCESSING CONDITIONS

INJECTION MOLDING

Barrel Temperature:
Rear, °F	350-400
Front, °F	380-420
Nozzle, °F	370-390
Melt, °F	390

Mold Temperature, °F: 120-180

Injection Pressure (psi): 10,000 to 15,000

Back Pressure (psi):   150-300

EXTRUSION

Barrel Temperature:
Rear, °F	325
Front, °F	350
Die, °F	350

Melt Temperature, °F   350-390

The performance of these materials under a variety of thermal, chemical, and weather exposures has been described in detail.[14] The Vistaflex materials, in general, retain their properties satisfactorily over a broad temperature range. A comparison of the flexural modulus of several Vistaflex thermoelastics with other materials is shown in Figure 6-1. It is evident that from a temperature of about −30 up to 70°C, these Vistaflex products manifest a much smaller change in flexural modulus than do the polyurethane systems shown. Similarly, the tensile strength dependence of two Vistaflex products is shown in Figure 6-2, and compared with a cured, highly extended ethylene propylene terpolymer compound of about 80 Shore A hardness. It is seen that the decay in tensile properties for the Vistaflex materials compares favorably with the thermoset EPDM.

It is clear from the data of Figures 1 and 2 that these thermoplastic olefins retain their properties over a range of temperatures. A final comparison of this

Table 6-8. Physical properties of Vistaflex thermoelastics.[13]

	701	801	902	903C	904C	905B	906C
General							
Color	Natural	Natural	Natural	Dark Black	Black	Black	Black
Specific Gravity	1.02	1.06	0.89	1.06	1.05	0.88	1.04
Cost, ¢/lb. (Jan., 1976)	47	46	54	53	48.5	50	49
Cost, ¢/cu. inch (Jan., 1976)	1.73	1.76	1.73	2.03	1.84	1.59	1.84
Flow							
Melt Flow Rate at 230C, Condition L (2.16 kg), g/10 min	1.5	1.5	4.1	11.4*	0.5	0.6	0.6
EXXON CHEMICALS Spiral Flow Test at 221C, cm	26	23	25	15	8.1	12.4	9.8
Hardness							
Hardness, Shore A							
Initial	75	82	91	92	—	—	—
15 Second Dwell	67	76	90	91	—	—	—
Hardness, Shore D							
Initial	19	22	35	41	45	40	40
15 Second Dwell	11	16	30	35	34	30	27
Tensile Properties, Injection Molded, Die C							
At Room Temperature							
Strength at Break, psi	860	1085	1820	2050	950	1200	1200
Elongation at Break, %	135	160	580	540	100	195	250
At 70C (158F)							
Strength at Break, psi	430	570	750	700	—	—	—
Elongation at Break, %	30	50	400	150	—	—	—
Stiffness							
Flexural Modulus, Secant at Room Temp., ASTM D 790, psi	5100	8000	18,200	17,500	22,000	28,000	15,000
Resiliency							
Recovery from 180 Degree Bend Chevrolet Test CTZ ZZ003AA,							
30 Second Retention, degrees	17	19	22	19	30	—	25
5 Minute Retention, degrees	14	16	19	16	25	27	17
Compression Set (B)							
Plied, 22 Hours at 70C, %	72	71	77	75	—	—	—

*Melt flow rate at 230C (10.0 kg), g/10 min

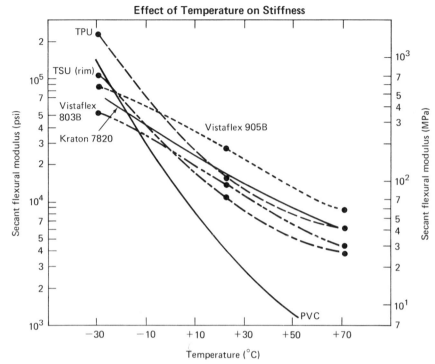

**Figure 6-1. Effect of temperature on stiffness. (Reprinted with permission, Copyright ©
Society of Automotive Engineers, Inc., 1976. All rights reserved.)**

characteristic with two well-known materials, plasticized PVC and ABS, is
shown in Figure 6-3. The lack of sharp transitions in the Vistaflex materials in
the temperature range of −50°C up to nearly 150°C is readily apparent and is in
sharp contrast to the behavior of the two conventional thermoplastic systems.
These data, of course, suggest that Vistaflex materials can be quite suitable for
use at low temperatures as well as elevated temperatures, without loss of their
elastomeric properties.

6.4.2 Fabrication

As with most thermoplastic elastomers, the conditions for processability are dependent upon the specific compound employed, the nature of the injection-
molding or extrusion equipment, and on the nature of the die or mold employed. When compared with plasticized PVC, Vistaflex materials may require
higher injection pressures and/or larger gate sizes to a specific part. As with
other TPEs, the location and size of gates and runners can have an effect on

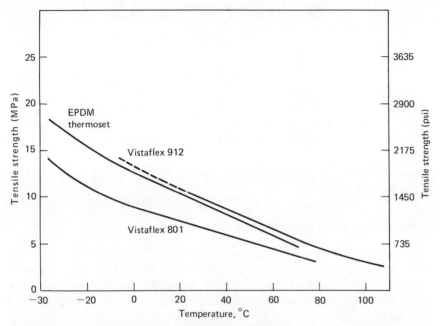

Figure 6-2. Vistaflex tensile strength at various test temperatures. (Reprinted with permission, Copyright © Society of Automotive Engineers, Inc., 1976. All rights reserved.)

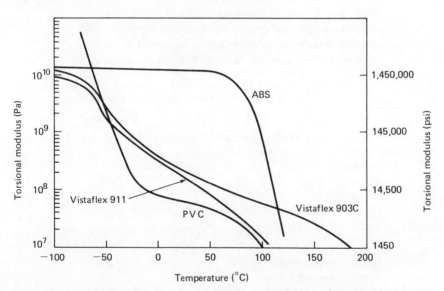

Figure 6-3. Vistaflex torsional modulus at various temperatures. (Reprinted with permission, Copyright © Society of Automotive Engineers, Inc., 1976. All rights reserved.)

the physical properties of the molded piece. Some suggested conditions for injection molding of a Vistaflex compound are:

Barrel temperature, °F	
Rear	400
Center	430
Front	430
Nozzle	440
Mold temperature, °F	100 to 130

In general, the cycle times for injection molding Vistaflex products are similar to those for PVC and TPU.

6.4.3 Environmental Resistance

The outdoor aging and Weatherometer exposure of several Vistaflex products have been described.[14, 15] Relatively little change in tensile properties was observed after Florida exposures up to 1 yr. Similarly, aging under intense ultraviolet light or in the Weatherometer caused relatively little change (10 to 20%) in tensile properties or in hardness. Some representative data obtained on Weatherometer-exposed samples are shown in Table 6-9.

Table 6-9. Effects of Weatherometer and South Florida exposure on physical properties of olefinic thermoelastics. (_Source_: Reprinted with permission, Copyright © Society of Automotive Engineers, Inc., 1976, All rights reserved.)

	Conductive	Non Conductive ·
	% retained	% retained
Weather-0meter (1000 hrs.)		
Hardness, Shore D	106	104
Tensile Strength	87	88
Elongation %	74	89
Flexural Modulus	119	109
1 Year South Florida		
Hardness, Shore D	109	100
Tensile Strength	109	85
Elongation	65	56
Flexural Modulus	115	112

The chemical resistance of these materials has been established by immersion in a number of different solvents and other reagents. A summary of the chemical resistance of Vistaflex 801 (initial Shore A Hardness of 82) as determined by immersion, is shown in Table 6-10. It is evident that, with the exception of acetic acid, the common aqueous bases and the organic alcohols and amines do not have a major effect on this material. However, esters, ketones, and hydrocarbons can significantly affect the volume swell of the immersed sample as judged by the weight change observed.

The ozone resistance of Vistaflex compounds appears to be good as judged by exposure at 100 pphm at 40°C.

While Vistaflex materials possess outstanding thermal stability, heat, chemical, and weather resistance, they can also be either colored or painted to extend their utility. Various olefinic color packages can be employed to tint Vistaflex directly. Alternatively, Vistaflex systems can be painted using commercially available flexible coatings. Electrostatic and conventional painting processes can be employed successfully.

The painted surfaces obtained, when decorated according to recommended procedures, can withstand various environmental exposures well. Considerable effort has been expended to demonstrate the performance integrity of these materials.[14, 15]

6.4.4 Applications

The excellent environmental resistance of Vistaflex products coupled with their excellent thermal stability makes these materials obvious candidates for automotive applications. In addition, they can be readily decorated by a variety of techniques, especially painting, which thus expands their utility in this particular market. Similarly, Vistaflex materials can be considered for electrical applications such as insulation or molded connectors, for extruded hose and tubing, for sporting goods, appliance parts, and similar applications.

6.5 POLYSILOXANE-BASED THERMOPLASTIC ELASTOMERS

Thermoplastic elastomers based on nonhydrocarbon elastomers have been reported in a number of patents and publications. Those based on polydimethylsiloxane have been of considerable interest.

The incentive to employ polydimethylsiloxane as the elastomeric phase stems from the apparently unique features of such systems. These have been reported as retention of flexibility at low temperature, excellent electrical properties, ozone resistance, durability toward weathering, and a high degree of permeability toward gases. The following discussion is directed at several systems that have been reviewed in the literature.

Table 6-10. Chemical resistance of Vistaflex 801. (Reprinted with permission, Copyright © Society of Automotive Engineers, Inc., 1976, All rights reserved.)

	14 days at room temperature			
		Shore A 15s Delay	Tensile Strength, psi	Elongation, %
Original Properties		79	830	410
Solvent	% Wt. Change	Δ Shore A 15s Delay	Tensile Strength, % Retained	Elongation, % Retained
Inorganic Acids, Bases, Salts				
10% Hydrochloric Acid	+ 0.1	− 5	101	85
10% Sodium Hydroxide	0.0	− 2	101	98
Sat'd Potassium Permanganate	0.0	− 1	101	90
Sat'd Calcium Hypochlorite	+ 0.2	+ 1	101	110
Organic Acids, Alcohols, Amines				
Acetic Acid	+ 37.7	− 8	78	48
Ethanol	− 4.4	0	105	60
Diethylene Triamine	+ 0.4	0	98	40

Esters, Hydrocarbons, Ketones

Toluene	−36.4	+13	117	129
Perchloroethylene	+171.5	−26	40	~10
Methyl Ethyl Ketone	−30.2	+13	116	107
Ethyl Acetate	−30.8	+14	116	115

Oil, Gasoline

ASTM #3 Oil	+29.4	−9	60	48
Primol 355	+19.6	−10	92	71
Hydraulic Oil	+11.0	−3	72	76
Gasoline	+17.7	−9	68	86

Detergent, Animal Fat

1% Cheer	0.0	+1	101	105
Chicken Fat	−3.8	−1	116	124

6.5.1 Block Copolymers of Polystyrene-Polydimethylsiloxane

Research efforts at Dow Corning Corp. have resulted in a family of block co-polymers based on short blocks of polystyrene and polydimethylsiloxane.[16] These systems differ from more typical block copolymers (such as those based on polystyrene-polybutadiene) in that the hard and soft blocks alternate six to eight times. Therefore, the hard blocks are relatively low in molecular weight (4000 to 15,000) in order to provide material that will perform adequately in melt fabrication.

The block polymers are apparently prepared via ring opening polymerization of hexamethyl cyclotrisiloxane with living α,ω-dilithiopolystyrene followed by termination with reactive Li silanolate functionality and further polymerization with stiochiometric amounts of dialkyldichlorosilanes as below.[16]

$$Li\,[CH_2CH(C_6H_5)]_n\,Li + 2m(Me_2SiO)_3 + \text{polar solvent}$$

$$Li(OMe_2Si)_m\,[CH_2CH(C_6H_5)]_n\,(SiMe_2O)_m\,Li$$

$$\searrow$$
$$R_2SiX_2$$

$$[(OMe_2Si)_m(CH_2-CH(C_6H_5))_n(SiMe_2O)_m]_x$$

The properties of the resulting materials can vary from that of thermoplastic elastomers to that of low modulus thermoplastics, depending on the ratio of hard block to soft block employed.[16]

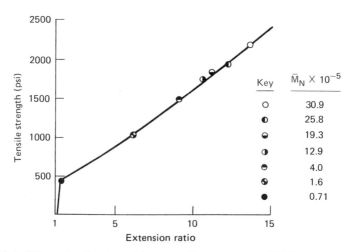

Figure 6-4. Effect of molecular weight on tensile properties of $(BAB)_x$. 30 wt% polystyrene. $M_A = 13,500$. (J. C. Saam, A. Howard, and F. W. G. Fearon. *J. Inst. Rubber Ind.* 1973, 7[2]: 69–71.)

Table 6-11. Effect of polystyrene block size on mechanical properties of compression-molded polystryene-polydimethylsiloxane block copolymers containing 30 percent polystyrene.[16]

Mn POLYSTYRENE BLOCK	DEGREE OF CONDENSATION (x)	TENSILE AT BREAK (PSI)	ELONGATION AT BREAK (%)
4,000	3.3	240	120
7,700	3.6	700	260
11,100	3.9	950	550
12,300	3.5	1,020	350
13,550	3.3	1,030	480

The stress-strain curve for typical polystyrene polydimethylsiloxane block copolymers is shown in Figure 6-4. As the molecular weight of the block polymers increases, the tensile strength at break increases until it levels off. In general, a block molecular weight for polystyrene of about 8000 is required to obtain useful mechanical properties, while a value above 12,000 gives little further improvement as shown in Table 6-11.

As expected, changing the amount of polystyrene in the block copolymer dominates the initial modulus and the yield point of the block copolymer. As

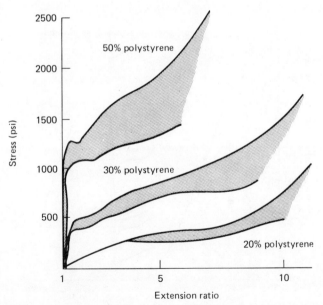

Figure 6-5. Effect of polystyrene content on tensile properties. (J. C. Saam, A. Howard, and F. W. G. Fearon. *J. Inst. Rubber Ind.* 1973, 7[2] : 69–71.)

Table 6-12. Effect of T_g of the hard 'A' block on tensile properties of $(BAB)_x$ containing 40 wt% of 'A'. (*Source*: J. C. Saam, A. Howard, and F. W. G. Fearon. *J. Inst. Rubber Ind.* 7(2): 69–71.)

TEMPERATURE (°C)	A = POLYSTYRENE		A = POLY(α-METHYLSTYRENE)	
	TENSILE AT BREAK (PSI)	ELONGATION AT BREAK	TENSILE AT BREAK (PSI)	ELONGATION AT BREAK (%)
25	1550	800	2400	700
50	1080	1000	–	–
100	90	300	870	800
130	–	–	300	1160
150	–	–	90	1100

shown in Figure 6-5, a range of 20 to 50% polystyrene is sufficient to alter the stress-strain curve from an elastomeric material to thermoplastic product.

Dow Corning workers have also shown that the use of α-methyl styrene blocks in place of polystyrene provides better ultimate tensile properties at a given temperature as well as a much increased use temperature at a given level of hard

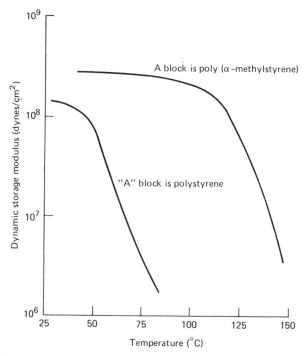

Figure 6-6. Effect of T_g of 'A' block on thermomechanical properties. (J. C. Saam, A. Howard, and F. W. G. Fearon. *J. Inst. Rubber Ind.* 1972, 7[2] : 69–71.)

block. The increase in tensile strength at a given temperature is shown in Table 6-12, where room-temperature tensile strengths of 2400 psi are shown for poly (α-methyl styrene) as contrasted to 1550 psi for polystyrene. Similarly, the modulus behavior as a function of temperature is shown in Figure 6-6 where the α-methyl styrene block softens about 70°C higher than the styrene block.

It is also reported that the copolymers based on poly-α-methyl styrene hard blocks show better oxidative thermal stability than those based on polystyrene after extended exposure in air at 150°C.

6.5.2 Alternating Block Polymers of Dimethyl Siloxane and Bisphenol A Carbonate

Block polymers having the elastomer block of polydimethylsiloxane and the hard block composed of poly (bisphenol A carbonate) have been described by workers at General Electric Co. laboratories.[17] These are alternating random block polymers of the –ABABA– type in which the blocks are polydisperse and of fairly low degrees of polymerization.

Typically, polycarbonate contents in these materials can range from 35% up to 85%. At polycarbonate levels of 50% and above, the copolymers were leathery with yield points in their stress-strain curves. The tensile strengths and elongations of these block polymers vary from elastomeric to thermoplastic as a function of polycarbonate content. Tensile strengths of 2000 to 3000 psi are achieved at polycarbonate levels of about 40 wt%.

One of the interesting characteristics of these materials, which distinguishes them from the typical ABA thermoplastic elastomers, is that while the polycarbonate blocks associate to form the domains that act as the physical cross-links, the matrix is composed of both silicone and bisphenol A carbonate blocks. As a consequence, it has been proposed that the mechanical behavior of the matrix, specifically its spectrum of relaxation times, can be quite different from that of either homopolymer.

6.5.3 Polysulfone-Polydimethylsiloxane Block Copolymers

Workers at Union Carbide Corp. laboratories have described a series of block copolymers based on a polysulfone hard block and a siloxane soft block.[18] These systems are synthesized from preformed oligomers bearing different, mutually reactive, end groups. As a consequence, the block structure of these materials is well defined and mutually controlled. The synthesis of these block copolymers is described in Equation 6-1.

These block copolymers have well-defined alternating $(AB)_n$ block sequence structures. Since the two oligomers can react with each other but not with themselves, the structure of the blocks in the polymer is the same as in the oligomer. The physical properties of these block copolymers are, of course, highly dependent upon the relative content of the two oligomers. Figure 6-9 describes the temperature modulus curves of three samples wherein the block length of the silicone block ranges in molecular weight from 350 to about 5100. About 50% of the siloxane block is required to insure the properties of a thermoplastic elastomer. The physical properties of a number of block copolymer compositions is shown in Table 6-13 wherein the block length (and therefore the composition) of the polysiloxane is varied over a broad range. The very high glass transition of the polysulfone homopolymer (190°C) is manifested in the phase separated block copolymers, but is moderately reduced to about 160 to 170°C.

These high-siloxane-content compositions are reported to display excellent recovery properties and behave like cross-linked silicone rubbers. These materials are clear and possess excellent resistance to oxidative abuse, such as extended exposure at 170°C in a forced air oven without substantial change. In addition, the hydrolytic stability is reported to be substantially superior to that of polyurethanes.

6.5.4 Silicone-Polyethylene Blends

An interesting approach to multicomponent polymer systems involves the blending of polyethylene with high molecular weight polydimethylsiloxane containing a low level of unsaturation.[19] When such blends are prepared under conditions of heat and mechanical shear, grafting of the two polymers occurs. This grafting and accompanying low level of cross-linking leads to the formation of two-phase blends, in which the silicone polymer generally comprises the dispersed phase and the polyethylene is the continuous phase.

While the specific phase compositions have not been unambiguously determined, it appears that there is a substantial gel fraction largely composed of the silicone fraction. The polyethylene is less tightly cross-linked. It is postulated that during the mixing reaction, the silicone is dispersed in the polyethylene, which, under shear, undergoes some breakdown with resultant free radicals. These radicals graft to the silicone unsaturation and promote cross-linking of the silicone rubber.

The effect of adding silicone under the conditions described by Dow Corning investigators is to decrease the tensile modulus sharply, even with minor amounts

Table 6-13. Effect of block $\overline{M}_n$ on block copolymer properties. (*Source:* A. Noshay, M. Matzner, and C. N. Merriam. *J. Polymer Science:* A-1, 1971 9(II), 3147.)

BLOCK $\overline{M}_n$		WEIGHT % SILOXANE	REDUCED VISCOSITY (a)	TENSILE MODULUS (PSI)	TENSILE STRENGTH (PSI)	ELONGATION (%)	T_g (b) (°C)
POLYSULFONE	POLYDIMETHYL-SILOXANE						
4700	350	10	0.4	240,000	6000	5	+125
4700	1700	28	1.1	170,000	4700	12	+140
9300	4900	41	0.4	29,000	2700	150	-110;+170
4700	5100	55	0.8	20,000	2400	350	-120;+160
4700	9200	67	1.5	2,000	1300	500	-120;+160
6500	25,000	79	1.3	300	900	550	-120;+160

(a) 0.2 g/dl in CH_2Cl_2 @ 25°C.
(b) Determined from temperature-modulus and resilience measurements.

Equation 6-1. Synthesis of polysulfone-polydimethysiloxane block copolymers. (Source: A. Noshay, M. Matzner, and C. N. Merriam. J. Polymer Science: A-1, 1971, 9(II), 3147.)

Table 6-14. Tensile and electrical properties. (*Source*: J. R. Falender, S. E. Lindsey, and J. C. Saam, *Polymer Engineering and Science*, 16(1): January 1976.)

	BLEND	DOW POLYETHYLENE 130®	SILASTIC 55® SILICONE
Tensile strength, psi	1300	2200	1300
Elongation, percent	550	760	600
Modulus, psi	4500	12,000	—
Volume resistivity	4×10^{15}	1×10^{16}	5×10^{14}
Dielectric constant			
100 cycles/sec	2.5	2.4	3.0
100 Kcycles/sec	2.6	2.4	—
Dissipation factor			
100 cycles/sec	.0019	.0011	.0015
100 Kcycles/sec	.0014	.0020	—

Blends consist of a 50% mixture of Dow polyethylene 130® and 4m% MeViSiO silicone mixed 20 min at 185°C/62 rpm/cam head/Brabender®.

of silicone. Consequently, the blends act typically as rubbery thermoplastics with the properties shown in Table 6-14.

It is reported that these polyethylene-silicone blends, despite the grafting and obvious presence of a gel fraction, can be readily processed. The presence of the silicone greatly lowers the energy requirements for mixing. The torque required to mix the 50% blend of the table above is reported to be less than half of that for polyethylene. Furthermore, it is reported that, under shear, the polymer melt behaves suitably for injection molding or extrusion. Under conditions of low shear, however, there is little flow. Certain electrical properties of these blends, such as corona resistance, are reported to be equal to or superior to those of polyethylene.

6.6 THERMOPLASTIC 1,2 POLYBUTADIENE

A substantial amount of work[20-22] by Japan Synthetic Rubber Company (JSR) has been reported in the literature dealing with 1,2 polybutadiene (1,2 PBD). This new thermoplastic is greater than 90% 1,2 content and has a controlled degree of crystallinity between 15 and 25%. The crystallinity of this new 1,2 PBD is markedly less than previously described syndiotactic 1,2 polybutadienes. Consequently, the crystalline melting point is 80 to 90°C, which permits fabrication on plastics fabrication equipment.

1,2 PBD, as described by JSR investigators,[21] is prepared via solution polymerization techniques with Ziegler-type catalyst systems. With the discovery of this polymer, JSR has conducted an intensive effort on the research and develop-

Table 6-15. Typical physical properties of JSR 1,2 polybutadiene.[23]

Properties	Testing methods	Units	Measured values	
			JSR RB810	JSR RB820
Density	Density-gradient tube method	g/cm^3	0.901	0.906
Crystallinity	Density-gradient tube method	%	approx. 15	approx. 25
Microstructure 1,2-unit content	Infrared ray spectrum (Morero method)	%	90	92
Refractive index n_{25}^d	ASTM D542		1.513	1.515
MFI (Melt flow index) 150°C, 2,160g	ASTM D1238	g/10min	3	3
Thermal properties Vicat softening point	ASTM D1525	°C	39	52
Melting point*	(DSC method)	°C	75	80
glass transition point	(DSC method)	°C	−30	−25

Tensile properties				
300% modulus	JIS K6301	kg/cm^2	40	60
Tensile strength		kg/cm^2	65	105
Elongation		%	750	700
Hardness				
Shore D	ASTM D1706	Degrees	25	34
JIS A	JIS K6301	Degrees	77	89
Izod impact (notched, at room temperature)	ASTM D256	kg-cm/cm	Not broken	Not broken
Light transmittance	JIS K6714	%	91	91
Haze	JIS K6714	%	1.0	1.0

Note: * Endothermic peak temperature according to the differential scanning calorimeter method.
(Speed of temperature rise: 20°C per minute)
The values shown in the above table are typical values measured at the JSR development research laboratory.

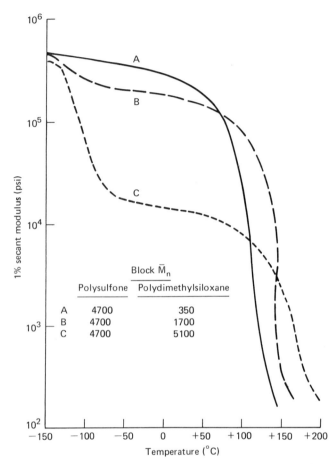

Figure 6-7. Temperature modulus curves. (A. Moshay, M. Matzner, and C. N. Merriam. *J. Polymer Science*, A-1, 1971, 9[11]: 3147.)

ment application studies and market development of this family of products. They reportedly have a plant capacity of 10,000 MT/yr.[21] There are two grades of PBD—designated JSR RB810 and JSR RB820—which differ in crystallinity.

6.6.1 Physical Properties

Some important physical properties of 1,2 PBD are shown in Table 6-15 and in Figures 6-7 through 6-9. In some respects, the properties of 1,2 PBD are similar to LDPE except for its greater flexibility. This can be seen also in Figure 6-10

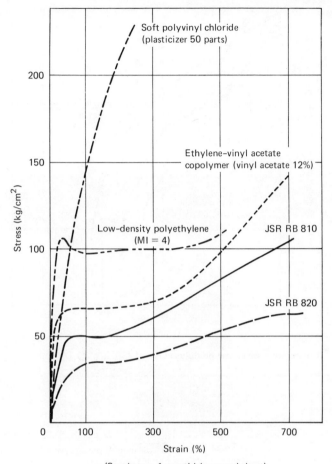

Figure 6-8. Stress vs. strain curve of 1,2 PBD.[23]

where the stress-strain curves of high-density polyethylene (HDPE), SBR gum, and 1,2 PBD are compared. It is seen that the 1,2 PBD has a stress-strain relation that is intermediate to that of the plastic and rubber.

Similarly, the "dynamic" elastic modulus of 1,2 PBD is shown in Figure 6-9 and compared with that of low-density polyethylene (LDPE) and ethylene vinyl acetate (12% vinyl acetate). At temperatures of below 20°C, the 1,2 PBD can be more flexible than either EVA or LDPE. These characteristics of flexibility over a useful temperature range and properties intermediate between conventional

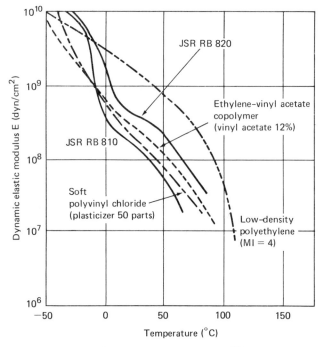

Figure 6-9. Temperature vs. elastic modulus curve of JSR RB.[23]

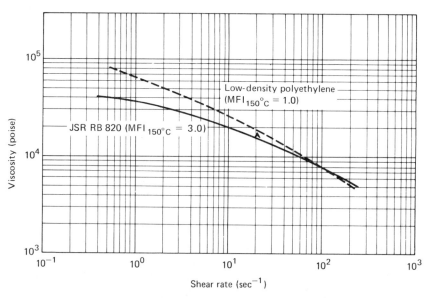

Figure 6-10. Viscosity curve of JSR RB820.[23]

plastics and elastomers combine to make 1,2 PBD an interesting thermoplastic elastomer candidate.

6.6.2 Chemical Properties

One distinctive characteristic of 1,2 PBD, which has received considerable study, is that this material can be readily sulfur vulcanized, if desired. Furthermore, it has been reported that the cured products based on 1,2 PBD exhibit excellent weatherability and ozone resistance similar to that of EPDM. A number of potential applications based on cured 1,2 PBD have been reviewed.[23]

Due to its structure, 1,2 PBD will readily react with selected chemical reagents and can be activated by heat and ultraviolet light. For example, the polymer will readily deteriorate (i.e., photodegrade) within a few months under outdoor exposure. This deterioration is due to a photoinduced cross-linking reaction, which can be modulated by various stabilizers. This concept has been exploited in a highly photosensitive printing system.[23]

6.6.3 Processing

The viscosity-shear rate relationship for 1,2 PBD of about 100,000 molecular weight is shown in Figure 6-10 and compared with LDPE. It is reported that the processing of 1,4 PBD is very similar to that of LDPE. In general, it is desirable to keep the temperature of fabrication relatively low in order to avoid cross-linking, which can occur with the polymer. The recommended maximum temperature is 150°C. Some suggested operating conditions for extrusion of 1,2 PBD are shown in Table 6-16.

JSR RB can be readily extruded in a blown film operation. The temperature of the cylinder and die should be set so that resin temperature ranges from 130 to 150°C. Some representative conditions for extruding blown film based on JSR RB820 are shown in Table 6-17.

6.6.4 Potential Applications

Due to its unique high functional reactivity, flexibility, and good processing characteristics, 1,2 PBD is reported to have applications in the following areas:

Table 6-16. Example of extruding temperatures of JSR RS820.[23]

	CYLINDER			ADAPTER	DIE
	C_1	C_2	C_3	A	D
Present temperature, °C	100	120	130	140	140

Table 6-17. Example of JSR RB820 blown film forming.[23]

MATERIAL	JSR RB820
Extruding machine	40 mm
Screw	
Type	Metering type
L/D	24
Compression ratio	2.0
Die	
Bore diameter	75 mm
Lip clearance	0.7 mm
Preset temperature	
C_1	100°C
C_2	120°C
C_3	130°C
D	150°C
Screw revolution	42 rpm
Resin pressure	250 kg/cm^2
Resin temperature	145°C
Discharge rate	10.7 kg/hr
Blow-up ratio	5.1
Haul-off speed	10 m/min
Film thickness	18 μm

Thermoplastics
Thermosetting resins
Coatings
Rubber
Fibers
Adhesive
Sponge

One area in which substantial applications work has been conducted is that of film. The properties of JSR RB820 film are compared with those of LDPD, EVA, and plasticized vinyl in Table 6-18. The outstanding characteristics of 1,2 PBD film are:

1. Good transparency
2. High gas permeability
3. High tear resistance
4. High coefficient of friction
5. Low heat-sealing temperature.

Based on these and other considerations, it is proposed that 1,2 PBD would be suitable for food packaging applications. In film areas, 1,2 PBD has been suggested as an excellent candidate for stretch film, shrinkable film, and laminated film.

Table 6-18. Physical properties of JSR RB820 film and other films.[23]

TEST ITEM	TESTING METHOD	UNIT	JSR RB820	LOW-DENSITY POLY-ETHYLENE	SOFT POLYVINYL CHLORIDE	ETHYLENE-VINYL ACETATE COPOLYMER
Film thickness		μm	50	50	50	50
Density		g/cm^3	0.91	0.92	1.26	0.93
Tensile strength		kg/cm^2				
machine direction	JIS Z 1702		200	170	250	175
transverse direction			200	140	250	180
Elongation	JIS Z 1702	%				
machine direction			500	290	240	400
transverse direction			570	410	240	560
Tear strength	Correspond to	kg/cm				
machine direction	JIS Z 1702		78	13	58	15
transverse direction			76	33	67	19
Moisture permeability	JIS Z 0208	g $\cdot$ 0.1 mm/m^2 $\cdot$ 24 hrs	98	25	100	45
Gas permeability:	ASTM D 1434	cc $\cdot$ 0.1 mm/m^2 $\cdot$ 24 hrs $\cdot$ atm				
Carbon dioxide			2.8×10^4	7.9×10^3	3.0×10^3	1.1×10^4
Oxygen			5.5×10^3	1.5×10^3	9.3×10^2	1.8×10^3
Ethylene oxide			3.2×10^5	2.1×10^4	—	
Light transmittance	JIS Z 6714	%	92	80	92	88
Haze		%	1	14	1	6
Gloss	JIS Z 8741	%	130	15	130	70

Note: All films are blown films (Blow ratio: 2.5)
Low-density polyethylene: MI = 4
Soft polyvinyl chloride: Plasticizer 50 parts
Ethylene-vinyl acetate copolymer: Vinyl acetate 12%

Table 6-19. Physical properties of JSR RB, EVA and
SB-TPE as sole materials for footwear.[23]

	JSR RB	EVA	SB-TPE
Lightness	O	Δ	X
Rubbery feeling	Δ	X	O
Hardness	Δ	O	X
Permanent set	Δ	X	O
Compression set	O	X	X
Tear strength	O	O	X
Flex resilience	O	X	Δ
Weatherability	Δ	O	X
Ozone resistance	O	O	X
Abrasion resistance	O	O	Δ
Oil resistance	O	O	X
Flowability	O	O	X

Note: O: Excellent
       Δ: Moderate
       X: Poor

Other applications include hot melt adhesives, injection-molded articles, and sponge or cellular applications such as expanded shoe soles. In the area of footwear, JSR RB is proposed as a suitable material for noncuring low blow-molded shoe soles. In physical properties, it is suggested that JSR RB ranks just between polyurethane and ethylene vinyl acetate in physical properties. A comparison of physical properties of JSR RB, EVA, and styrenebutadiene block copolymers is provided in Table 6-19.

6.7 REFERENCES

1. U.S. Patent 3,997,487, R. W. Rees and H. G. Reinhardt to E. I. du Pont de Nemours & Co., Inc., Dec. 14, 1976.
2. D. Brenner and R. D. Lundberg, Paper No. 55, 110th Rubber Div. ACS Meeting, San Francisco, California, Oct. 1976.
3. J. Bock, R. D. Lundberg, and H. S. Makowski, Abstract in *Rubber Age* 108: 33 (September 1976).
4. J. C. Danjard, C. Niemerich, and M. Pineri, *Rev. Gen. Caout. Plast.* 50(9): 723–727 (1973).

5. Data from Technical Information Brochure (A 95645), E. I. du Pont de Nemours & Company.
6. Data from Technical Information Brochure (A 73984), E. I. du Pont de Nemours & Company.
7. *Materials Engineering*, August 1974, p. 40.
8. H. P. Brown, *Rubber Chemistry and Technology* **36**: 931 (1963).
9. D. K. Jenkins and E. W. Duck, Chapter 2 of *Ionic Polymers* (L. Holliday, ed.), p. 184.
10. *Thionic Polymers—A New Family of Thermoelastics*, Technical Information Brochure from Exxon Research and Engineering Co., Corporate Research Laboratories.
11. *Thionic Polymer 352*, Technical Information Brochure from Exxon Research and Engineering Co., Corporate Research Laboratories.
12. *Materials Engineering*, December 1975, Manual 258.
13. Data available from Technical Information Brochure, Exxon Chemical Company, 1975.
14. S. A. Banks, J. A. Brillinger, R. C. Puydak, G. N. Schmit, and C. A. Coffey, 108th Rubber Div. Mtg. of ACS, Minneapolis, Minn., April 27–30, 1976.
15. S. A. Banks, J. H. Brillinger, and D. G. Perham, Publication 760728, Society of Automotive Engineers Meeting, October 1976.
16. J. C. Saam, A. Howard, and F. W. G. Fearon, *Journal Inst. Rubber Ind.* **7**(2): 69–71 (April 1973).
17. Vaughn, H. A., *J. Poly. Sci.* (1969) I Part B, p. 569
    Kambour, R. P., *J. Poly. Sci.* (1969) I Part B, p. 573
    Legrand, D. G., *J. Poly. Sci.* (1969) I Part B, p. 579
    R. P. Kambour, *Block Polymers*, Proc. of Symposium held in 1968, Ed. by S. L. Aggarwal, p. 263, Pub. by Plenum Press, 1970.
18. A. Noshay, M. Matzner, and C. N. Merriam, *J. Polymer Science* A-1, **9**(11): 3147 (1971).
19. J. R. Falender, S. E. Lindsey, and J. C. Saam, *Polymer Engineering and Science* **16**(1): January 1976.
20. S. Kimura, N. Shiraishi, S. Yanagisara, and M. Abe, *Polymer Plastics Technology and Engineering* **5**(1): 83 (1975).
21. Y. Takeuchi, A. Sekimoto, and M. Abe, *ACS Symposium Series* **4** (New Industrial Polymer Symposium): 15 (1974).
22. Ibid., p. 26.
23. *JSR RB810, JSR RB820*, Technical Information Booklet of Japan Synthetic Rubber Co., Ltd.
24. U.S. Patent 3,997,487, R. W. Rees and H. G. Reinhardt, E. I. du Pont de Nemours & Co., Inc., December 14, 1976.

7

Compounding Thermoplastic Elastomers for Specific Applications

Patrick A. DePaolo
and
David P. DaVia
Prolastomer, Inc.
Cheshire, Connecticut

7.1 INTRODUCTION

7.1.1 Emergence of Thermoplastic Elastomers in the Marketplace

Thermoplastic elastomers (TPE) are becoming increasingly important in many major polymer markets. The concept of combining the processing ease and economics of a thermoplastic polymer with desirable end-product characteristics normally derived only from vulcanized elastomers has become well established.

Various TPE polymer types have been introduced since Shell Chemical Company commercialized the first styrene-butadiene-styrene block copolymers. Product design engineers can now choose from a wide variety of TPEs including styrene-butadiene and styrene-isoprene block copolymers (Kraton, Solprene), thermoplastic urethanes (TPU), polyolefin plastic/rubber compositions (TPR, Somel, Telcar, Vistaflex, etc.), block copolymers of styrene-ethylene-butylene-styrene (Kraton G), and borderline elastomers such as Surlyn Ionomer and Trans-Pip polyisoprene.

New TPE materials now in the development stage are expected to be introduced shortly, including polymers and compounds designed to overcome one or more deficiencies of current materials, such as high cost, poor compression set, oil-solvent resistance, flammability, and limited high temperature capabilities. The wide variety of potential applications in nearly all major end-use markets assures a continued market for higher quality as well as more economical TPE polymers and compounds.

The use of each TPE polymer type is growing in specific markets and applications for which these compounds are best suited. The styrene-butadiene-styrene block copolymers are used primarily in compounds for the large-volume casual footwear and low-cost sneaker sole market. Solution and hot melt adhesives are a primary market for S-isoprene-S as well as S-B-S copolymers. The major outlet for polyolefin rubber/plastic compositions is automotive painted sight shields and filler panels. Thermoplastic urethanes are used in cable jacketing, skateboard wheels, and molded and extruded goods requiring maximum abrasion resistance.

Improved TPE polymers and compounds are anticipated, which should result in major growth in applications such as gaskets and seals, hose, wire and cable, construction, and automotive and industrial products.

7.1.2 Projected Growth of TPEs vs. Conventional Elastomers and Flexible Plastics

Thermoplastic elastomers as a class have the potential for significant sales growth via three separate routes: replacement of conventional vulcanized rubbers, replacement of flexible thermoplastics (primarily PVC compound), and use in newly designed products that utilize the unique combination of properties and processing offered by the different TPE types.

Many current applications for TPE are being found in the "overlap" markets, defined as *the group of applications that utilize both vulcanized elastomers and flexible plastics.* An example is the automotive use of flexible body panels and sight shields, where plastics (such as PVC) and vulcanized elastomers (such as EPDM rubber) have been replaced with TPE materials. Another example is the low-cost sneaker sole and unit sole market where SBS block copolymers have replaced a large part of the PVC and SBR rubber products. In addition, thermoplastic urethanes have replaced neoprene rubber as well as PVC in wire jacketing due to better properties and possibilities for improved cable designs. Many other examples can be cited where a TPE polymer or compound has replaced vulcanized rubber and/or flexible plastics, including telephone bumper feet, spatulas, sports grips, closures, housewares, respirator masks, gaskets, tubing, and syringe bulbs.

Examples of new applications designed specifically around TPEs include snow treads for tires (injection-molded TPU replaces metal chain); cushion-grip tape

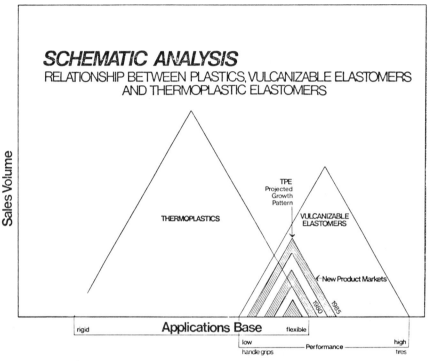

Figure 7-1. Schematic analysis: relationship among plastics, vulcanizable elastomers, and thermoplastic elastomers. (Courtesy of Prolastomer, Inc.)

for bicycles, tools, and sporting goods (extruded TPE replaces leather, cloth, etc.); and flu-gas filtration balls (blow-molded TPE used in new unit for pollution control).

It seems apparent that TPEs will continue to grow in the "overlap" market as improved grades are developed. Figure 7-1 is a schematic analysis of the relationship among TPE markets and those for conventional plastics and vulcanizable elastomers. By 1980, improved grades of TPE will likely shift the growth trend toward the right on Figure 7-1, providing increased sales at the expense of lower performance vulcanized rubber compounds.

A key to this growth, which many project will reach the billion lb/yr category by 1985, will be the industry's ability to develop and efficiently market not just a few large-volume grades but a large number of relatively small-volume grades. This point is supported by the fact that TPEs are growing primarily in a market area based on a myriad of multicomponent rubber and flexible PVC compounds. A relatively few TPE grades could not be expected to meet the requirements of this market.

7.1.3 Potential Demand for Special "Nonstandard" Grades

Compounding TPEs to meet specific applications will likely become as important to the growth of TPE markets as formulation development has been in the growth of both conventional elastomers and PVC. In fact, many similarities in the technical aspects of commercial products are becoming apparent.

PVC powder, unvulcanized rubber, and the styrene-based block copolymers all have to be compounded with other ingredients to produce a usable compound. In many cases, the compounding equipment is identical, and may consist of a Banbury-type internal mixer, FCM continuous mixer, or extrusion-blending line. Even the TPE grades consisting of nearly 100% polymer, such as the thermoplastic urethanes and polyolefin rubber/plastic compositions, are reported to require extensive hot-melt mixing in this type of equipment.

Variation of properties to meet specific applications is currently accomplished in PVC and rubber compounds more by altering ingredients and levels of ingredients than by changing molecular weight, copolymer ratio, or other polymerization-controlled variables in the polymer itself. The technique of compounding TPEs to meet specific requirements also appears to be the most feasible method to service the "overlap" market described in Figure 7-1.

There are two types of basic TPE polymer produced by the major manufacturers:

1. Polymer that is the primary thermoplastic elastomer component, but must be blended with significant amounts of other ingredients (fillers, plasticizing oils, rigid plastics, etc.) to produce a finished compound ready for fabrication into an end product.
2. Polymer that is essentially the finished product ready for fabrication into end products. These polymers may also be modified with compounding ingredients if all end-use requirements are not met initially.

Since there is a practical limitation to the number of base TPE polymers that major manufacturers can produce and support in the marketplace, large growth should occur with type 1 polymers. It is estimated that these polymers, mainly styrene block copolymers, currently hold 85 to 90% of the United States TPE polymer market in applications such as footwear, adhesives, and molded goods. This growth also assumes that improved grades will be developed.

The major factor in growth of type 2 polymers will be the emergence of large-volume applications for individual grades. Possibilities include wire coating to replace cross-linked polyethylene or other large-volume power or communications cable insulators, flexible automotive body panels, if the industry goes that way, or possibly a breakthrough in packaging, the largest single market for thermoplastics.

These factors suggest that the number of "standard" TPE polymer grades made available by manufacturers will be limited by economic and marketing considerations. It is assumed, therefore, that a significant compounding technology in the field of thermoplastic elastomers will evolve in order that the wide variety of potential applications are developed.

7.2 DEVELOPING SPECIFIC GRADES

7.2.1 Sequence for Developing Grades of TPE Compounds

A thorough knowledge of the end-use requirements for both TPE compound and fabricated part is essential. These requirements may include a specific combination of physical properties, raw material cost limitation, processing characteristics to match in-place fabrication equipment, and special features such as nonburning, nontoxic, stabilized for outdoor use, or good adhesion to other substrates.

Once these requirements are analyzed and force-rated to determine "essential," "important," and "desirable" properties, a feasibility review should be made by polymer engineers with knowledge of available TPE polymers and ingredients to determine if these requirements can be satisfied. An end-user or original equipment manufacturer will in many instances initiate the project because he or she cannot find a suitable material "on the shelf" from a large TPE manufacturer. Experience indicates that sharply pointed questions must be asked regarding "essential-important-desirable" properties at the initial project stage in order to assure any chance of success in developing a suitable TPE compound. Some end-users provide exact requirements, while others may not be certain of the properties they require in a compound, only that "it must work" in the application ("sound" like a balata golf ball, "squeeze" like a rubber syringe bulb, or hold up twice as long as current materials).

Specific information that has proven useful in establishing requirements for a TPE compound are listed in Table 7-1.

Defining the specific requirements of the application to the maximum extent possible is an effort well spent. This analysis of needs, when balanced against the available knowledge of TPE compounds, should determine the feasibility of developing a suitable TPE compound for a specific application.

A promising project is also examined from the supplier's point of view (assuming the end-user is not set up to conduct compound development studies). Volume and profit potential from sale of the TPE compound must be sufficient to justify research and development costs. Otherwise, the end-user may drop the project, settle for a less than satisfactory polymer, or seek outside help from contract development laboratories.

Aside from the considerations in Table 7-1, the sequence in developing a TPE compound for a specific application would proceed as follows:

Table 7-1. Typical factors to determine in evaluation requirements of a TPE compound.

Hardness
Service temperature
Tensile strength
Modulus at elongations encountered in use
Maximum elongation and elongation set (snap-back)
Resistance to compression set at service temperature
Wear resistance—abrasion, flex life
Tear strength, impact strength
Oil, solvent, and chemical resistance related to end-use environment
Heat, ultraviolet, and ozone resistance related to end-use environment
Melt flow rate and sensitivity to shear
Cost parameters—acceptable part cost, scrap factor, process rate requirements, price limitations on TPE compound
Specific gravity
Design of tooling—gate, runner, sprue and die dimensions; possible alterations of in-place tooling
Shrinkage—injection molding
Die swell—extrusion
Capabilities and limitations of available fabricating equipment
Special requirements of the compound-clarity, nontoxic, nonburning, conductive or semi-conductive, surface texture and appearance, colorability, adhesion to certain substrates, etc.

1. Research the best possible TPE or other elastomers to use as the backbone of the compounds.
2. Decide what modifications in properties are required: must the compound be harder, softer, stronger, stiffer, more resistant to abrasion or tear?
3. Choose ingredients that will modify the elastomer backbone in a desired manner. Then design experimental formulations. This will usually involve five to 10 initial formulations utilizing ingredients such as fillers, oils and plasticizers, plastics, hydrocarbon resins, stabilizers, processing aids, and other specialty ingredients.
4. Blend the ingredients to produce homogeneous compounds (using a Banbury-type internal mixer or other suitable hot-melt compounding equipment).
5. Prepare test samples, analyze results of the screening study, modify formulations, and retest. Submit for end-product tests.
6. A promising formulation is then scaled-up. Trial quantities are produced on production equipment, at which time blending conditions and production costs are usually worked up.
7. Full fabrication trials are arranged, and, if all goes well, the compound is commercialized.

A thorough knowledge of compounding techniques as well as interactions between ingredients is obviously essential in such a program. Blending methods and equipment are basically the same as those used for PVC and conventional elastomer compounds, with some variations in finishing lines and physical handling of ingredients. However, the interactions of ingredients in TPE compounds are considerably farther from being a mature technology than are flexible PVC and vulcanized rubber compounds.

7.2.2 Key Compounding Ingredients

TPE compounds can be formulated using commercial TPE polymers and/or carefully chosen unvulcanized elastomers as basic starting materials. The TPE polymers such as SBS and SEBS block copolymers are desirable in many cases due to their high tolerance for fillers and oils and highly resilient properties at room temperature. Unvulcanized or partially vulcanized elastomers can also be excellent base polymers for TPE compounds, but care must be exercised in choosing polymer types and grades.

A thorough evaluation of application requirements is essential for choosing the correct elastomer base. The key requirements to check are high temperature properties, oil resistance, and degree of elasticity.

If high temperature properties are critical, the polyolefin compositions of EP rubber/polypropylene are best starting materials. SBS block copolymers give the best room temperature elasticity but cannot be used with confidence for applications requiring oil resistance, outdoor aging, or exposure to temperatures of 150°F or above. TPU polymers have excellent properties but are expensive and have not been evaluated extensively as starting materials for special compounds. The polyurethane chemistry is quite versatile, and it is likely that modifications of these polymers for specific applications would be accomplished through chemical rather than compounding methods.

Certain unvulcanized elastomers, particularly EPDM and EPR, offer enough resilience, environmental stability, and compounding versatility to be good starting materials for TPE compounds. Several products of this type are offered commercially by major chemicals companies. The prime compounds are EPDM/polypropylene compositions, which offer good high temperature capabilities and low temperature impact. A major limitation is their lack of true resilience. Most of these compounds have high hardness (85 to 95 Shore A) and are used for painted automotive sight shields for bumper systems.

Other unvulcanized elastomers have also shown promise in particular compounds, but care must be taken to assure the proper combination of physical properties, environmental stability, and processing ease. Unsaturated rubbers can degrade rapidly in TPE compounds. An incorrect polymer choice can also cause rough extrudates, long injection-molding cycles, and high shrinkage in parts molded from TPE compounds based on the unvulcanized rubber.

It should be noted that the technology of developing TPE compounds from conventional vulcanizable rubbers is just recently emerging. Much work is still to be done in developing new, improved elastomers and in studying polymer/ ingredient interactions in physical blends of this type.

Several other ingredients are typically used in TPE compounds. Classes of ingredients include commercial plastics, fillers, process oils, petroleum resins, low molecular weight polymers, waxes, pigments and polymer chemicals such as stabilizers, processing aids, and blowing agents.

The major difference between TPE compounds and conventional rubber compounds is the absence of cross-linking agents and accelerators in TPE. TPE compounds also have much lower loadings of carbon black (if any), thermoplastic components not usually found in rubber compounds, and antioxidant/ultraviolet stabilizer systems designed to protect plastic as well as rubber polymers. The number of ingredients in a typical TPE compound is only half that used in a typical vulcanized rubber compound (4 to 8 vs. 8 to 16).

Table 7-2 gives a list of suggested ingredients that may be used in developing TPE compounds.

7.2.3 Blending Methods

The method used to prepare a specialty thermoplastic elastomer compound will be determined by the following factors:

1. Physical form of the raw materials.
2. The rheological characteristics of the raw materials.
3. The energy required to prepare an intimate mix.
4. Physical characteristics of the final product.
5. Production rate required.
6. Desired physical form of the finished product.

Most of this information can be acquired from manufacturers' product literature, although some is subjective or requires extensive experimentation. Physical form and rheology of raw materials are published, while energy required is subjective. Generally, energy requirements range from 4 lb/hp-hr for materials such as TPR and Hytrel to 10 lb/hp-hr for some styrene block copolymers.

Internal batch mixing is the most common method for compounding specialty thermoplastic elastomers. The Banbury can handle baled and crumb rubbers, pellets, high levels of oil, and fillers. Extrusion compounding is practical only when blending polymers of similar rheology in pellet form or adding low levels of oil (approximately 10% by weight maximum) or fillers (approximately 20% by weight maximum). The continuous mixer falls into the same limitations as the extrusion compounding equipment, but does allow high output rates on sim-

Table 7-2. Typical ingredients for TPE compounds.

CLASS	EXAMPLES
Commercial Thermoplastic Elastomers Give basic elastomeric properties and govern maximum service tem- perature to a large degree	S-B-S, S-I-S block copolymers TPU polyurethanes Polyolefin plastic/rubber compositions Polyester TPEs Borderline materials—ionomers, ET polymers, trans polyisoprenes
Unvulcanized Elastomers Give improved resiliency, softness, low temperature properties, im- pact strength, and helps bind ingredients	EPDM, EPR, polyisobutylene, butyl, SBR, natural rubber, neoprene, polyisoprene
Commercial Plastics Give improved stiffness, tensile, tear, abrasion and higher tempera- ture properties, higher hardness	PP, PE, EVA, PS, ionomer (Surlyn), nylon, EEA, alpha-methyl styrene, EP copolymers
Fillers Give lower cost, increased hardness, modulus, tear resistance, help con- trol die swell, shrinkage of molded parts, etc.	Soft and hard clays, hydrated and amorphous silica, calcium car- bonate, barytes, wood flour, car- bon black, talc, metal oxides, etc.
Modifying Oils Give softer, lower cost, easier pro- cessing compounds; will bind other ingredients, but reduce properties	Naphthenic, paraffinic and aromatic oils, DOP-type plasticizers
Modifying Resins and Low *Molecular Weight Polymers*	Paraffin wax, amorphous polymers, polyindene, coumarone-indene, hydrogenated rosin esters
Polymer Chemicals and Additives	Antioxidants, ultraviolet stabilizers, process aids, flame retardants, blowing agents, conductive addi- tives, coupling agents, pigments, and color concentrates

ple blends such as minor modifications of thermoplastic elastomers with pellet and flake plastics.

Powder blending of styrene block copolymers in high-intensity blenders, such as Henschel or Wellex, permits melt compounding of the ingredients in the machine that forms the finished part. The process involves charging a crumb polymer, fillers, and chemicals to the blender. The charge is heated by intensive blending, and the liquid modifiers (oils and/or plasticizers) are absorbed into the crumb polymers. Care must be taken to prevent excessive heating, which will gel the blend before it can be discharged from the blender. The powder blend is fed to the injection-molding machine or extruder and, compounding occurs in the plasticating unit and forms the final product without the cost and heat history of a separate compounding step between the raw materials and the finished parts. The twin screw extruders and transfer mixers offer the opportunity to tailor the compounding equipment to produce thermoplastic elastomers on a continuous mixing basis. This type of equipment can be justified when the types of TPE produced are very similar or when the compounding line is dedicated to a single product. The segmented screw, additive injection ports, vents, and filler feed ports must all be designed to incorporate the modifiers at the appropriate points along the barrel.

After selecting the appropriate upstream compounding equipment (i.e., Banbury, continuous mixer, extruder, dry blender, transfer mixer, or twin screw extruder), the downstream equipment must be selected to finish the compound into a physical form that can be handled by the final processing equipment. This means, in most cases, that the product must be converted into a free-flowing pellet form.

If a Banbury-type batch mixer is used, the batch may be stripped from a mill through a water-cooling trough, the strip dried with an air knife, and granulated through a "dicer." The disadvantage of granulating a mill strip is that the equipment is limited to compounds of about 70 Shore A hardness or higher. Softer compounds tend to bounce and deflect rather than cut through cleanly to form a pellet.

For compounds between about 55 to 70 Shore A hardness, a "hot melt feed" extruder can be used to convert the batch to $\frac{1}{8}$-inch-diameter strands. The strands would be water cooled, dried, and granulated through a strand chopper. The strand chopper can also be used with extrusion and transfer mixer compounding.

Thermoplastic elastomer compounds with Shore A Durometers below about 55 require hot face cutting or underwater pelletizing. These types of pelletizing involve extruding the compound through holes in a die plate, cutting the hot melt rod with rotating knives, and cooling the product in the pellet form before they come in contact with each other. This is the most flexible type of finishing equipment because it allows pelletizing of not only the low Durometer materials, but the higher compounds as well.

After the compound has been pelletized, "blocking" or caking in storage must be considered. Some thermoplastic elastomers, especially the soft, oil-extended or unvulcanized rubber modified compounds develop a surface tack, which results in the pellets sticking together in the storage containers. This problem becomes more serious as the storage life increases. The problem can be eliminated by coating the pellet surfaces with a powdered partitioning agent. It is most practical to apply the powder after the pellets are formed and dried and before they are packaged. Powdered high-density polyethylene at 0.5 to 1% by weight has been used successfully.

Compounding of specialty thermoplastic elastomers will involve modifiers in bale, liquid, powder, and pellet form. Because of this wide range of physical forms, the upstream equipment is generally adapted from rubber compounding industries, while the downstream equipment is generally adapted from the plastics compounding equipment. Selection of specific pieces of equipment from these two industries will depend on the characteristics of the ingredients and the finished compound.

7.3 MODIFYING COMMERCIAL TPEs

As mentioned previously, the most important starting materials for developing specific TPE compounds are the commercial TPE polymers and polymer blends. These polymers are available in several forms, including neat crumb, oiled crumb, and pellets.

7.3.1 SBS and SIS Block Copolymers

The SBS and SIS polymers from Shell Chemical Company (Kraton) and Phillips Petroleum Co. (Solprene) are used for many TPE compounds. The large-volume footwear and adhesive applications are based almost entirely on these polymers, which make up an estimated 80 to 85% of the total United States TPE polymer market.

Both Shell Chemical and Phillips offer finished compounds for specific applications as well as uncompounded polymer for use by outside converters. The suppliers have published considerable literature on compounding with these polymers, including blending methods and formulations for particular uses.

The most economical means for developing a TPE compound is to start with the neat crumb. If high levels of oil are anticipated, the oiled crumb form will allow faster mixing cycles and may be preferred. The ingredients of most importance in SBS and SIS TPE compounds, along with their general effects on properties follow:

- *Polystyrene*: increases hardness, tear strength, abrasion resistance and tensile; reduces flex life and elongation.
- *Naphthenic and paraffinic oils*: reduces cost, hardness, tensile, tear and abrasion resistance; increases processability and melt flow.
- *Alpha-methyl styrene*: improves high temperature performance.
- *Calcium carbonate, silicas, clay, talc*: reduces cost, melt flow, and tensile; increases hardness, tear, and specific gravity.
- *Hydrocarbon resins* (can associate with either styrene or rubber phase, several types): improves processability, adhesion; can increase tensile strength, flex life, and melt flow.
- *Stabilizers*: typical combination of hindered phenolic antioxidant, thiodipropionate synergist, hydroxy benzophenone, or hydroxy benzotriazole

ultraviolet absorbers. Zinc dibutyl dithiocarbonate, zinc oxide, carbon black, and titanium dioxide are also effective.

Other ingredients that have been used include polyethylene, EVA, EPDM, carbon black, zinc stearate, and microcrystalline wax.

Typical applications for SBS and SIS compounds are: unit soles, sneaker soles, rubber bands, erasers, molded gaskets, cove base, milk tubing, disposable respirators, and squeeze bulbs. Many other applications have been evaluated but the inherently low service temperature and limited environmental stability have prevented broader use of these compounds.

7.3.2 SEBS Block Copolymers (Kraton G)

These styrene-poly (ethylene-butylene) copolymers have essentially no unsaturation and are claimed to overcome the limitations noted above for SBS and SIS types. Higher service temperature in the range of $250°F$ and above in some compounds should lead to broad use in molding, extrusion, and adhesive and sealant applications that must withstand weathering and high use temperatures.

SEBS copolymers are available in neat crumb, oiled crumb, and pelletized compounds. These polymers are also said to be the basis for a new series of wire and cable compounds sold under Shell Chemical's Elexar trade name.

These relatively new polymers are believed to have a broad field of potential applications if suitable compounds can be developed. Suggested applications include adhesives, coatings, sports grips, packaging, automotive rub strips, sight shields, flexible front ends, steering wheels, armrests, inflatable bags for crash protection, garden hose, stair treads, wire insulation and jacketing, respirator masks, syringe bulbs, waterproof sheeting, medical and pharmaceutical parts, flexible tubing, and spatulas.

Although limited information has been published on compounding SEBS copolymers, the authors have evaluated two grades of neat crumb in several formulations and find these materials to be versatile compounding polymers. SEBS copolymers appear to be compatible with ingredients such as naphthenic and paraffinic oils, alpha methyl styrene, polystyrene, polyethylene, EPDM, EVA, EEA, various fillers and pigments, hydrocarbon resins, and waxes.

As with all TPE compounds, the interactions of ingredients should be evaluated in final compounds, and the effects on processing characteristics as well as properties and economics measured. Commercial Kraton G compounds and developmental compounds* appear to process well on conventional thermoplastic processing equipment. Higher initial cost for neat crumb compared with SBS and SIS types will result in generally high TPE compound costs. Initial indica-

---

*Prolastomer, Inc. *Compound Research Book No. 3-76.*

tions are that formulation changes can produce soft or hard, tough, semiconductive, strong, clear, highly resilient, and heat-resistant TPE compounds.

The SEBS-based compounds should compete with polyolefin TPE compositions, flexible PVC, and conventional elastomers in several major markets.

7.3.3   Polyolefin Rubber/Plastic Compositions: TPR, Somel, Telcar, Vistaflex, Prolastic

The polyolefin-type thermoplastic elastomers can be modified by ethylene propylene rubbers or paraffinic naphthenic oils to reduce the hardness while sacrificing tensile strength and compression and elongation set. The effects on these physical properties can be controlled to some extent by selecting high molecular weight grades. The softening efficiency of rubber modifiers will depend on crystallinity of the EPR selected. The low ethylene copolymers will reduce the hardness more, at an equivalent modifier level, than a high ethylene EPR.

Hardness, modulus, tensile, and tear strengths can be increased by incorporating polyolefin plastics such as polypropylene, polyethylene and polyethylene copolymers. These modifiers, however, will reduce the resilience and elastomeric characteristics of the product.

To compound rubber and plastic modifiers into polyolefin thermoplastic rubbers requires stock temperatures in excess of 320°F, while oil modifiers are most efficiently incorporated at temperatures above 340°F. Batch mixing cycle times are moderately fast for the rubber and plastic modifiers. The oils are incorporated easily, but cycles are longer than oil modification of the block copolymers. The finished compounds present no special problems to finish by dicing a cooled mill strip for harder grades or underwater pelletizing of soft grades. Partitioning of the pellets with powder for storage is generally required for compounds under 70 Shore A hardness.

Polyolefin thermoplastic elastomers are basically compounds as supplied by the manufacturers and therefore do not tolerate high levels of inert fillers. The small particle size fillers (under 5μ in diameter) will increase compound modulus levels below the point where cost of the compound, on a pound-volume basis, is reduced. Cost reduction may be possible using large particle size fillers in applications that can tolerate some loss of elastomeric characteristics and increased viscosity. Fillers coated with titanate coupling agents have shown some promise in increasing the tolerance of polyolefin thermoplastic elastomer compounds for fillers.

In most polyolefin thermoplastic elastomers, the crystalline structure is used to impart some of the physical characteristics of cross-links in thermoset rubbers (i.e., set, tensile strength, tear strength, high service temperature, etc.). Most noncrystalline modifiers such as oils and fillers will interfere with the arrangement of crystalline sites. Modification with high molecular weight amorphous rubbers will also interfere with crystalline arrangement, but will not deteriorate the elastomeric properties to the extent of oils and fillers due to polymer chain entanglement.

Modifying polyolefin types for flame retardance and semiconductance requires such high levels of fillers that the compounds are generally hard and "boardy" and lose much of their elastomeric properties.

In general, the polyolefin-type thermoplastic elastomers do not tolerate the high degree of modification found in the block copolymers. Practical modifications are generally limited to rather minor changes in specific physical properties to tailor a compound to an application where the standard polyolefin grade needs small changes to succeed.

7.3.4 TPU Thermoplastic Urethanes

During the 1960s and 1970s, many thermoplastic urethanes were commercialized. These polymers are today among the toughest and most resilient elastomers available.

A major drawback is the high price ($1.30 to $2.25/lb) compared with conventional vulcanized elastomers ($.35 to $.90/lb) and other thermoplastic elastomers ($.45 to $1.00/lb).

As an example of this problem, TPU was replaced by lower cost polyolefin TPE compositions in large-volume automotive sight shield and filler panel applications soon after the parts were designed.

The versatility of polyether- and polyester-based TPUs is such that many high performance applications have been designed around these polymers. Superior abrasion resistance qualifies TPUs for rollers, drive belts, gears, casters, tires, and various industrial components. Excellent oil resistance, low temperature flexibility, and load-bearing properties also qualify TPU for cable jacketing, military and marine devices, fuel line hose, gaskets, seals, and automotive components.

Compounding as a means to meet specific applications has not become a significant aspect of the TPU technology. The main reason may be the flexibility of urethane polymer chemistry, which allows development of properties via changes in prepolymer type, molecular weight, and isocyanate component. Another reason may be the relatively small hardness range (about 80 Shore A to 65 Shore D) in which most TPU applications fall.

Polyether types have better hydrolytic stability and low temperature flexibility and usually cost more. Polyester types generally offer better mechanical properties. Both classes can be formulated to enhance one or more specific property.

Many of the commercial TPU polymers are modified with small amounts of proprietary thermoplastics other than urethanes, and may also contain additives to improve dimensional stability, stiffness, flame retardancy, heat resistance, and outdoor aging. However, the basic physical properties are derived from the TPU polymer itself.

An area of compounding, which will likely be explored further, is blending for cost reduction via the use of compatible, lower cost ingredients.

7.3.5 Additional Thermoplastic Elastomer Types

A number of polymers are supplied as specialty materials or have some physical characteristics that may qualify them as thermoplastic elastomers. Within this group are:

1. Surlyn ionomer (E. I. du Pont de Nemours & Company)
2. Hytrel polyester (E. I. du Pont de Nemours & Company)
3. Trans-Pip polyisoprene (Polysar)
4. ET grafted polyethylene (Allied Chemical Corporation).

Some of these polymers are designed for low-volume specialty applications and are therefore high-priced.

Surlyn ionomers are in the hard (90+ Shore A range), which would exclude them from many thermoplastic elastomer applications, but they are tough, resilient, and have high elongations with poor set characteristics. They have been successfully modified with inert fillers of large particle size to high loadings (up to approximately 50% by weight). This results in higher modulus and lower elongations. Polymer modifications have involved polyethylene and polyethylene copolymers to about 10% by weight. These modifications also increase modulus and decrease elongation with the advantage of slightly increasing the ionomer's heat distortion temperature. Compounding presents a problem because of the severe sticking to hot metal surfaces, such as the rotors and sides of a Banbury mixer.

Du Pont's Hytrel thermoplastic polyester has been modified with polyvinyl chloride resins and compounds to improve surface mar resistance and processability. Most elastomeric physical properties of Hytrel modified with PVC/DOP compounds improve while rigid PVC modifiers increase plastics physical properties. Dipropyl glycol dibenzoate has been reported by Du Pont as being effective at reducing hardness. Du Pont has also reported improved weather resistance by using commercially available concentrates.

Although considerable technical information is available on Hytrel polyester elastomers (see Chapter 4), limited work has been published on modification of these polymers via compounding techniques.

Trans-Pip is synthetic trans polyisoprene supplied by Polysar. This high hardness, low temperature polymer is very similar to balata rubber and is limited by its high cost. Compounding studies to reduce cost have been started.

ET polymers from Allied Chemical can be more readily modified with powdered additives. Allied Chemical has reported semiconductive and flame-retardant compounds that retain much of the physicals of unmodified polymers.

7.4 SUMMARY

Thermoplastic elastomers are becoming an increasingly important class of materials to product designers, materials engineers, and processors. The potential to replace conventional rubbers and flexible plastics is enormous. Many predict that, by 1985, TPE will become the next billion lb/yr polymer category.

Current applications are developing, mainly in the "overlap" market described in Figure 7-1. This market is characterized by a wide variety of applications and a large number of compounds servicing these applications. Relatively few high-volume (25 million lb/yr) applications have been developed to date. Casual footwear, adhesives, and automotive sight shields are the only examples.

Available TPE polymers and compounds lend themselves to modification of properties to meet specific applications. A wide variety of compounding ingredients is available as is the blending equipment needed to produce the TPE compounds. In addition, much research is in progress to produce base polymers with higher temperature capabilities and better resistance to oils, compression set, and other current product limitations.

With many tools in place and plenty of materials to work with, the only major hindrance to the rapid growth of TPE markets would be the lack of commitment to a multiapplications-oriented marketing and development effort.

Since many polymer manufacturers have set objectives to manufacture and sell the fewest grades possible, their primary efforts will be to concentrate in developing large-volume applications such as wire and cable, hose, and packaging.

Whoever fills the void in the multiapplications market will require compounding technology. It may be that development of compounding technology will be as important to the growth of the TPE industry as it was with vulcanized elastomers.

8

Borderline Materials

Benjamin M. Walker, Ph.D.
Walker Engineering Associates
Madison, Connecticut

8.1 GENERAL

Elastomers are, by definition, clearly differentiated from plastics in regard to properties. According to ASTM D883, *Standard Nomenclature Relating to Plastics*, an *elastomer* is *a material which at room temperature can be stretched repeatedly to at least twice its original length, and, upon immediate release of the stress, will return with force to its approximate original length.* (This is interpreted to mean an elongation of at least 100% at the yield point.) According to this definition, it would seem possible to unequivocally categorize a material as either "plastic" or "elastomeric." In practice, however, the properties of thermoplastic materials cover a broad and continuous range of elastic properties. Although some of them are very clearly elastomeric—and others very definitely not—there are many "borderline" materials.

These borderline materials may not completely satisfy the formal definition of an elastomer, but are sufficiently close to being elastomeric to be useful and competitive with true elastomers in many applications. Also, some modifications or formulations of a polymeric system might satisfy the definition, while others do not. Among the borderline materials are EVA (ethylene vinyl acetate copolymer), EEA (ethylene ethyl acrylate copolymer), *ionomer* resins, and *transpolyisoprenes*.

The first two borderline materials, EVA and EEA, are sometimes included in statistical and other lists and tabulations of elastomers. Of the other two classes of borderline materials, ionomers are not considered to be elastomeric and thermoplastic materials, and trans-1,4-polyisoprenes appear to be more thermoplastic than elastic. However, each of them is a unique material possessing a balance of elastomeric and thermoplastic properties sufficient to warrant its mention. Therefore, a brief description of these two classes of material follows.

8.2 IONOMERS

This group of polymers, introduced and supplied by the E. I. du Pont de Nemours & Company under the trademark Surlyn, consists of modified polyolefins containing some cross-chain ionic bonds. Their chemical structure results in properties that are substantially different from those of the unmodified polyethylenes; some of these compounds have elastomeric properties.

8.2.1 Chemistry

Surlyn ionomers consist primarily of polyethylene/methacrylic acid copolymers, reacted selectively with metallic ions, such as zinc or sodium. The net effect is a polymer containing both organic and inorganic materials linked by both covalent and ionic bonds.[1]

8.2.2 General Properties

Many of the general properties of the Surlyn ionomers are similar to those of the polyolefins, including chemical resistance, melting range, and density. Processing techniques are similar to LDPE and EVA polymers. The many resins available differ in molecular weight and amount of cross-linking, and therefore differ in properties and processing characteristics. (See Table 8-1.)

8.2.3 Some Outstanding Properties

- Toughness
- Impact strength
- Low temperature impact toughness
- High abrasion resistance
- High solvent resistance, including low permeation by oil
- Transparency
- High melt strength
- Direct adhesion to epoxy, polyurethane finishes, and to metal, glass, and natural fibers by heat lamination.

Table 8-1. General properties of Surlyn.[4]

Specific gravity	0.93–0.97
Izod impact, ft lb/in.	5.7–14.6
Tensile impact, ft lb/in.^{2} @ 23°C	240–565
@ –40°C	205–390
Elmendorf tear, g/mil	20–80
Brittleness temperature, °F	Below –160
Tensile strength, psi	2100–4400
Yield strength, psi	1300–4200
Elongation, %	280–520
Modulus, psi	10,000–55,000
Power factor, 1000 cps	0.001–0.003
Dielectric constant, 1000 cps	2.4
Softening point, Vicat, °C	61–80
Permeability	
WVTR, g/24 hr/100 in.^{2}/mil/	
100°F, 90% RH Creased	1.5–2.5
Oxygen, cm^3/24 hr/100 in.^{2}/mil	500–800
Resistance to Chemicals:	
Acids	Slow attack
Bases	Resistant
Hydrocarbons	Slow swell
Ketones-Alcohols	Some alcohols stress crack
Vegetable oil	High resistance
Animal oil	High resistance
Mineral oil	Good resistance

8.2.4 Elastomeric Properties

Although most commercial ionomers do not satisfy the definition of "elastomer," they do have many of the characteristics associated with elastomers, such as high elongation, toughness, and impact strength. A few of them do qualify as elastomers—they have high elongation at the tensile yield point and return to the original length after stretching. For example, Surlyn 1855 and 1856 show 520% elongation at a yield stress of 3700 to 4200 psi, and Surlyn 1702 has 437% elongation at a yield stress of 3610 psi.

REFERENCES for Sections 8.1 and 8.2

1. Kinsey, Roy H., Ionomers, Chemistry and New Developments, *Applied Polymer Symposia*, Vol. No. 11, 77–94 (1969).
2. Kinsey, Roy H., Ionomers in the Polyolefin Marketplace, *SPE RETEC*, 1975.
3. *Properties of Surlyn Ionomer Resins*, Du Pont Bulletin A-87537, January 1974.
4. *Selector Guide for Molding and Extrusions of Surlyn Ionomer Resins*, Du Pont Bulletin E-14884, June 1977.
5. Du Pont product bulletins describing Surlyn compounds, 1970–1974. Refer to E. I. du Pont de Nemours & Company, Polyolefin Div., Plastics Dept., Wilmington, Delaware 19898.

8.3 TRANS-1,4-POLYISOPRENE

Polysar Limited developed trans-1,4-polyisoprene and has marketed it since 1963 under the registered trademarks Trans-Pip and Polysar. The compound has some unique end uses and many applications as a substitute for natural balata. This compound is synthesized in pure form to produce a product that is almost identical with naturally occurring trans-1,4-polyisoprene, a polymer found in natural balata. This material is similar to natural rubber and to most synthetic rubbers insofar as it is vulcanizable with sulfur. It differs from most rubbers insofar as it is relatively crystalline at room temperature. The crystals, however, melt at 140°F (60°C), so that the compound exhibits thermoplastic characteristics.[1]

8.3.1 Chemistry

Balata is a rubberlike hydrocarbon polymer gum obtained from the latex of *Mimosops balata*, which grows wild in Central and South America. It is an isomeric form of natural rubber. Natural rubber is the *cis* form, or cis-1,4-polyisoprene, with chain bonds on the same side of the double bonds. Balata is the *trans* form, or trans-1,4-polyisoprene, with chain bonds on opposite sides of the double bonds. The chemical composition is the same for the two compounds, but the difference in the stereoisomeric structure, or spatial arrangement of the component groups, results in differences in properties. An important difference is that natural (cis form) rubber crystallizes very slowly at room temperature, usually existing as a noncrystalline polymer with low hardness and tensile strength. Balata (the trans form), on the other hand, crystallizes rapidly at temperatures below 140°F (60°C) and at room temperature exists as a crystalline polymer with higher hardness and tensile strength. These properties of balata are equivalent to those of synthetic trans-1,4-polyisoprene.[1] The properties of trans-1,4-polyisoprene are shown in Table 8-2.

Table 8-2. Typical properties of synthetic trans-1,4-polyisoprene.[1]

Viscosity, ML-4' at 212°F (100°C)	23–33
Hardness, instantaneous, Shore C	70
Tensile strength, kg/cm^2 (psi)	352 (5000)
Modulus at 300% elongation, kg/cm^2 (psi)	190 (2700)
Elongation at break, %	460–500
Tear strength, kg/cm (lb/in.)	20.5 (115)
Melting point, °F (°C)	140 (60)
Dielectric constant	2.6
Refractive index at 68°F (20°C)	1.55
Mill shrinkage, %	49
Cold brittle point, °F (°C)	−9 (−23)
Specific heat, cal/gram	0.67
Coefficient of expansion per °C	0.008

8.3.2 Processing

This material may be compression molded, injection molded, extruded, and calendered by rubber or plastics techniques. On cooling, it recovers its crystalline structure, strength, and hardness. With orientation, films of 0.012 mm (0.5 mil) thickness may achieve strength values of over 700 kg/cm^2 (10,000 psi).

8.3.3 Vulcanization

The properties of molded products are given a permanent character by curing a stock that has been compounded with sulfur and an accelerator. By choosing a suitable accelerator, compounds may be molded at a temperature as low as 140°F (60°C), then vulcanized to develop improved resistance to heat and chemicals, while retaining physical properties under service conditions.

8.3.4 Applications

Some applications for which trans-1,4-polyisoprene has proved very successful are:

- Golf-ball covers (largest present-day application).
- Heat-sealable coating on paper, fabric, leather, repair patches, etc.
- Pressure-sensitive adhesives.
- Caulking compounds (with butyl rubber).
- Modifiers for thermoplastics to improve impact resistance and elongation at break.
- Inserts for toes of safety shoes; impregnants for fabrics.
- Gaskets for low temperature service.
- Coatings for mining equipment, cable covering, and tank linings.
- Orthopedic devices; casts, prepared by softening sheet in warm water, become rigid upon recrystallization at room temperature.

8.4 REFERENCES for Section 8.3

1. E. G. Kent and F. B. Swinney, Properties and Applications of Trans-1,4-Polyisoprene, *I & EC Product Research and Development* 5(2): 134 (June 1966).
2. Synthetic Trans-1,4-Polyisoprene, *Journal of the IRI* 1(5): 259 (Sept/October 1967).
3. J. S. Lansky, H. K. Garner, and R. H. Ewart, Catalysts for the Polymerization of Isoprene to Trans-1,4-Polyisoprene (Synthetic Balata), *I & EC Product Research and Development* 1(2): 82 (June 1962).

4. F. Kirchhof, Von der naturlichen zur synthetischen Guttapercha, *Gummi Asbest Kunstoffe* **1**(4): 302.
5. R. H. Jones and Y. K. Wei, Application of Trans-1,4-Polyisoprene in Orthopedic and Rehabilitative Medicine, *J. Biomedical Materials Research Symposium* **1**: 19 (1971).
6. Polysar Rubbers in Golf Balls, *Polysar News*, July/August 1964.
7. *X-414, The Future in Orthopedics*, Polysar Brochure.
8. Communication from W. S. Edwards on behalf of Dr. L. Breitman, Polysar Limited, Sarnia, Ontario, Canada N75 7M2, March 1976.

9

Markets, Applications, Desirable Future Improvements

Robert D. Lundberg, Ph.D.
Exxon Research and Engineering Company
Linden, New Jersey

Clarence M. Alsys
Fisher Body Division, General Motors Corp.

Benjamin M. Walker, Ph.D.
Walker Engineering Associates
Madison, Connecticut

9.1 INTRODUCTION

Since the introduction of Kraton on a commercial scale by Shell Chemical Company in 1965, thermoplastic elastomers have emerged as a new family of rubbery materials. While "thermoplastic elastomers" encompasses a broad range of materials differing in composition, physical properties, and flow behavior, they all have the common characteristic of rapid processibility, similar to thermoplastics. In addition, TPEs generally meet the ASTM definition of an elastomer: "a material which at room temperature can be stretched repeatedly to at least twice its original length, and, upon release of the stress, will return immediately to its approximate original length."

While these two characteristics are generally descriptive of the field of TPEs, substantial differences exist among the various commercially available TPEs in their respective properties. The primary advantage of a thermoplastic elastomer over a cured rubber system is typically ease of processibility and, consequently,

306

economics. Both injection molding and extrusion operations can be conducted substantially more rapidly with TPEs than with cured rubber systems. In addition, the potential of recycling rejected parts or scrap based on TPEs affords a substantial cost savings over rubber. While the advantages of thermoplastic elastomers over cured rubber systems are quite apparent, it should be emphasized that there are several classes of materials that can perform in a similar manner to TPEs, but are typically not described as such. Plasticized PVC has been available for many decades, performing many of the functions of a TPE while lacking some of the rubbery characteristics. Similarly, ethylene/ethyl acrylate and ethylene/vinyl acetate copolymers can be processed as well or better than many TPEs and, with certain compositions, can be elastomeric. From an application viewpoint, TPEs are effectively penetrating markets largely served by cured rubber, flexible vinyl, and selected thermoplastics (such as low-density polyethylene and ethylene copolymers). The processibility advantages of TPEs over cured rubber systems are readily apparent and represent one major reason why TPEs can compete with cured materials. However, the advantages of TPEs over more conventional flexible thermoplastics are more property-oriented. The improved low temperature properties (i.e., reduced sensitivity of modulus to temperature) of TPEs as compared to flexible vinyl make these materials more desirable in applications where flexibility over a broad temperature range is desired. In addition, TPEs have coefficients of friction similar to those of conventional rubbers, and therefore are on the order of 30 to 50% higher than the flexible thermoplastics.

9.2 CURRENT APPLICATIONS AND MARKETS FOR TPEs

Because TPEs are competing in markets that are currently served by both cured rubbers and flexible thermoplastics, the range of potential applications is extremely broad. Table 9-1 provides a partial list of applications suggested for TPEs.[1]

9.2.1 Markets for Elastomers

The current United States consumption of specialty and general purpose elastomers is shown in Table 9-2.[2] It is readily evident that the total volume of TPEs (including EVA and EEA) is extremely small relative to total elastomer consumption with an estimated consumption of 50 to 75 thousand long tons in 1974. There is a broad range of estimates for current volumes of TPE because of the diversity of applications, and also because the classification of TPEs is somewhat subjective. For example, in some estimates, such as Table 9-2, the flexible plastics such as EVA and EEA are included as TPEs, in others, they are not.

Table 9-1. Suggested applications for typical thermoplastic elastomers.[1]

Adhesives
Asphalt products
Coatings
Impact modification of thermoplastics
Food packaging
Medical/pharmaceutical products
Sealants
Low-cost rubber items
Sheeting
Belting
Tubing
Unit soles/heels
Sneaker soles
Automotive sight shields
Mechanical goods (gaskets, grommets, fasteners, knobs)
Sporting goods (swim fins, ski boots)
Garden hose
Wire and cable insulation
Grips for sporting goods, tools, etc.

It has been emphasized that many of these newer thermoplastic elastomers have not been typically classified as rubbers due to their plastic orientation.[3] Consequently, some of the more rubber-oriented statistics significantly understate the growth of this new class of materials. According to one source,[3] there are now 20 distinct group classifications, 215 individual products, and over 100 different manufacturers of the newer specialty elastomers. Of these manufacturers, only one-fifth are members of the International Institute of Synthetic Rubber.

The markets served by thermoplastic elastomers in 1973 are shown in Table 9-3. The total volumes[4] shown here include soluble polyurethanes, which do not fall within the thermoplastic elastomer category, and therefore the consumption level is higher than would be the case for thermoplastic materials. Except for polyurethanes, the major markets are seen to be automotive, footwear, wire and cable, hose and tubing, and adhesives.

One of the most interesting aspects of thermoplastic elastomers is that they compete with flexible PVC, cured rubber, and flexible plastics. The substitution of PVC for rubber is a process that has been occurring for several decades. While the total volume of rubber displaced by this process is small relative to rubber consumption, the amount of penetration can be a substantial volume, as shown in Table 9-4. Thus, according to this analysis, nearly a billion pounds of rubber are estimated to be displaced by vinyl.[4] Interestingly, the higher costs of vinyl resins and the lower processing cost of thermoplastic elastomers have recently resulted in a trend back to rubber to replace vinyl.

For example, TPEs are replacing vinyls in footwear, and a similar displacement

Table 9-2. U.S. consumption in long tons of specialty and general purpose elastomers. (Reprinted with permission from *Rubber World* magazine, February 1975, p. 43.)

	1966	1969	1973	1974	1978	Est. of '75 price, $/lb.
SBR	1,150,700	1,300,026	1,478,000	1,400,000	1,730,000	0.28-0.32
Natural	549,700	587,996	685,000	660,000	800,000	0.25-0.35
Butyl	83,800	92,007	115,000	111,000	132,000	0.37
NBR	59,800	64,357	63,000	71,000	84,000	0.52-0.58
Polybutadiene	140,000	270,432	314,000	330,000	370,000	0.32-0.35
Polyisoprene	50,000	84,939	119,000	105,000	150,000	0.35-0.45
EPDM	22,000	43,255	96,500	106,000	175,000	0.39-0.46
Neoprene	107,200	120,000	143,000	130,000	154,000	0.59-0.61
Polyurethane Millable	450	500	625	650	988	
Chlorosulfonated polyethylene	11,300	9,600	12,000	14,000	18,000	0.62-0.64
Chlorohydrin*	340	450	3,000	4,000	9,000	1.15-1.40
Chlorinated polyethylene	mincr	minor	2,000	3,000	10,000	
Chlorobutyl & Bromobutyl	—	10,100	26,000	30,000	57,000	0.40
Polysulfide (solid)	900	1,000	1,200	1,200	1,200	
Polyacrylate	1,900	2,200	2,460	2,600	2,940	1.40
Silicone (solid)	3,900	4,900	7,500	8,000	9,600	
Fluoroelastomers	540	790	1,012	1,100	1,413	11.50
Trans-polyisoprene	580	760	900	1,000	1,230	
Crosslinked polyethylene**	20,000	36,000	90,000	100,000	150,000	0.41
Polypropylene Oxide	—	—	440	500	4,460	0.99
Thermoplastic elastomers						
SB, SI, S/EP	670	1,170	16,500	20,000	30,000	0.37-0.75
EVA, EEA	4,500	5,350	14,000	15,000	19,000	0.40
TPR	—	—	900	1,400	6,700	0.55-0.70
Polyester	—	—	1,340	1,600	2,700	1.40-1.60
Urethane Soluble	2,200	11,200	11,800	27,000	40,000	
Moldable			12,700			
			24,500			

Table 9-3. 1973 end-use consumption of thermoplastic elastomers. (Reprinted with permission from *Rubber World* magazine, February 1975, p. 45, and from the author, David Dworkin, Fairfield Associates, Inc.)

	SB, SI, S/EP*	Poly-olefin	Polyur-ethanes	Poly-ester	EVA, EEA	Total
Adhesives	6	—	3.0	—	—	9.0
Misc. molded &						
extruded goods	—	—	4.5	—	—	4.5
(including automotive)	15	2	—	—	7	24.0
Footwear	13	—	2.5	—	—	15.5
Resin modification	7	—	—	—	—	1.0
Hose & tubing	—	—	0.3	0.5	12	12.8
Sheeting	—	—	1.0	—	2	3.0
Wire & cable	—	—	4.0	0.5	10	14.5
Off-road tires	—	—	—	1.0	—	1.0
Belting	—	—	—	0.5	—	0.5
Coated fabrics	—	—	21.0	—	—	21.0
Coatings	—	—	15.6	—	—	15.6
Other	2	—	3.0	0.5	1	6.5
Total	37	2	54.9**	3.0	32	128.9

*Styrene types.
**28.4 million lbs. are plastic processing types, the remainder are soluble types.

Table 9-4. Vinyl resin substitution for rubber (million lbs.). (Reprinted with permission from *Rubber World* magazine, February 1975, p. 45, and from the author, David Dworkin, Fairfield Associates, Inc.)

	1965	1966	1969	1973
Wire and cable	220	251	390	427
Garden hose	25	30	35	40
Weatherstripping & gaskets	45	46	48	55
Sealants	14	15	20	23
Footwear	31	89	100	145
Toys	45	50	58	84
Other (auto mats, medical tubing, misc.—estimated)	100	100	100	100
Total	480	581	751	874

is occurring with garden hose and rubber molded goods. This displacement of one class of materials by another is one that will be dictated by material cost, material availability, trends in rubber and plastics compounding, and fabrication—which reduce labor/capital costs, performance needs, and, more recently, government regulations (i.e., toxicity, safety, etc.).

9.2.2 Specific Applications: Footwear

A review[5] by Shell Chemical personnel has provided considerable insight on the use of Kraton thermoplastic rubber in shoe-soling applications. This application for thermoplastic elastomers is especially interesting for it involves competition with cured rubber, flexible vinyl, and, to a modest extent, ethylene copolymers. In addition, this market is currently undergoing a significant change in the manufacturing process due to competitive pressures. Therefore, the less labor-intensive operation of direct injection molding of canvas and noncanvas shoes is displacing the process of hand-building the shoes. As a result of this latter change, new markets have been created for thermoplastic elastomers, plasticized PVC, and thermosetting polyurethanes.

The potential footwear markets for TPEs can be subdivided into direct injection-molded canvas, direct injection-molded noncanvas, and unit sole footwear applications. Generally, canvas upper footwear constitutes approximately 20% of this total market. In the past, shoe construction has been very labor-intensive, and therefore, due to the higher wage rates in the United States, there has been continuing penetration into the United States markets by imported shoes. For example, it is estimated that 40% of shoes consumed in the United States in 1975 were imported.[5]

As a consequence of this pressure from imported footwear, United States manufacturers have changed their manufacturing processes to less labor-intensive methods. The direct injection molding of both canvas and noncanvas footwear and the use of unit soles have permitted a substantial decrease in this area. A detailed discussion[5] by Lantz et al. has analyzed the various factors determining the growth and future potential of TPEs in these markets.

In the case of injection-molded canvas footwear, plasticized PVC was first introduced in 1964. PVC was the first substitute for vulcanized rubber in this application, and, even though PVC was inferior to rubber in skid resistance, appearance, and feel, it did achieve market penetration. Within 2 years or so of the introduction of PVC, thermoplastic elastomers were introduced and have since constituted the largest share of this market. However, there are essentially three major polymers being used in this market in the United States. Technically, these materials perform somewhat differently in this application, as shown in Table 9-5.

Table 9-5. Canvaswear soling materials. (W. L. Lante, J. A. Sanford, and J. F. Young, Presentation at ACS Rubber Division Meeting, San Francisco, California, October 5, 1976.)

POLYMER	FEEL	SKID RESISTANCE	BONDING TO UPPER	ABRASION RESISTANCE
Thermoplastic rubber	Best	Best	Fair	Fair
PVC	Plastic	Poor	Best	Good
SBR/NR	Best	Best	Best	Best

It has been estimated[5] that the canvas footwear market has changed significantly during the past 10 years in the selection of polymers for this application. Data in Table 9-6 describe the market share of this market for the major polymers from 1968 to 1976. Based on this evaluation, it is evident that the thermoplastic elastomer market share has increased from about 7% in 1968 to about 30% in 1976. In contrast, the share of this market held by PVC is seen to decline from about 24% to about 8%, while the market share attributed to SBR/NR is seen to be about constant. The other major impact in this area is the continued growth of the import market for canvas footwear.

In summary, it is seen that the injection-molded canvas footwear market in a period of about 8 years has had a substantial displacement of PVC by TPEs. Based on the property analysis of Table 9-5, the rubbery feel and improved skid resistance of TPEs could be significant factors in this displacement; however, other factors such as materials cost cannot be ignored.

A second significant market exists for TPE soling in direct injection molding in noncanvas applications. TPEs have not competed in this market because of inadequate bonding to leather or PVC uppers. If this problem is overcome, TPEs could participate in this application as well.

A third and rapidly growing footwear application is that of unit soles, where an injection-molded sole is simply cemented to the uppers. This approach affords considerable labor savings and provides styling flexibility. The potential for substantial TPE participation in this large market is good. It is estimated that TPEs represented 50% of this market in 1975 even though currently restricted to the non-dress-shoe applications.

In summary, TPEs have penetrated the canvas footwear markets at the expense largely of PVC. It is postulated by Shell Chemical personnel[5] that substantial growth will occur over the next 5 years in noncanvas injection-molded applications and in unit sole applications. They attribute this growth to a cost/performance balance, as summarized in Table 9-7.

Table 9-6. Summary of canvas footwear market shares. (W. L. Lantz, J. A. Sanford, and J. F. Young, Presentation at ACS Rubber Division Meeting, San Francisco, California, October 5, 1976.)

CATEGORY	1968		1973		1974		1975		1976 PROJECTED	
	MM PAIRS	% MARKET SHARES	MM PAIRS	% MARKET SHARES	MM PAIRS	% MARKET SHARES	MM PAIRS	% MARKET SHARES	MM PAIRS	% MARKET SHARES
Injection molded	62.0	31.0	112.9	44.0	102.7	41.3	94.8	39.3	93.0	39.0
PVC	47.0	23.5	74.4	29.0	56.7	22.8	40.3	16.7	20.0	8.4
Thermoplastic rubber	14.3	7.2	38.5	15.0	46.0	18.5	54.5	22.5	73.0	30.6
Hand built SBR/NR	50.0	25.0	61.2	23.9	62.6	25.1	58.0	23.9	54.0	22.7
Direct vulcanized SBR/NR	45.0	22.5	16.0	6.4	16.0	6.4	16.0	6.6	16.0	6.7
Imports	43.0	21.5	66.3	25.7	67.9	27.2	73.0	30.2	75.0	31.6
Totals	200.0		256.4		249.2		241.8		238.0	
% Rubber		76.5		71.0		77.2		83.3		91.6

Table 9-7. Thermoplastic rubber as a soling material. (W. L. Lantz, J. A. Sanford, and J. F. Young, ACS Rubber Division Meeting, San Francisco, California, October 5, 1976.)

ADVANTAGES	DISADVANTAGES
Processes easily by injection molding	Poor wear in athletic shoes
Low-cost compounds for unit soles	Poor oil resistance and wear in work shoes
Excellent traction on ice and wet surfaces	High mold costs for short runs
Easily decorated and painted	Long cycle for thick soles
Excellent low temperature flexibility	
Excellent wear in casual, dress, and children's shoes	
Lightweight vs. vinyl	
Offer shoe design flexibility	

9.2.3 Specific Applications: Adhesives

A major market for styrene-based thermoplastic elastomers is found in adhesive formulations. Currently, it has been estimated[6] that about 12% of TPE markets are found in adhesives in the United States. Here, the TPEs (such as Shell Chemical Kraton and Phillips Petroleum Co. Solprene) are displacing more conventional rubber systems. In selected areas, such as hot melt applications and pressure-sensitive labels, the polystyrene-isoprene block copolymers offer better tack and faster and ecologically better systems than typical solvent-based formulations.[7] A summary on the use of Solprene plastomers in adhesive formulations has been presented.[8]

The styrenic-based TPEs possess selected properties that make them well suited to this application. First, they are soluble in common solvents; second, they accept oils and tackifiers; and third, their thermoplastic character allows them to be employed as hot melts. In this respect, only polyurethanes function sufficiently well to compete in a segment of this market.

The adhesives market can be subdivided into four segments: pressure sensitive adhesives, solvent cements, construction adhesives, and hot melt adhesives. This section highlights some general observations about the four adhesive applications and the general performance of the styrenic TPEs in those areas.

9.2.3.1 Pressure-Sensitive Adhesives

The use of block polymers in this application provides formulations with outstanding creep resistance due to the existence of the polystyrene-based domains. However, this same characteristic can reduce the tack of these systems to an undesirable level; therefore, a compromise of these two properties is achieved by suitable compounding. In effect, the use of tackifying resins, which primarily

Table 9-8. Effect of resin type on adhesive properties. (B. D. Simpson, Presentation at 110th Rubber Division Meeting, ACS, San Francisco, California, October 5, 1976.)

85 Isoprene-15 styrene plastomer	100	100	100
Synthetic terpene resin	100	100	100
Coumarone-indene resin	–	10	20
Naphthenic oil	40	40	40
Stabilizer	3	3	3
Rolling ball tack, cm	2.3	5.0	5.8
Polyken probe tack, gram	875	735	630
180° peel, kN/m	0.53	0.51	0.56
Creep[a] after 72 hr, cm	Failed	0.2	0

[a]Load = 0.014 MPa.

solvate the rubbery midblock, permit a substantial improvement in tack of the final coating. Some representative formulations of pressure-sensitive adhesives are shown in Table 9-8. In these systems, the terpene resin performs the task of tackifying the system, while the use of a coumarone-indene resin provides an interaction with the polystyrene blocks and thereby improves performance, both at ambient and elevated temperatures. This capability of selective interaction of resins and plasticizers provides an unusual capability to alter the performance of this class of TPEs.

9.2.3.2 Solvent Cements

The two-phase structure of TPEs employed in this application requires suitable selection of a solvent that will solvate both phases of the polymer, or a combination of solvents, to perform this function. As with pressure-sensitive adhesive formulations, different resin additives can be employed to strengthen these formulations or to tackify them.

9.2.3.3 Construction Adhesives

TPEs have been employed in mastics for wall panels and plywood subflooring due to their high strength. Such formulations contain substantial levels of clay and resin, which make them competitive yet provide adequate compressive strength.[8]

9.2.3.4 Hot Melt Adhesives

Pressure-sensitive adhesive coaters have been under increasing pressure to control solvent emissions to the atmosphere and reduce costs due to increased solvent costs. The use of rubbery hot melt adhesives provides one approach to achieve this objective. The thermoplastic nature of TPEs has made this approach practical and competitive. Again, a compromise must be sought between tack and peel strength. This can be achieved by appropriate formulation.

9.2.4 Specific Applications: Impact Modification

It has been reported[9] that Phillips Solprene thermoplastic elastomers enhance certain performance aspects of selected thermoplastics when present at additive levels. Specifically, polystyrene, polypropylene, high-density polyethylene, and low-density polyethylene have been studied. Improvements in impact resistance, flexural modulus, and hardness are claimed. For example, Izod impact is described as increasing from 0.7 in medium impact to 4.0 in a blend of impact polystyrene and 15% Solprene 41. Also, increases of tear strength are reported for LDPE film through the blending of 50% LDPE with 50% Solprene 475 from values of 90 up to 144. It is claimed that in some cases, the TPEs are superior to conventional rubber when employed as additives to achieve impact resistance.

The use of Kraton 4000 TPEs as impact modifiers for polystyrene has been described by Shell Chemical.[10] The combination of about 10% Kraton with high-impact polystyrene provides physical properties comparable to those achieved with commercial super high impact polystyrene at lower cost.

9.3 COST PERFORMANCE COMPARISONS OF TPEs AND COMPETITIVE MATERIALS

Those thermoplastic elastomers now available commercially in significant volumes are summarized in Table 9-9 along with the estimated selling prices and the names of the larger producers.[11] In addition, a few of the more significant advantages and limitations of these classes of materials are included. It is important to note that these materials traverse a range in selling prices that differ by as much as a factor of 5, and serve substantially different markets.

It is highly misleading to compare the polymer costs of various thermoplastic elastomers against competitive materials such as curable elastomers unless this is done on the basis of the total cost of a fabricated part. For example, as shown in Table 9-10, the cost of fabricating a cured extruded product can be substantially greater than the simple raw materials cost.

An interesting analysis of the relative costs of producing insulation and jacket for wire and cable applications has been made.[12] Thermoset vs. thermoplastic processing were compared employing a $3\frac{1}{2}$-in. extruder as the base piece of equipment in each case. A summary of manufacturing costs of these two scenarios is provided in Table 9-10.

In the case of thermosets, the requirement of continuous vulcanization equipment and the attendant higher labor costs result in a total production cost that is

Table 9-9. Summary of cost performance features of commercial TPEs. (Information abstracted from *Materials Engineering*, December 1975.)

TPE TYPE	PRICE RANGE $/LB	PRODUCERS	MAJOR ADVANTAGES	MAJOR LIMITATIONS
Olefinics	.50–.70	Uniroyal Goodrich Du Pont Exxon Chemical Hercules	Broad use temperature range.	Somewhat plastic in recovery.
Styrenics Unsaturated midblock	.32–.66	Shell Chemical Phillips	Rubbery feel. Good processibility.	Limited use temperature and weatherability.
Saturated midblock	.50–.92	Shell Chemical	Improved weatherability.	
Copolyesters	1.40–1.65	Du Pont	Use temperature range.	Availability in softer Shore A range.
Polyurethanes	1.30–1.80	Uniroyal Upjohn Goodrich Mobay Hooker	Abrasion resistance. Set characteristics.	Water sensitivity. Low temperature properties.

Table 9-10. Manufacturing costs thermoset vs. thermoplastic. (C. F. Blaich, Rubber Division ACS Meeting, San Francisco, California, October 5, 1976.)

	Thermoset* Continuous Vulcanization	Thermoplastics
3½" Extruder/Tuber 100 HP Installed Cost	$ 75,000	$ 75,000
Take-Up and Payout	50,000	50,000
Cooling Equipment	15,000	15,000
Plant Space 150 x 25	82,500	82,500
CV—Tube, etc. 200 ft. tube	150,000	—
Total Plant	$372,500	$222,500
10 yr. amortization	$ 37,250	$ 22,250
Int. at 10% (10 yr. avg.)	30,000	17,750
Maintenance at 6%	—	13,350
Maintenance at 10%	37,250	—
Total Fixed	$104,500	$ 53,350
Fixed Cost/hr. (6,000 hr. yr.)	$ 17.40	$ 8.90
Manpower at $12/hr.	$ 24.00	$ 12.00
Steam 50#/min.	18.00	—
Electric Power	5.00	7.50
Cooling Water	1.00	1.00
Variable Cost/hour	$ 48.00	$ 20.50
Total Prod. Cost/hour	$ 65.40	$ 29.40

*Basis: $6.00/1000# —3,000 lbs./hr.

OPTIMUM EXTRUSION RATES   1 HR.

Neoprene	450	PVC	600
SBR	550	TPR	400
ROYLAR	350		

*Does not include the cost of Boiler

essentially double that required for a thermoplastics process. Blaich[12] recognized that such estimates will certainly vary from plant to plant, but he estimated that the values in Table 9-10 were within ±10% of actual plant operating costs.

In addition to this difference in production costs, there is the factor of material scrap, again estimated at 5 to 6% for thermosets vs. 2 to 3% for thermoplastics. As indicated in Table 9-11, these cost advantages for thermoplastics processing hold for the range of the cable industry, including flexible cord, welding cable up to power cable systems. Blaich offered a number of comparisons in this area, including SBR, neoprene, PVC, and TPR. (See Table 9-11.)

It is seen that for this set of assumptions the thermoplastic systems end up with an effective cost that is significantly less than for the thermosets, even allowing for a significantly higher raw materials cost for the thermoplastics. In addition, it is often possible to achieve considerably higher extrusion rates with the thermoplastic materials, especially with the newer systems that are being designed for better processability.

The thermoplastic elastomers have been on the market for only a few years, and there has not, therefore, been sufficient feedback on the relative performance of these systems to determine if they will meet the requirements of the wire and cable industry. Blaich[12] has emphasized that even in the short history of TPEs, materials are now available that can compete from a performance viewpoint for 50% of the needs of this industry. In view of current research and development efforts, it is likely that TPEs will be available to meet all of the requirements of this industry.

While the analysis provided by Blaich is quite specific to various applications in the wire and cable industry, his general observations of lower production costs for TPEs relative to thermosets should also extend to other extruded goods.

While such analyses are appropriate if one is considering an investment in a new facility, it is not necessarily relevant if one has a fully amortized facility capable of producing cured extruded product. For example, many of the current thermoplastic elastomers cannot be properly fabricated on conventional rubber extrusion equipment, while they can be extruded satisfactorily on plastics extrusion equipment. From the viewpoint of fabricators who have the amortized rubber fabrication equipment, it may be more economical from their viewpoint to continue making a cured rubber product. Therefore, the displacement of cured rubber products by thermoplastic elastomers will be slower than might be expected on a strict comparison of the fabrication costs. Finally, the economic climate prevailing at the time the comparison is made is significant, for it is important in determining whether the equipment will be utilized at 50 or 90% capacity.

Table 9-11. Estimated costs of various extruded insulated cords. (C. F. Blaich, Rubber Division ACS Meeting, San Francisco, California, October 5, 1976.)

POLYMER	SBR	NEOPRENE NBR/PVC	PVC	TPR-5200 THERMOPLASTIC OLEFIN ELASTOMERS	MODIFIED THERMOPLASTIC OLEFIN ELASTOMERS
Specific Gravity	1.45	1.45	1.36	.88	1.30
Cost/# at the Extruder	.35	.50	.37	.68	.54
#/1,000 includes material scrap	10.14	10.14	9.5	5.91	9.1
Material Cost/1,000 ft. $	$ 3.55	$ 5.07	$3.52	$4.02	$4.91
Line speed	400+	200+	800	1200	800
$/1,000 Extrusion/Cure Cost	$ 2.73	$ 5.45	$ .61	$ .41	$ .61
Startup Scrap Cost $/1,000 ft.	$ .08	$ .09	$ .02	$ .02	$ .02
Cost for Insulation $/1,000 ft.	$ 6.36	$10.61	$4.15	$4.45	$5.54

+Limited by CV

9.4 AUTOMOTIVE APPLICATIONS: TPEs vs. CONVENTIONAL RUBBERS

Automotive applications of thermoplastic elastomers represent a special class of materials for a variety of reasons. As potential markets for polymer systems, automotive uses are extremely varied in terms of performance criteria, while simultaneously representing one of the largest markets for flexible polymeric materials. In addition to the usual performance criteria of hardness, moduli, tensile strength, impact performance, etc., there are also stringent requirements relating to more aesthetic aspects such as weatherability, scratch or mar resistance, and paintability. Because there are many polymer systems competing for these various automotive applications, this section will deal exclusively with these applications.

The thermoplastic urethanes, blends of EDM rubber and a hard plastic, and blends of various block copolymer rubbers with hard plastics are used extensively for automotive body extensions and filler panels. These TPE compounds compete typically with EPDM and flexible polyolefin compounds such as ethylene vinyl acetate and PVC.

As a representative example, Figure 9-1 illustrates typical part configurations and colors manufactured from the thermoplastic urethanes. Rear quarter extensions are shown mounted on a body mock-up commonly called a *buck*. A pendulum is shown in the cocked position, which, when released, will strike the

Figure 9-1. Rear quarter extensions made from TP urethanes.

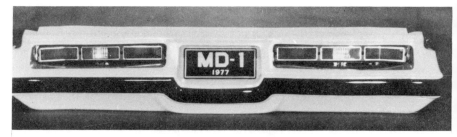

Figure 9-2. MD-1 bumper. Experimental full-width bumper for standard size car. Molded from urethane TPE (Texin) by Mobay Chemical Corp. (Courtesy of General Motors Corp.)

bumper into the fender extension at a rate of 5 mph. This is typical of the testing done to develop automotive applications. Other typical applications of thermoplastic urethane elastomers are shown in Figures 9-2 through 9-7.

Representative parts made from EPDM rubber/hard plastic blends are shown in Figure 9-8. They appear to be similar in size and shape to TPU parts, yet they

Figure 9-3. The Pontiac front grill frame stretches across the entire front of the car and encompasses both headlamps. The above TPE part was repainted and used after replacement of some of the metal in the fenders. Molded of TP urethane. (Courtesy of General Motors Corp.)

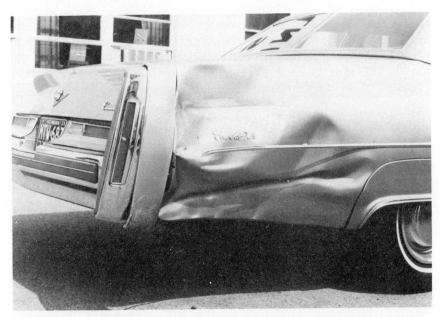

Figure 9-4. Cadillac rear fender extension. Extension section molded of TP urethane. Shows damage to metal fender, but no damage to molded extension piece. (Courtesy of General Motors Corp.)

are not interchangeable with TPU in most applications in automotive. These blends are limited to parts that will experience limited scuffing action from either the bumper or the environment due to their more limited abrasion resistance and resilience.

Some of the TPEs are made from natural resin light enough in color to make pigmentation to a color match possible. In automotive applications, paint is preferably applied to achieve a decorative color since it is easier to control gloss and match by this means. The topcoat is flexible and often requires that the substrate be treated with a reactive primer to achieve good adhesion under adverse conditions.

There are at least 15 different chemical varieties of the commercially available conventional rubbers. They are produced in approximately 250 compositions that compete with a similar number of TPE compounds. Six of the most widely used conventional rubbers are SBR, EPDM, chloroprene (neoprene), nitrile, butyl, and natural rubber. They all require vulcanization with sulfur, and compounding with oils, carbon black, and other ingredients in order to achieve useful performance characteristics.

Many of the same formulation ingredients used in preparing conventional rubbers are used in the manufacture of TPEs. Carbon black and oil can be compounded into TPEs in greater proportions than are used in the conventional rubber formulations. Carbon black, in TPEs, acts as a reinforcing agent. Oils and mineral fillers aid in processing and cost reduction. Less stabilizer is generally required in TPEs since they have less residual unsaturation than conventional rubber compounds and are therefore less subject to ozone and oxidative attack.

9.4.1 Comparative Costs

The unprocessed rubber raw material costs of the six rubber compounds listed previously fall within the same general price and availability range as those used in TPEs. However, the conventional rubbers must be compounded with various ingredients such as sulfur, accelerators, carbon black, oil, fillers, and stabilizers to produce economical formulations designed for specific product applications, all of which add to costs. Processing costs for the conventional rubber formula-

Figure 9-5. Cadillac rear quarter extension. Shows molded TP urethane extension piece (black) used to prevent damage when bumper is struck. (Courtesy of General Motors Corp.)

Figure 9-6. Cadillac front filler parts. All front filler areas between bumper and steel section of fender and grille are of molded TPE parts in line with bumper. Used to prevent damage when bumper is struck. (Courtesy of General Motors Corp.)

tions are somewhat higher than for comparable TPE processing because of the additional curing step that is needed.

9.4.2 Competitive Comparison Example

The thermoplastic elastomers compete with the conventional rubber products as well as with other TPEs. Each competitive situation requires a thorough and careful analysis in order to determine which material would make the most effective choice.

An example of the competitive analysis of various compounds is shown by the evaluation that was done by automotive design engineers when considering a material for flexible filler panel applications. As is usual in such problems, the engineer starts with a list of likely candidate materials (see Table 9-12).

The data presented in Table 9-12 show that the thermoplastic elastomers are slightly less expensive than EPDM or PVC. However, the comparison must be carried several steps further, as shown in Table 9-13.

Product thickness increases on EPDM and PVC were believed to be necessary to maintain a satisfactory shape for the parts to be used in this application. The

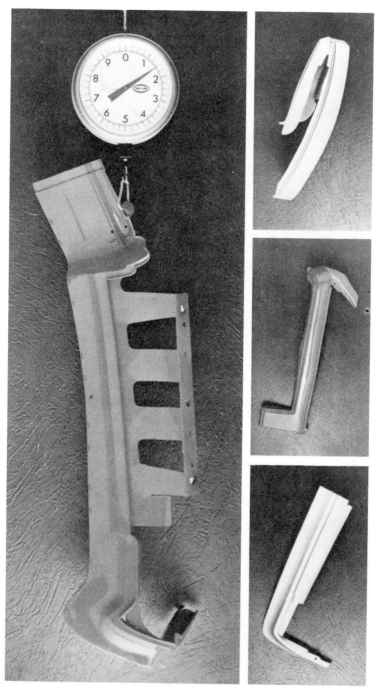

Figure 9-7. Filler and quarter extension panels for General Motors cars. Molded of Estane polyurethane elastomer. (Courtesy of B. F. Goodrich Co., Chemical Division)

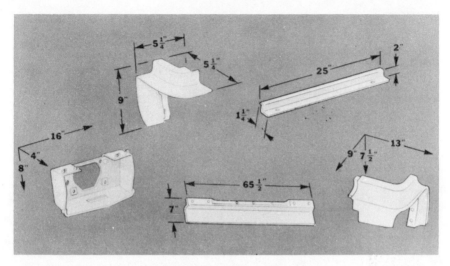

Figure 9-8. Parts made from blends of EDM rubber and hard plastic.

data show that the cost of a PVC part, and other questionable performance parameters, would, in the engineer's opinion, make it unacceptable for this application. EPDM was eliminated since there wasn't a cost advantage over TPE and since it would require major operational changes in the manufacturing facility where the materials were being considered for production.

Extensive testing of this part, molded in both TPU and TPE under service conditions, indicated that neither surface scuffing nor resiliency were major factors in its function. While the testing procedures used were as realistic as possible, they could have, by different selection and emphasis, drastically altered the decision that was made. General discussion of testing and evaluation procedures will be presented in a later section of this chapter.

Table 9-12.

MATERIAL	DENSITY	COST[a]	PART COST[b]
TPU	1.22	1.45	1.57
TPE	0.90	0.45	0.36
EPDM	1.25	0.35	0.39
PVC	1.33	0.37	0.43

[a]Costs in $/lb are valid for mid-1976 only.
[b]Part cost is calculated as (Density) × (Material cost/lb) × (Standard part weight). Standard part weight is 0.89 lb. It is the product of the part volume (which in this example is 24.6 in.^{3}) multiplied by 0.0361 lb/in.^{3} (the weight of 1 in.^{3} of material having a density of 1).

Table 9-13.

MATERIAL	ESTIMATED THICKNESS INCREASE	REVISED COST	PAINT COATING PROCESS	PERFORMANCE CHARACTERISTIC	COMMENTS
TPU	None	$1.57	No prime	Excellent	Good resistance to damage
TPE	None	0.36	Prime topcoat	Easy to damage surface	Marginal resilience
EPDM	10%	0.43	Sensitize prime topcoat	Good	Thermoset, can't use scrap
PVC	15%	0.47	Prime topcoat	Poor at elevated temperatures	Stain resistance questionable

9.4.3 Comparison Summary

The TPE compounds are involved in a dynamic competitive situation both within their own class and with the conventional rubbers. The examples given in Tables 9-12 and 9-13 represent only a few of the many possibilities that could be considered. Microcellular urethanes made by the RIM process, ethylene-vinyl acetate compounds, and various polyolefins could have also been involved in this evaluation.

Automotive is only one of the many market areas to provide considerable utility for the thermoplastic elastomers. In footwear, the unit sole applications include such TPE compounds as the SBR block copolymers, thermoplastic urethanes, and various EPR formulations. The advantages for TPE in this case are similar to those cited in other applications. They include production of soles by injection molding, the ability to reprocess scrap, and outstanding wear characteristics. As previously stated, each projected application requires careful analysis to determine the most effective material choice.

9.4.4 Processing Comparisons of TPEs and Conventional Rubbers

Injection molding is the principal process used in the fabrication of TPE parts. Extrusion follows closely in importance and is used to produce profiles, sheet stock, and wire-coated products. Rotational and compression molding, fluidized bed coating, and solvent casting are also used to product a variety of specialized products.

The primary manufacturing processes for conventional rubber compounded products are injection molding, extrusion, and compression molding. The injection-molding machines used to mold conventional rubbers require special nozzles, high mold temperatures, and a minimum impact of work energy into the feedstock.

This special equipment limits the versatility of a molding operation since switching to other feedstocks would require revision by the molder. The TPE molding operation does not require such equipment modifications and can therefore change readily among many thermoplastic feedstocks.

Conventional rubber products require extensive part curing to achieve optimum physical properties. The nonpolar surfaces of conventional rubber products must be treated with reactive primers, radiation, electrical discharge, etc. in order to achieve sufficient paint adhesion where this decorative option is required. This surface treatment is also required on a majority of the TPEs, with the notable exception of the thermoplastic urethanes.

The molders of TPE products have an additional advantage over the manufacturer of conventional rubber parts: the runners, sprues, and other scrap produced can be reprocessed. Conventional rubber products not meeting quality standards are either repaired or scrapped as unsalvageable. The scrapped material is often an ecological and economical problem since it can only be sent to landfill sites.

Extruded TPE sheet stock can be thermoformed into many products. The neutral color of most natural TPE resins ranges from a light tan to a translucent white, enabling color chemists to formulate a range of precolored products reducing the need for a painting step.

The natural TPE resins are widely compatible within their chemical groupings and also accept modification with both hard polyolefins and soft elastomers. This enables even the small processors the luxury of developing proprietary formulations through simple blending that gives their products a competitive edge.

Secondary operations such as spin and hot melt welding, sonic bonding, and solvent cementing are possible with TPEs and not with the conventional rubber compounds. Techniques for joining or adhering TPEs to other plastics, metals, wood, and other materials of construction have not been extensively developed. Generally, processors have assiduously avoided secondary operations of this kind primarily through creative designs.

9.5 TESTING OF TPE ELASTOMERS

The testing of plastics has many facets, and some are so subtle that only a specialist can appreciate them. Elastomers, particularly the TPEs, have their own peculiarities, and consequently the selection of meaningful tests and interpretation of the results require experienced judgment. Continual follow-up is also necessary to maintain correlation between test evaluation and field performance.

9.5.1 General Test Considerations

The performance of various TPE compounds is sensitive to many factors, some of which go as far back as the polymerization reaction. Each step along the way to a finished product contributes its own set of variables to the total process. These include the additives (stabilizers, pigments, fillers, oil extenders, etc.), their order of addition, the in-plant processing equipment, the customer's molding equipment, the mold configuration, the condition of the mold, and finally, the posttreatment of the molded part.

The standard tests usually performed on the TPE compounds include tensile strength, elongation, stiffness modulus, specific gravity, and tear strength. They are of necessity conducted on carefully prepared test specimens in order to obtain the intrinsic reproducible values. Since a molded product produced for the consumer represents the "real world" and not the ideal conditions of the polymer chemist's laboratory, each user industry has found it desirable to develop specific tests that can be relied upon to determine product performance levels. An example from the automotive industry will be used to illustrate this point.

9.5.2 Special Automotive Functional Tests

Many TPE applications in the automotive industry are for exterior filler panels that will be flexed when the bumpers are stressed. The stressed part is required to return to its original shape without structural or cosmetic damage after the stress has been removed. In addition, the vehicle will be required to operate in a range of ambient temperature conditions that reach a high of 65°C and a low of -30°C. Given these two parameters, a flex impact and a sag test were developed to evaluate proposed TPE compounds for this application.

9.5.3 Flex Impact Test

The effect of bumper stress on TPE filler panels was evaluated by developing a flex-impact test. The principle of this test is to generate stresses that approximate those experienced in a low-speed collision. Stress-strain analysis studies of the test specimen indicate that the upper boundary layers are being elongated at the rate of 223.5 cm/sec as compared to a usual test rate of 0.127 cm/sec. This more rapid strain rate approximates the effect of flexing elastomeric automotive filler panels at a rate that would be expected in a 5 mile/hr collision.

A typical apparatus for the flex-impact test is shown in Figure 9-9. It basically consists of a hemispherical dart fastened to a guided cross-head. The weight of the impact head and the cross-arm assembly is made just heavy enough to com-

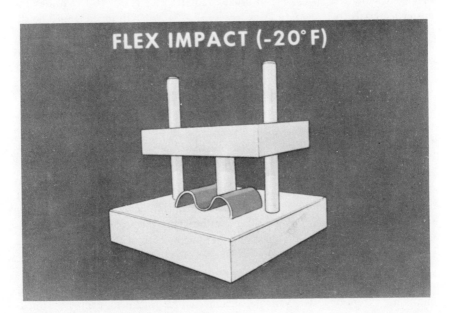

Figure 9-9. Apparatus for flex-impact test.

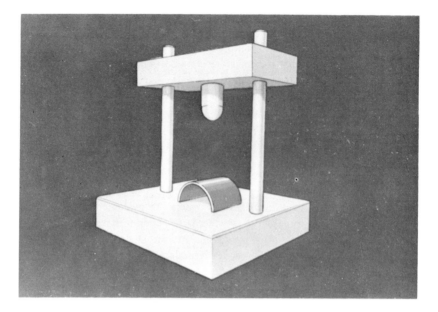

Figure 9-10. Fully flexed test specimen.

pletely flex the test specimen. It usually requires a weight of 100 kg to flex the stiffer materials to temperatures as low as $-30°C$. When dropped from a height of approximately 28 cm, the speed of the head due to the acceleration of gravity approaches 223 cm/sec at the impact point (about 5 mph). The specimens for flex impact evaluation are typically 7.0 by 15.0 cm and have a thickness of approximately 0.3 cm. The impact plate is solid steel and has two machined slots 5.0 cm on each side of the impact point of the dart. When the ends of the test sample are inserted in these slots, the test piece bows up into a dome-shaped structure. Refer to Figure 9-9 for an illustration of the specimen ready for impact. The falling dart tip hits the apex of the dome and causes the test specimen to flex into a double wave pattern. TPE formulations that resist failure are completely flexed into the double wave pattern configuration with no apparent damage to the substrate. Figure 9-10 shows the fully flexed test specimen that did not fail. The failure mode of a test specimen is usually of a catastrophic nature, exhibiting well-defined glasslike fracture along the broken edges. The failure is usually initiated at the crest of either one or both of the waves formed by the nose of the dart. Failure almost never occurs at the point of impact of the dart, indicating compressive stresses are not particularly damaging.

There are many sample preparation variables to consider in most tests, and this one is no exception. The variables include sample thickness, paint film thickness, and level of paint cure. In general, the thicker the sample, the more prone it is to result in failure. Paint film thickness follows a similar trend. Overcured paint will promote more failures than undercured paint.

At -30°C (and even using the best finishes available), paint crack failures are evident when the specimen is held in the flexed position. However, when the stress is released and the substrate has returned to its original position, the paint cracks are not visible enough to cause cosmetic problems. Since paint loss does not occur and corrosion is not a problem, the paint cracking experienced after severe flexing goes largely unnoticed.

All of these effects indicate that formation of stress risers promotes breakage. Since it is fairly easy to mold and paint flex impact size samples, the test fixture is relatively inexpensive, and material and paint suppliers have used flex impact for development and improvement of their products.

9.5.4 Sag Test

The sag test is another relatively simple test used in the development of automotive filler panels. This test will be described in some detail as was the flex impact test, in order to illustrate what usually occurs in most segments of the automotive industry.

Dimensional change at elevated temperatures (commonly referred to as *sag*) is an important parameter of product performance. The most commonly used test can be described as a *cantilever beam test*. This test is usually run at elevated temperatures (121°C) on a test specimen 1.27 by 7.62 by 0.254 cm. The test material is usually exposed for a period of 30 min at the required temperature. Experience has shown that a sag value of 2.0 cm or less is considered adequate for most automotive applications. Higher sag numbers generally mean poor green strength and portend paint rack deformation. Competitive materials such as flexible vinyl compounds have trouble meeting both this test and the flex impact requirement at -30°C. The addition of fillers such as glass and mineral reinforcements have helped in overcoming this kind of deficiency.

9.6 DESIRED IMPROVEMENTS IN THERMOPLASTIC ELASTOMERS

Thermoplastic elastomers have been available commercially in significant volume since the introduction of Kraton TPEs by Shell Chemical around 1965. Prior to that time, thermoplastic polyurethanes were available but were generally used as a specialty elastomer. Therefore, TPEs have been recognized as a special class of materials intermediate in properties between thermoplastics and cured rubber for a relatively brief period of 10 years or so. Nevertheless, during that time there has been a proliferation of new types of thermoplastic elastomers. Nearly every supplier of thermoplastics has a candidate either available commercially or under development designed to serve the thermoplastic elastomer market.

Many of the TPEs that were initially available commercially competed with flexible polyvinyl chloride from a performance viewpoint. Those initial TPE candidates generally were defensive in performance in several characteristics, which precluded their achieving substantial penetration in markets served by cured rubber. The second-generation thermoplastic elastomers, such as Uniroyal Inc. TPR, E. I. du Pont de Nemours & Company Hytrel, and so on, had improvements in some performance areas, and recent developments suggest future TPEs may be significantly better. This section deals with selected needs of thermoplastic elastomers, which, if met, might permit significantly greater market penetration against both cured rubber and plasticized vinyl.

9.6.1 Requirements of Future TPEs

Thermoplastic elastomers now available commercially generally can be considered defensive to either cured rubber or vinyl in the following areas:[6]

1. Compression set, especially at high temperature
2. Use temperature range (i.e., tensile strength at 100° to 150°C)
3. Processibility
4. Flame retardance
5. Weatherability
6. Stress-strain characteristics.

The following comments compare TPEs versus competitive materials in the property areas described above. In addition, there are other considerations that are also important to particular applications.

9.6.2 Compression Set

One of the primary reasons that cured rubber or TPEs are selected for an elastomeric application resides in the capability of those materials to recover from applied stress without substantial permanent deformation. Cured elastomers are generally outstanding in this characteristic, especially at elevated temperatures. By definition, the physical cross-links of thermoplastic elastomers are thermally reversible, which generally results in high compression set values. Therefore, tensile set or compression set values for cured rubber systems generally are low compared to many TPEs. Furthermore, the temperature dependence of compression set (and similar deformation tests) is considerably less for a covalently cross-linked material than for one based on physical cross-links. Thus, for many thermoplastic elastomers, compression set values (ASTM D-395 Method B) measured at room temperature are comparable to or somewhat better than flexible vinyl (20 to 30% at 23°C after 30-min. recovery). At elevated temperatures (70°C), the compression sets of many TPEs are in the region of 80 to 100%, while cured elastomers would be substantially less. Those thermoplastic elastomers developed more recently have shown improved compression set values as compared with first-generation materials.

There have been some classes of TPEs described that have shown outstanding compression set values even at elevated temperatures. Specifically, graft copolymers of ethylene propylene terpolymers and polypivalolactone have been shown to be capable of compression set values as low as 10 to 20% at temperatures of 70 to 100°C.[13]

These findings and other developments suggest that substantial improvements in compression set values of TPEs are feasible over that of many of the current materials available commercially. While TPEs may not equal cured rubber systems in compression set values, improvements in this area would permit TPEs to capture some of the markets now held exclusively by cured products.

9.6.3 Broader Use Temperature Range

The physical cross-links of TPEs are thermally reversible; therefore, a deterioration of physical properties at elevated temperature is unavoidable. For many applications, this limitation may not be critical. However, in many wire and cable applications, automotive under-hood applications, and in those areas where temperatures greater than 100°C are encountered, there is a need for better high temperature tensile properties. Some of the second-generation TPEs, such as Du Pont Hytrel and the thermoplastic polyolefins, offer substantial improvements here.

In recent publications, it has been indicated that further improvements in high temperature tensile properties are feasible. Again, graft copolymers of EPDM and polypivalolactone have been shown to provide good tensile properties at elevated temperatures.[13] While there have been promising developments in this area, it is likely that TPEs possessing a combination of good tensile properties at elevated temperatures (~150°C), good flow behavior from a processibility viewpoint, and a Shore A hardness in the range of 50 to 70 will be difficult to achieve.

This discussion has been directed only at the high temperature aspects of TPE performance since nearly all TPEs currently available possess excellent low temperature flexibility.

9.6.4 Improved Processibility

In view of the wide range of TPEs now available, it is apparent that a wide variation in flow behavior is achievable. However, nearly all TPEs are designed to be fabricated on thermoplastics fabrication equipment. In some cases, the injection molding of selected polyolefin-based TPEs can be achieved only on relatively high-pressure injection-molding equipment. Other systems, especially the polystyrene-based block copolymers, exhibit excellent processibility even on low-pressure machines.

Despite the range of processing characteristics, the TPEs available today are more suited to thermoplastics equipment than to typical rubber processing machines. Thus, the use of extruders possessing L/Ds of 20 to 30 are commonly employed. In many cases, the employment of extruder screws of special design are preferred for thermoplastic elastomers. The use of equipment with relatively low L/D, as is often the case with rubber equipment, is not recommended. Similarly, TPEs typically require higher processing temperatures than can be achieved with rubber processing equipment. Therefore, from the viewpoint of the fabricator with rubber fabrication capability, many of the TPEs are not compatible with this situation. The availability of TPEs capable of being fabricated on such equipment without major compromise of properties would offer some opportunities in this area.

9.6.5 Flame Retardance

Many of the thermoplastic elastomers commercially available today are based on polyolefins or polystyrene-based block copolymers. As compared with polyvinyl chloride-based materials, they are defensive in terms of flammability. Flame-retardant compositions have been supplied for specific applications, and, as the markets grow for TPEs, there will be other flame-retardant TPEs.

9.6.6 Weatherability

After some 30 years of improvement of stabilizers and plasticizers, flexible vinyl now possesses excellent weathering characteristics, generally superior to rubber. The initial generations of TPEs, based on diene elastomer blocks or polyurethanes, were clearly inferior to flexible vinyl in weatherability. Indeed, most polyolefin-based thermoplastics do not perform as well as vinyl in that respect. Nevertheless, subsequent thermoplastic elastomers based on polyolefins have demonstrated much improved weathering performance. The use of elastomer systems with inherently better resistance to oxidation and ultraviolet attack, in addition to improved stabilizer packages, has resulted in materials that apparently perform satisfactorily under accelerated aging conditions.[14]

It is certain that substantial improvements in this important area will be made in subsequent TPEs as these materials penetrate markets such as garden hose, automotive applications, weather stripping, and so on.

9.6.7 Stress-Strain Characteristics

The stress-strain behavior achieved with thermoplastic elastomers varies substantially depending on the specific TPE being considered. Nevertheless, many of the current materials available commercially display stress-strain curves where there is pronounced strain hardening. For many applications, a more desirable stress-strain curve would be one in which the stress was more proportional to the strain. With many thermoplastic elastomers, the application of a certain level of stress induces an excessive elongation. Thus, the load-bearing capability of such materials is limited, not by the tensile properties at break, but by the nature of the stress-strain curve of the particular material employed.

In view of the wide variety of TPEs now available, and the number of additional new materials under development, it is likely that products with more desirable stress-strain relationships will be available to suit a wide variety of applications. In addition, the stress-strain behavior of many TPEs can be altered substantially simply by appropriate compounding of suitable fillers and extenders. Such compounding guidance is now available from certain of the suppliers of TPEs.

9.7 THE FUTURE OF TPE COMPOUNDS

The market availability of plastic raw materials usually stays in a "lock step" fashion with the rest of the industry. This suggests that the future supply of TPE compounds will increase to meet increased requirements. Since most users of TPE compounds consider the present supply adequate, they are confident about the future in this regard.

The TPE compounds should increase their market penetration in footwear, adhesives, and wire coating industries. Other growth areas include industrial products such as hoses, bushings, flexible couplings, seals, and solvent coatings. This list is by no means complete, and it is expected that the majority of the products that will be developed during the next few years do not as yet exist and are unknown at this time.

The successful development of the homogeneous, termination controlled, anionic polymerization systems makes it possible to produce an endless variety of copolymeric materials. The placement of polymer segments, molecular weight, and composition can be controlled. As our knowledge of the polymerization chemistry, the morphology of the products, and the variables in processing increases, many new TPE materials and new applications will be developed. The wide range of compatibilities that exist within chemically similar groups of TPEs and with other thermoplastic polyolefins makes it possible even for small processors to develop proprietary formulations that will give them a competitive edge over conventional rubber products.

9.8 REFERENCES

1. *Modern Plastics Encyclopedia*, 1974–75, p. 114.
2. *Rubber World*, February 1975, p. 43.
3. *Chemical Week*, April 14, 1976, p. 22.
4. *Rubber World*, February 1975, p. 45.
5. W. L. Lantz, J. A. Sanford, and J. F. Young, 110th ACS Rubber Division Meeting, San Francisco, California, October 5, 1976.
6. *Modern Plastics*, December 1974, p. 51.
7. *European Plastic News*, June 1976, p. 13.
8. B. D. Simpson, 110th Rubber Division Meeting, ACS, San Francisco, California, October 5, 1976.
9. *Modern Plastics*, April 1976, p. 18.
10. Shell Technical Information Bulletin, SC:70-4, February, 1970.
11. Information abstracted from article in *Materials Engineering*, December 1975.
12. C. F. Blaich, Rubber Division Meeting, ACS Division, San Francisco, California, October 5, 1976.
13. R. C. Thamm and W. H. Buck, *Polym. Preprints* **17**: 205 (1976).
14. S. A. Banks, J. H. Brillinger, and D. G. Perham, Society of Automotive Engineers Meeting, October 18, 1976, Paper No. 760728.

Index